SO FAR TO GO

Rhodri Jones

KT-378-725

CANONGATE · KELPIES

First published 1987 by Andre Deutch Ltd
First published in Kelpies 1989

© 1987 Rhodri Jones

Cover illustration by Alexa Rutherford

Printed in Great Britain
by Cox and Wyman Ltd, Reading

ISBN 0 86241 249 8

CANONGATE PUBLISHING LTD
17 JEFFREY STREET, EDINBURGH EH1 1DR

1

What a send-off! Everybody was there. The forecourt in front of the flats was packed with people.

Ian was amazed. Who'd have thought they'd all turn out to see them go? Unless they were just glad to see the back of them.

Even the grey sky with a suggestion of drizzle hadn't put them off. It was supposed to be summer, but you'd never have guessed it. Ian's particular friends were there — Andy and Maisie and Jean. It was good of them to come. Especially as it was Sunday morning and not yet ten o'clock. Though on a morning like this, there wasn't much else to do.

'I envy you,' Andy was saying. 'Going to the great metropolis. Seeing all they sights. It's a rare place.'

He'd never been.

Maisie and Jean joined in.

'Aye, Buckingham Palace.'

'The Tower of London.'

'Westminster Abbey.'

'Big Ben.'

'And Soho,' said Andy with a leer. 'You watch it. That Soho's an awfie place. All kind of things go on there. You'd never believe some of the stories I've been tellt aboot it.'

His freckled face burned with envy. He sounded as though he

would have given his right arm to go there and find out if what he had heard was true.

'I'll be careful,' Ian said.

'But it's that far away,' Maisie moaned.

'Aye,' said Jean. 'It's so far to go.' She seemed genuinely sorry to see him leave.

Maisie gave a sniff. 'You'll let us know how you get on, won't you? You'll write me now?'

She sniffed again to prevent the tears from coming, and Jean patted her arm.

'Oh, aye,' Ian said absently.

Maisie had been putting it around for years that she was Ian's girlfriend, and he had never bothered to deny it. She didn't interest him enough for him to make the effort.

'I'll miss you,' Maisie went on, the corners of her mouth dragging down in a clown's face of despair. She was making a meal of it.

'Oh, aye,' Ian responded. 'I'll miss you too.'

This confession cheered Maisie up no end. Ian wondered if he had said too much.

He searched the mob for the rest of his family. Across the way, Mum was surrounded by a crowd of neighbours clucking like broody hens. She was blowing her nose into a scrap of a handkerchief that already looked as damp as a used dishcloth.

Auntie Sarah was there, and Auntie Morag. They were looking right miserable. As though the end of the world had come.

Further over, Dad was talking loudly and boasting to his cronies as usual. There was a roar of laughter, and they started to slap him on the back. He enjoyed being the centre of attention.

Ian's older brother Jimmy was huddled against the wall with his mates. He was looking furtive and arguing. They probably wanted the money back they'd lent him.

His sister Bella had her arms around her latest boyfriend. They called her Big Bella. You could see why. She was swallowing her boyfriend up in a bear hug so that you could hardly see him. She was brazen, that one. She didn't care who knew it.

It had all happened so suddenly that Ian couldn't quite take it all in. Dad had been away for nearly a year. After three years without a job, he had decided to go to London and try to find one. Somebody had said, 'Get on your bike,' so he had. And surprise, surprise, it had actually worked. He had been taken on as a corporation dustman.

Then the night before, he'd arrived back home. Somehow he'd managed to wangle a council flat for them. They were all moving to London.

He hadn't asked any of them whether or not they wanted to go. He had decided and that was it. He was like that.

Mum had cried and said she couldn't leave all her friends. But she always did what Dad wanted in the end. Jimmy had jumped at the chance to get away. He might even get a job in London like Dad. There were bound to be more openings. Big Bella had said she didn't want to leave her boyfriend, but there was a gleam in her eye that suggested she was already thinking of new conquests.

As for Ian, he wasn't sure. He hadn't known anything else but his life in Glasgow with his friends and his family. Yet here was Dad uprooting them all and carting them off to London. As Jean said, it was so far to go. It was another world.

After all, what did he know about London? There were all those places Andy and Maisie and Jean had mentioned. It was where the Queen lived and the Houses of Parliament that rule Scotland as though it was some outlying colony. It was where people had lots of money and spoke posh and lived in big houses. And hadn't they pinched Scotland's North Sea oil? He didn't fancy the idea of living there.

Not that it mattered. He was the youngest. Nobody bothered to ask his opinion.

They had spent most of the night loading the furniture onto the lorry Dad had borrowed from a workmate in London — four beds, a three-piece suite, a fridge, a TV, table and chairs, and endless boxes and plastic bags.

As usual, the lifts hadn't been working, so they'd had to lug it all down five flights of stairs. Ian had only had a couple of hours' sleep. His stomach muscles were still knotted and his legs still buckling under the effort. It was a good job they didn't have a piano. It was a good job they didn't live on the twentieth storey as well.

Now they were ready to go. The lorry stood waiting. It was a wonder how they'd got all the stuff in. Though looking at it, Ian suspected that the lorry would never get through the journey, loaded down as it was. It was so ancient. Like something left over from the First World War. Or a covered wagon that had somehow survived wave upon wave of marauding Indians.

Probably that was how he ought to think of it. As a big adventure into the unknown. Establishing a settlement in a foreign country. But he didn't feel like John Wayne.

At last, Dad broke away from his friends and staggered towards the lorry. Ian's heart gave a jolt. He wasn't drunk already, was he? If he was, it was hard luck on them. He was the only one who could drive.

Mum blew and wiped her nose and picked up her bag. She shuffled across the forecourt with all the other wives and aunties in her wake.

Jimmy said, 'I'll have to be on ma way,' and rushed over to the lorry before any of his mates could stop him.

Bella gave her boyfriend a last slobbery kiss and let him go. She had a quick squint in her mirror to see her make-up was all right, straightened her skirt and tittuped across to join Mum and Dad.

'I'd better be off,' Ian said.

'Be seeing you then,' said Andy.

'Oh, aye.'

'You'll be sure to write, won't you?' Maisie pleaded.

'I said I would,' Ian retorted.

'Here,' said Jean. 'I nearly forgot.'

She held out a piece of white heather.

'We bought this to bring you luck.'

'Oh,' said Ian, surprised. 'That wis good of you.'

He took the white heather and wondered what to do with it. Finally, he slipped it into the breast pocket of his shirt.

'I think we're about to leave.'

'I'll miss you,' said Maisie, and she began to snivel.

'Well, it's the way it is,' said Ian. 'Thanks fur everything,' he added, though he didn't quite know why.

He strode across to the lorry, ready to leave his past behind him.

Dad, Mum and Bella were to sit in front. It was a tight squeeze, but they just about managed it. Jimmy and Ian had to climb into the back. They made themselves as comfortable as they could on the mattresses thrown on top of all the other furniture.

At the third attempt, the lorry shuddered into life. It began to roll forward. There was a cheer from the crowd. Dad beat out a jaunty tune on the hooter, and they were off.

As the lorry ground to a halt at the corner leading into the main road, two grinning figures came chasing up to them. It was Wee Lin and his wife from the Chinese take-away. They made the best fish and chips in the whole of Glasgow.

Wee Lin handed up a big parcel. It felt hot and greasy.

Before Ian could say anything, the lorry gave a jolt and juddered forward. Wee Lin and his wife waved their hands delightedly in the air.

'Lang may yer lum leek,' Wee Lin shrieked in his highpitched voice, a gash of teeth slitting his face.

You had to forgive him. He meant well.

'Thanks,' Ian yelled back.

Ian woke with a start.

'Get your arm oot ma face,' Jimmy was saying. He shoved his brother further over the mattress.

It must have been the chips, giving his stomach a full comfortable feeling, that had sent him to sleep. They used to have them once or twice a week until they put VAT on them. It was nice of Wee Lin to give them a farewell present.

Or it could have been the rhythm of the lorry as it trundled along with a regular bump, bump, bump. It couldn't have been doing much more than thirty miles an hour.

Jimmy was lying back on the mattress, his head cupped in his hands, gazing up at the rusty struts of the lorry's hood a couple of feet away from his face. Out of the back Ian watched the steady stream of cars and vans and lorries come zooming towards them like angry bees and then, flashing their lights furiously, overtake them.

Then he caught sight of a big sign far away on the north-bound side of the motorway. It said, 'Welcome to Scotland'. They must have crossed the border. That was it then. Glasgow, Scotland, were left behind. He felt a sudden pang. Was it regret? He didn't know.

He tried to work out what Glasgow had meant to him. The flat in the tower block on the estate. The gang and the games they had played in the forecourt and the empty garages or on the rubbish tips and wasteland next to the factory. The school which had bored him silly and which it was a relief to play truant from even if there was the pain of the tawse if you got caught. The visits once or twice a year, at Christmas or on birthdays, to the city centre to look at the shops or to the Barras in search of bargains.

It wasn't much.

Mum and Dad were always talking about the old days when they lived in the Gorbals, and Argyle Street and Sauchiehall Street were full of bustle and excitement. But then they'd been moved to the estate, and the corporation had dug a big hole in the centre of Glasgow to make motorways and by-passes. It wasn't the same, they said. The spirit had gone.

Ian turned to his brother. 'Are you glad to be going?'

Jimmy gave him a scornful look. 'Whit d'you think? Glasgow's dead. There's nothing there fur me. London. That's where it's all happening. That's where all the jobs is. They English keep everything fur themselves. It's aboot time I had ma share. It's time I had some money in ma pocket.'

Jimmy hadn't had a job since he left school, and that was three years ago now. Bella who was nearly eighteen hadn't been much luckier. She'd had the odd job, but none of them had lasted long. She'd made a scene and been given the sack. Or else there'd been cut-backs, and she was the one to go. It was six months since she'd last been in work. The way things were going, it wasn't likely to be any better for Ian when he left school in two years' time.

Unless what Jimmy said was true, and there was more chance in London.

He was just dozing off again when the lorry began to slacken speed and go even slower. It couldn't be a hill, could it, that the lorry was having difficulty getting up. Ian thought they didn't have hills on the motorway.

Then the lorry veered off to the left, and he saw that they were stopping at a service station.

The place was jam-packed with cars piled high with suitcases and rucksacks and folding chairs. It looked as though everybody was off to the seaside on holiday. It was all right for some people.

After going backwards and forwards a couple of times, Dad ended up parking beside a line-up of huge container lorries. Ian thought theirs was big enough, but it was a pigmy by comparison.

He jumped down and jogged about. It was a relief to be able to stretch his legs. The clouds had cleared, and the sun was shining from a blue sky. The rays struck sharp against the top of his head.

'It's baking,' he cried, and he began to peel off his sweater.

'It's like I said,' Jimmy pointed out grimly. 'It's like jobs. They English keep everything fur themselves. Even the guid weather.'

The others clambered down from the cab and joined them. Bella dragged off her cardigan and mopped her brow.

'It's time you had air-conditioning fitted,' she said. 'It's like the black hole of Calcutta in there.'

'You dinny ken when you're well off,' said Jimmy. 'I'll swap you.'

'Aw naw. I'm no getting in the back.'

'Nivver mind arguing,' said Mum. 'Where's the toilet? I've been dying to go fur the last hour.'

They all went.

Then they made for the cafeteria. When they got there, they found a long queue stretching out of the doors.

'This is awfie,' said Dad. He stamped his feet impatiently.

'It'll soon go down,' said Mum. Though she didn't sound too hopeful.

There were people everywhere. The tables were hidden under trays and dirty cups and greasy plates thick with left-over chips and fish bones and half-eaten sausages.

Gradually, the queue moved along until they came level with the first display cabinets of food from which you could help yourself. Dad was still fuming at the time it was taking.

'I want steak and chips,' said Bella.

Mum gulped. She'd just caught sight of the price list set up on the wall above them and was scanning it anxiously. 'My, just look at they prices.'

Dad stopped fidgetting long enough to run his eyes down the menu and do some quick calculations.

'It's sausages, beans and chips fur me,' said Jimmy.

Dad had gone all red. He glared wildly up and down the queue.

'Can I have yin of they cakes?' Ian asked, pointing at the glass case crammed with chocolate gateaux, lemon meringue and apple pie.

'No, you can't,' snapped Mum. 'D'you think we're made of money? You can have cake at hame.'

'Aw, Mum,' Ian protested. But he knew there was no point in saying more.

'I've had enough of this,' Dad announced suddenly. He pushed his way towards the end of the queue, threw his tray back on top of the pile, and stomped out. There was nothing for it but for the rest of them to follow him.

'Whit aboot ma dinner?' Bella stormed when they were outside.

'I don't get you,' said Jimmy. 'Standing in that queue fur half an hour, and then just when we're getting served you walk oot.'

'There's nae need to speak like that,' said Mum.

'Go boil your heid,' said Dad.

'Oh aye, I'll do that,' retorted Jimmy.

They found a stall nearby and made do with hamburgers and orange squash. Bella still went on complaining. 'D'you call this a meal? It's no enough to keep a dog alive.'

Mum gave her a reproachful look.

Dad went all furtive, squinting up and down at the people standing around and walking past. He turned his back on them and took a half-bottle of whisky from his jacket pocket. One of his cronies must have given it to him as a parting gift. He refreshed himself with a couple of quick swigs.

Then it was back to the lorry.

'D'you think we'll get there afore tomorrow?' Jimmy asked sarcastically before climbing in.

Dad just stared at him with pursed lips and held his breath.

Once more, the steady rumbling of the lorry lulled Ian into a kind of coma. He had lost track of time, but it would still be hours before they reached their destination.

Beside him, Jimmy was lying flat out with his mouth open. He was snoring. The snorts and grunts were so loud they even outdid the chugging and coughing of the lorry. Ian was used to the sound. He and his brother had shared a bedroom in Glasgow. He wondered if they would have to share again in London. Nobody had said. It wasn't something he was looking forward to.

It had been all right while they had both been at school, but since Jimmy had left he'd got all bad-tempered. A right pain in the neck. There were always rows.

Gazing out of the back of the lorry, Ian couldn't tell how much closer they were getting to London. The motorway stretched endlessly behind them. The countryside, flat fields and outcrops of towns all looked the same. All he could tell was that the journey seemed to be taking an eternity. Cars and lorries went on speeding up to them, signalling furiously and passing them. They were in some kind of crazy chase and were being left further and further behind. At this rate, they'd never get there.

Then the lorry dropped back even more. It shuddered and juddered and rolled onto the hard shoulder where it came to a halt. We haven't run out of petrol, have we? Ian thought. No, that couldn't be it because Dad had filled up at the service station. But there must be something wrong.

Ian slid over the tailboard onto the road. He hurried round to the front. Billowing clouds of smoke were rising from the engine. It looked as though it was on fire.

Dad stumbled down from the cab and began waving his arms around wildly to try to clear the smoke. Mum and Bella peered anxiously through the windscreen.

'We've run oot of water,' Dad shouted. 'I forgot to check.'

The lorry had one of those old-fashioned radiators in front with a big metal cap on top. It was so antiquated it ought to have been in a museum. Dad stretched up to try to unscrew the cap and fell back with a yelp of pain. Then he was dancing up and down, cursing furiously and shaking his burnt fingers in the air.

Ian listened with interest. Dad had learnt some new swear words since he'd been away.

By now, Mum and Bella had climbed down to join them. They stared aghast at the whirling clouds. It was like those pictures on TV of volcanoes when they're about to erupt.

'Oh my,' Mum said.

'D'you think it's gonny blow up?' Bella asked fearfully.

'How do I ken?' retorted Dad, and he stuck his throbbing fingers in his mouth.

Then he noticed the cardigan Bella had hanging round her shoulders. Before she could protest, he grabbed it and yanked it off.

'Hey,' Bella cried. 'Whit are you doing?'

Dad ignored her. He wrapped the cardigan round his hand and approached the radiator again. He thrust his arm into the smoke and grasped the cap. He tried to turn it. His face got redder and redder. The veins on his forehead bulged out and beads of sweat sprang up and ran down his cheeks. He gritted his teeth.

Everyone watched and waited with bated breath.

Suddenly Dad let out a triumphant gasp. The cap was moving. Inch by inch he worked it round, His face was tense with effort and concentration. The sweat was pouring off him.

Then it all happened at once. The cap shot off. Dad was thrown back yelling onto the road. A column of steam shrieked upwards with tremendous force, desperate to be free. Ian half expected a genie to appear.

Gradually, the steam evaporated, and there were sighs of relief all round. Dad picked himself up and wiped his face with the cardigan still wrapped round his hand and arm.

'That's a mercy anyway,' said Mum.

'Aye,' said Dad. 'All we need noo is some water.'

Bella eyed him grimly. 'That's ma best cardy.'

Dad looked at her as though he didn't know what she was talking about. Then he unwound the cardigan and threw it at her. She caught it, shook it out and held it up for inspection. There were dark oily stripes across the back.

'Look at it,' she cried. 'It's ruined.'

'Nivver mind,' said Mum, patting her on the back. 'It's all in a good cause.'

Bella went on muttering.

'Where's Jimmy?' Dad asked.

It was only then that Ian realised that his brother wasn't there. 'He's sleeping in the back.'

Dad gave a tut of annoyance. 'Is that no typical? Tell me when he ever does anything else.'

He stalked round to the back of the lorry and began hammering on the tailboard with the flat of his palm. 'Come on oot, you,' he shouted. 'You're wanted.'

Jimmy's bleary face appeared. He blinked his eyes. 'Whit is it?'

'You'll have to gang to the next service station and get some water,' Dad told him.

'What?' Jimmy yelled back in shock. He was awake now all right. 'Why can't he go?' he demanded, jerking his head in Ian's direction.

11

'You're bigger,' Dad explained. 'You can carry more.'

Jimmy muttered to himself, 'It's always me, intit?' and began to climb reluctantly over the tailboard.

Dad watched him with a baleful eye. He waited until Jimmy landed on the road. Then he said, 'You'll need a pail.'

Jimmy looked at him as though he could have murdered him. But he gritted his teeth and held himself in. He jumped at the tailboard and hauled himself over. From inside came the clatter of furniture being shunted about and upturned and Jimmy's curses of anger.

'Oh my,' said Mum. 'Whit's he doing to ma furniture?'

Ian shrugged his shoulders. He knew he'd be in for it when Jimmy got him on his own. He was sure to get the blame.

Some time later, Jimmy emerged with a metal bucket. He dropped it on the road with a clang and leapt out after it. Without a word, he picked it up and set off along the hard shoulder. Everyone watched him go.

He had only walked a few yards when he stopped and turned round. 'How far is it anyway?' he shouted.

'I dinny ken,' Dad replied. 'I think it's aboot two mile.'

'Two mile!' They must have heard the shriek in the next county.

For a moment it looked as though Jimmy was going to throw the bucket down and kick it flat. But he thought better of it. He heaved in a deep breath and began to trudge along the road.

The others settled down on the grassy slope to wait. Dad unscrewed the top of his whisky bottle and took a drink. The bottle was half empty, Ian noticed. Mum gave a disapproving sniff but didn't say anything.

The sun was lower in the sky, but it was still hot. Bella stretched herself out full-length on the grass and drew up her skirt to show her pale fleshy thighs.

Mum tutted. 'Pull your skirt doon, Bella. Whit a way to behave.'

'It's all right, Mum,' said Bella without opening her eyes. 'I'm only sun-bathing.'

'It's enough to give they drivers a heart attack,' Dad muttered.

A lot of them were certainly giving her their full attention. As huge lorries thundered towards them, their drivers caught sight of her and grinned and shouted and waved. Ian couldn't hear what they were saying, but he could guess. Cars slowed down and swerved. Passengers gawped speechless at the spectacle of Bella's legs. There'd be an accident yet.

Ian chewed at a stalk of grass and watched the traffic. It was going to be a long wait. If it was two miles to the next service station, it was two miles back. It would take Jimmy at least an hour. He'd be in a right mood when he got back. He'd be flaming mad.

Dad would probably have finished his whisky by then as well.

'Where's that lad?' Dad fumed after an hour had passed. 'He must be crawling on his hands and knees.'

'Dinny fret,' soothed Mum. 'I'm sure he's doing his best.'

'Aye,' muttered Dad. 'The trouble is his best is everybody else's worst.'

He got out his whisky bottle.

At last they spied him — a tiny speck at the point where the motorway curved round. Gradually, he grew larger, walking lop-sided, weighed down by his bucket.

'Whit kept you?' Dad demanded when he came within hailing distance.

'That's all the thanks I get,' moaned Jimmy.

Dad examined the bucket. It was half-empty. 'Is that the best you could do?'

'It kept slopping oot,' said Jimmy. 'Ma troosers is wet through with it.'

'They dinny look wet to me.'

'Well, they've dried in the sun, haven't they?'

Dad groaned and grabbed hold of the bucket. 'Give it here.'

He carried the bucket round to the front of the lorry and began pouring water into the radiator.

'Just you wait,' Jimmy muttered to Ian.

Dad screwed on the cap, and they were ready to set off again.

13

'Whit a waste,' Bella grumbled, tidying herself up. 'I wis just getting a good tan.'

In the back of the lorry, Jimmy punched Ian in the ribs. 'That's fur no going to get the water.'

Ian yelped and slipped along the mattress away from his brother. 'It wisny ma fault,' he protested.

'Oh yes it wis,' Jimmy maintained, giving him another jab. 'You get away with everything. I'm the yin that aye gets lumbered.'

Nothing had changed.

When night fell, they seemed to be no nearer their destination. They stopped at another service station to have sandwiches and to fill up with petrol. This time Dad remembered to check the water.

'It'll no be long noo, son,' Mum comforted. Ian didn't believe her.

Mile after mile, he watched the headlights of the cars and trucks behind them grow larger and then flash past them out of sight. It was quite hypnotic. It could send you into a trance.

Then he noticed there were houses on either side of the road, and then shops. They had come off the motorway. This must be it. This must be London. He sat up and took more interest, but it just went on and on the same. He looked out for all the famous places and buildings he had heard about, but he didn't catch sight of any of them.

He was disappointed really. It wasn't much different from Glasgow except that there was more of it, and there was more traffic about and more people than there would have been in Glasgow at that time of night. Why did everyone go on about London all the time? It didn't look anything special to him.

Then suddenly they were there. The lorry came to a halt. Ian stuck his head out of the back and peered about him. They had stopped outside a large red-brick block. It was set back a few feet from the road. Without warning, the lorry started up again and began reversing into an alleyway at the side. Ian was thrown backwards onto the mattress.

14

'Get off,' Jimmy protested, pushing him away.

'I think we're here,' said Ian.

Jimmy struggled to his feet, and together they clung to the struts of the roof as the lorry shunted into position. The front doors were opened and slammed. Dad came round to the back, slapping his hand on the side.

'Wakey, wakey,' he called.

He sounded more cheerful. He was probably glad the driving was over and done with. He unbolted the tailboard and let it fall with a crash fit to rouse the dead. It went on banging backwards and forwards.

Ian and Jimmy jumped down.

'Come on then,' said Jimmy. 'Let's see it.'

He too seemed to have lost some of his bad-temper.

'Oh ma legs,' said Bella, coming round to join them. 'It's great to be on ma feet again. All that sitting doon.'

Mum was looking apprehensively about her, trying to take it all in.

'Oh my,' she said. 'I hope we've done the right thing.'

'Of course we have,' said Dad confidently. 'You wait till you see the flat.'

'Whit are we waiting fur then?' Jimmy demanded.

Dad led the way to an entrance, and they went up a flight of stairs.

'It's on the first floor,' he explained. 'Nae mair hauling up all they stairs when the lift's no working.'

'That'll be a blessing any road,' said Mum. 'They stairs just aboot killed me.'

The door to the flat was in an open walkway at the back. While Dad was searching in his pocket for the key, Ian leaned over the parapet. There was a concrete yard below and some garages. Beyond them there seemed to be trees.

Dad unlocked the door and switched on the light. They went from room to room, eyeing them up and down.

'It's a nice big kitchen,' said Mum.

'I want the room at the front,' said Bella.

'At least the wallpaper's on the walls,' said Jimmy. 'No like the last place.'

'Aye,' said Dad, 'and there's no cracks to let the water in either.'

It didn't look too bad. There were only three bedrooms, so Ian would have to share with Jimmy again, but that was life.

'I think it's lovely,' said Mum when they had completed the tour of inspection. 'If only the neighbours could see it, they'd be green with envy.'

She gave Dad a grateful glance. 'You've done well.'

'Aye, it's no sae bad,' said Dad, pleased in spite of himself. He almost smiled. Then he pulled himself together. 'We canny stand here talking all night. There's work to be done.'

Unloading the furniture was easier than Ian expected. He was tired and his bones ached. But at least it only had to be carted up one flight of stairs, and the feeling of relief that they had actually arrived gave them all renewed energy.

Dad stood in the truck and threw things out to them or manhandled them to the edge so that he could drop them off. Ian and Jimmy humped them up the stairs. Mum and Bella decided where they should be dumped and set about creating some kind of order.

The only problem was the noise. The clatter of their shoes on the stairs, the heaves and groans, the shuffling as they worked round corners and through doors, the awful crash when something fell or their strength gave way.

Twice, a door on the ground floor opened, and an irate figure in pyjamas burst out to yell at them.

'Some of us are trying to sleep,' he informed them.

Ian and Jimmy tried to carry on with bated breath and on tip-toe, but it was difficult. This first view of their new neighbours wasn't encouraging either.

But at last it was all done. Two hours later, they were sitting round the kitchen table with mugs of strong tea and a packet of chocolate digestive biscuits that Mum had kept as a treat.

16

Nobody had much to say. They were just too exhausted.

'My, it's been a long day,' said Mum.

'Aye,' Dad agreed. 'It's time we wis all in bed.'

Mum gathered up the mugs. 'I'll just wash these.'

Ian undressed in a dream. As he took his shirt off, he felt the white heather he had put in his pocket. It looked a bit crumpled. But it was a nice gesture, he thought vaguely. He put the white heather in the drawer of the chest under the clothes he had unpacked.

He finished undressing and climbed into bed. He curled up under the bedclothes and tried to sleep. His body was throbbing with tiredness, but his brain was still a whirl with all the things that had happened that day. He would have so much to tell Andy and Maisie and Jean when he next saw them.

Then it hit him that he would probably never see them again. He had left his friends behind. They were four hundred miles away, and he was in London with his family, starting a new life.

What would it be like? Would he find new friends? He suddenly felt very alone. Even though Jimmy in the bed just across from him was snoring loud enough to shake the walls.

He remembered that Maisie had asked him to write to her. He had said he would, but it wasn't on. He was no good at writing letters. Besides, what would he say? They all thought how marvellous it was for him to be going to London and what a wonderful time he would have. He wasn't so sure about that. Still, he couldn't disappoint them.

As he drifted off to sleep, he began to compose the letter that he knew he would never write.

Dear Maisie, We had a great journey down. It took no time at all. We were going at seventy miles an hour most of the way. We went right through the middle of London. I saw Big Ben and Westminster Abbey and the Tower of London and Soho. I better not tell you what was going on in Soho. I'll tell Andy the next time I see him. The new flat is all right. Everything is going to be fine. So you don't need to worry. I hope you and Jean are well.

That was enough, wasn't it? He tried to think what you put at the end of a letter. *Yours faithfully? Ever yours? Love?*

But before he could decide, he was asleep.

2

Ian stared out of the window of his new bedroom. There were no curtains up yet. Beneath his bare feet the lino left by the previous tenants was cool and slippery, but the air was warm. Jimmy seemed to have been right. The English did keep all the best weather to themselves. Across from him, Jimmy was still fast asleep. He had pulled the bedclothes round him and pressed his head into the pillow to keep out the light.

From the window, Ian watched the traffic racing past. Perhaps it was the unaccustomed rumbling that had woken him. You couldn't hear the traffic five flights up. Besides, there hadn't been many cars on the estate.

Beyond the busy road, the ground sank away to a railway line, and as the trains hurtled past the whole earth seemed to shake. On the other side of the track was a row of grimy terraced houses with narrow straggly gardens.

Ian put on a T-shirt and jeans and went into the kitchen. If it had been Glasgow, he'd have needed a sweater as well.

Mum was standing in the middle of the floor surrounded by bags and boxes.

'I'll nivver get this place straight,' she groaned. 'You'll have to get your own breakfast.'

Dad had gone to work ages ago. He'd only had the weekend for the move. He couldn't have had much sleep.

Ian helped himself to a cup of tea from the pot and had a slice of bread and jam while Mum emptied the contents of a bag — tins and bottles and packets — onto the table and began to put them on the shelves.

'Can I help?' Ian asked.

'Naw,' said Mum, 'you'll only get in the way. If I dinny put things in their place maself I'll nivver ken where to find them.'

She dithered over a tin of soup before deciding where to store it.

'You go on oot,' she continued. 'You go and find some friends.'

Friends? Ian had a feeling it wasn't going to be as easy as that. It was worth a try though. It was still the school holidays so there ought to be people his own age around.

He paused on the walkway outside and looked in either direction. There was no one in sight. The place seemed deserted. Behind the garages were the trees he had noticed the night before. He was almost on a level with the tops. They stretched in an irregular pattern of points and curves of green for quite a distance. Beyond them peeped the roofs of houses in the next street. It was like an uneven carpet. All you had to do was to step off the parapet and you could stride across it with giant steps from one pinnacle of green to another until you reached the other side.

It was strange for there to be so many trees right in the middle of a city, Ian thought. He wondered what they were doing there. It couldn't be somebody's garden. It was far too vast.

There hadn't been many trees where he had lived before. The corporation had planted a few to cheer up the concrete forecourt of the flats, with thick wooden poles to support them and rolls of wire netting to protect them. But they hadn't stood a chance. Within a week most of them had been snapped in two by kids swinging on them. The corporation didn't bother to replace them.

Ian turned and padded down the stairs. The walls were sprayed and scratched with words and slogans and crude drawings. This

20

at least was the same. Except that the football teams were English — Tottenham and Arsenal instead of Rangers and Celtic.

Some of the other words didn't make sense. Someone had chalked up the letters KBW in huge print. What could that mean? Perhaps it was the initials of someone's name.

In the paved area in front of the main entrance there were some children playing. Other human beings at last. But they were only little girls. They couldn't have been much more than seven or eight. There were three of them, bouncing a rubber ball against the wall and taking turns to catch it. When they saw Ian, they stopped and stared at him open-mouthed.

Ian gave a nervous nod of his head. 'Hi,' he said, trying to be friendly.

The girls just went on staring.

'We've just moved in,' Ian explained.

'You what?' one of the girls asked.

You'd think he was speaking a foreign language. 'We've just moved in.'

'Don't 'e talk funny?' the girl said to her two friends. Then she fixed Ian with a bold look and said, 'My mum told me not to speak to strange men.'

She picked up the ball, and pushing the others in front of her, began to move away.

'Come on,' she said. 'Let's go play round the back.'

Before they vanished round the corner, they halted for a moment to give him a final stare. He might have been some creature from outer space.

Not that it mattered. Who wanted to be friends with eight-year-old little girls. Only other eight-year-old little girls.

He walked down to the pavement and gazed back at the block of flats. There were only three storeys. There couldn't have been more then twelve flats altogether. Not like the huge tower block he'd come from — twenty storeys high with ten flats on each floor. You couldn't help making friends there with so many people

21

around. There had been lots of people his own age there — Andy and Maisie and Jean and lots of others.

Here, it looked as though he might not be so lucky. Unless there were more flats further on.

He walked along the pavement to find out.

But there weren't any more flats. The next building was a large house with a set of wrought iron gates and a gravel path leading up to the front door. It looked very grand. He stared up at the pillared entrance and the broad bow windows. He'd seen houses like this in Glasgow, but he'd never been so close to them. You'd have to have a lot of money to live in a house like that. You'd need a fortune.

He started guiltily. If someone saw him staring in, they might get suspicious. He moved on.

The next house was just as big and imposing. And the next. What kind of place had they landed in? They certainly were coming up in the world.

The pavement continued to his right in a curve. A street sign fixed to a low wall said 'Trinity Park'. But straight ahead of him was a broad expanse of open grass. A busy main road cut through the middle of it, and then the grass continued on the other side until it reached a row of houses that looked quite small in the distance. A sign on the pavement said 'Trinity Common'.

There were people walking about, taking a short cut to the shops or to work, letting their dogs romp about in the long grass. This was different from the rubbish tip next to the estate all right.

A line of trees ran round the edge. They were tall with wide spreading branches. A gang of small children was squealing and chasing round one of them. They were throwing sticks up into the branches, trying to knock down chestnuts. When they succeeded and a piece of tree came fluttering down, they rushed over to examine their prize. Then they quarrelled and argued about whose it was.

Ian moved on. He was too old to be interested in conkers.

22

Further on, some boys were playing football. That was more like it. He hurried towards them.

But when he got closer, he got a shock. The boys were all black.

He's never really thought about it. He supposed he knew there were a lot of black people in London. He'd seen them on television in news programmes and things like that. But it still came as a surprise. Somehow it hadn't really sunk in.

You hardly ever saw black people in Glasgow. Not the part he used to live in. Except sometimes Lascars off the boats, looking cold and miserable. Or shops run by Asians. There were no black people living on the estate. Unless you counted Wee Lin and his wife. And he didn't think you did.

There were five of them. They had rolled up a couple of shirts to act as goal posts. One of them stood guard while the others passed the ball and took shots at goal. The goalkeeper was good. He dived at the ball and thrust it away with his hands. Or curved his body round the ball and hugged it to his chest. Then he sprang to his feet, took a few skipping steps and kicked the ball back into play, his leg coming out straight and his toe pointing outwards.

Ian stood behind the goal posts and watched. The boys were about the same age as himself. They went on with their passing and tackling and shooting at goal. They did a lot of shouting and yelling at each other. They must have known he was there, but he might as well have been invisible for all the attention they paid him.

The ball bounced onto the road and one of them had to risk his life among the traffic to retrieve it. It was then that the goalkeeper turned round and acknowledged Ian's presence with a cool stare.

The boy was slightly taller than Ian and more heavily built. He had taken his T-shirt off, and his bare chest was shiny with sweat. From the way his arms and chest were developed, he must have done weight training.

It was difficult to tell from the expression on his face what he was thinking. His lips were slightly open and pulled back from his teeth. It wasn't exactly a sneer and yet it wasn't friendly either. His brown eyes were round and large. They stared at Ian without blinking. They seemed to see him and yet not see him. As though the boy was looking right through him.

Then there was a shout. One of the players was driving the ball before him towards the goal. He stopped to steady it and then lobbed it into the air. The goalkeeper leapt up, caught it in his hands and dragged it down.

Ian watched a bit longer. It looked like a good game. He wanted to join in. But none of the players gave him any encouragement. As far as they were concerned, he might as well not have been there.

He was just about to turn away when the ball slipped through the goalkeeper's fingers and came bumping over the turfy grass towards him. He trapped it with his foot and stooped to pick it up. Before he could do anything with it, the goalkeeper had bounded over to him.

For a moment, Ian thought of asking if he could play. He even took breath and opened his mouth to speak. But one glance at the black boy's face was enough to stop him. There was an angry scowl on it that looked almost dangerous. Those narrowed glinting eyes. That skin tight over the cheekbones. As though he was accusing Ian of trying to steal their ball. He grabbed it from Ian's hands and strode back to the goal. The others had gathered there, and they stood for a while talking among themselves and giving Ian dirty looks before starting the game again.

Ian thrust his hands in his pockets and walked away. Talk about not being wanted. They couldn't have made it more obvious if they'd actually shoved him away with their hands.

Well, he didn't care. Who wanted to play football with black kids anyway? Only other black kids.

And yet . . .

He went on worrying about it as he trailed aimlessly across the grass. Was there something wrong with him? Or did people down here just think they were superior? That was what Andy had said.

He wondered what Andy was doing now — and Maisie and

Jean. They could have gone looking for useful scraps on the rubbish tip by the factory. Andy was very good with his hands. He made all kind of models out of bits of metal and wire and plastic.

Or perhaps they had gone bramble-picking. He hadn't checked lately, but it was about time for that, wasn't it? There were dense thickets of brambles running wild and practically taking over part of the rubbish tip. They had great times cutting paths through them and filling jam-jar after jam-jar. Mum was glad to have them. She told him off for getting his clothes stained and tearing his shirt. But she made pounds and pounds of bramble jelly.

Ian sighed. It seemed as though those days had gone forever.

'There's nae jobs,' Jimmy complained for the fourth or fifth time in the week since they had arrived. 'I don't know why we came. Call this the land of opportunity? That's a laugh.'

Jimmy and Bella had signed on at Social Security. They had been to the Job Centre. But they hadn't had any luck.

They were all sitting round the kitchen table having their tea. Mum still liked them to sit down as a family to one meal in the day. She gave Jimmy a sympathetic glance.

'I'm sure something'll turn up,' she said, trying to comfort him.

'Aye,' said Jimmy glumly. 'And I'm sure elephants can fly.'

'You've got to keep trying,' Mum urged.

'Keep trying?' Jimmy exploded. 'Whit d'you think I've bin doing fur the past three years? I look in the paper every day. I write letters. I phone up. I go to the Job Centre. And whit good does it do? None.'

'Aye, it's all a waste of time,' agreed Bella. 'There's nae jobs to be had.'

A cloud of gloom descended on them. Mum tried to think of something cheerful to say but couldn't. Dad sipped his tea and stared blankly into space. Ian looked from face to face and thought. If that was the way things were, then why had they moved? Would it be the same for him when he left school?

Then Mum remembered something. 'You ken that newsagent's on the corner of the main road? I noticed the day they've got these adverts in the window. Gas cookers fur sale and things like that.'

Dad came to suddenly. 'You've got a cooker,' he cried. He sounded alarmed.

'I ken that,' said Mum, dismissing his protest. 'But they've got these adverts fur cleaners as well.'

Bella gasped. 'Whit? You're no getting me going oot cleaning.'

'I wisny thinking of you,' said Mum. 'I meant me.'

'That's all right then,' Bella muttered.

'They want people fur two hours a day or something like that,' Mum went on. 'I could manage that. And we could do with the money. Everything's that expensive doon here.'

'That's true enough,' agreed Dad.

'Whit d'you think?'

Dad pursed his lips and considered it. 'It's worth a try. You could make enquiries.'

'Right then. I'll do that.'

Mum looked quite pleased with herself. At last she had found something to bring a ray of hope into the day. She searched about for more news to cheer them up. What else had happened?

'Oh aye,' she said. 'I met one of the neighbours the day.'

'Did you?' said Dad, not really interested.

'She seemed very nice. I'd run oot of milk and she lent me some. She's got two bonny bairns. One's one and the ither one's three. A boy and a girl. Bright as buttons they are.'

She thought for a moment. 'I don't think I've ever spoken to a black person afore.'

Dad stared at her. 'Black?' He grunted. 'You'll soon get used to that. They're everywhere doon here. It's like living in the Casbah.'

Ian thought about the black boys he had seen on the Common.

'Well, she seemed very nice,' Mum maintained. 'Her name's Hyacinth. That's a pretty name.'

'I dinny ken whit the country's coming to,' Dad grumbled on.

'Letting all they black folks come here to take oor hooses and take oor jobs.'

Jimmy looked up. 'That's whit somebody said to me the day at the Job Centre.'

'Well, he wis right,' said Dad.

'Naw, it wisny like that.'

'How d'you mean then?'

'He wis blaming me.'

'You! But you're no black.'

'It's the same difference, intit?'

Dad gave an exasperated sigh. 'I dinny ken whit you're on aboot.'

'Do I need to spell it oot to you?' Jimmy asked contemptuously. 'He wis saying it wis people like me frae Glasgow and Liverpool and Newcastle that wis coming doon here and stealing their jobs.'

Dad was astounded. 'It's no the same at all. We're British.'

'Hyacinth said she wis born in London,' Mum put in.

Dad stared at her as though he thought she was an idiot. What did that have to do with anything? But he was too exhausted to go on with the argument. So was Jimmy. They lapsed into a gloomy silence.

After a while, Bella had had enough.

'It's like the morgue in here,' she said. She got up. 'I'm going oot.'

'Where to?' Mum asked.

'I'm meeting a fella.'

'That wis quick,' said Jimmy pointedly. 'I suppose he's doing the paying.'

'Mind your own business,' Bella snapped back.

'Whit aboot Fergus then?' Mum asked.

'Fergus?' Bella cried scornfully. 'He's four hundred mile away. That's nae use to me.'

She swept out of the kitchen to get ready.

'I don't know,' said Mum. 'There's times I despair.'

Jimmy pushed his chair away from the table and stood up.

'I'm going to bed,' he announced.

'Whit?' exclaimed Dad. 'At this hour?'

'I've nae money so whit else is there to do? You tell me.'

He scowled at them all and went out.

'I don't know,' said Mum again, and she and Dad exchanged despondent glances.

'Come on,' said Dad. 'I'll help you clear away the things.'

Ian piled the plates up for them and then went into the living room. He was feeling depressed. Everything seemed to be in such a mess. There were no jobs for Jimmy and Bella. There were no new friends for him. Why hadn't they just stayed where they were?

He switched on the television. It was the news. It was all about the miners' strike and unemployment and famine in Africa.

That was all he needed.

The wall at the back of the flats had crumbled in places. Or else it had been deliberately hacked at and vandalised. Piles of broken bricks and mortar littered the ground. It would be easy to climb through one of the gaps.

Ian had been meaning to explore what lay beyond for some time. This was his chance.

He looked up at the flats to see if anyone was watching. He could hear a baby crying, loud and squally. It was probably one of Hyacinth's. But there was no one in sight.

He gripped the uneven bricks and pulled himself up to a ledge. Then he stepped over and dropped down on the other side.

He didn't know what to expect. From the balcony on the first floor, it looked like a sea of trees. Like a wild stretch of forest that had somehow been left behind and forgotten. He half-expected that no human being had set foot in it for years. Even so he crouched down where he had landed and looked about cautiously just in case.

Everything was quiet. You couldn't even hear the rumble of the traffic on the main road or the rattle of the trains. The only sound was the chattering and chirping of the birds.

28

He stood up and took a few steps forward. It was cool and shady. A canopy of branches and leaves closed in above his head. Here and there, the sun penetrated the thick foliage and sent slanting rays down to light up patches of undergrowth.

He waded through the long straggly grass and came to a path. He had been wrong. People did know this place existed. The path was made of hardened earth and ran parallel to the wall. He checked to the right and to the left. There didn't seem to be anyone about. He set off to follow the path.

On his left, the wall continued in line with the path, but it was higher here, well over six feet, and in a good state of repair. It was impossible to see over. Every now and then, there were doors set into the wall. Ian tried to open one of them, but it was locked. He screwed his eye up to the key-hole and peered through. He could just make out a slice of well-kept lawn and the edge of a shed. It must have been the back garden of one of the big houses facing the Common. He walked on.

On either side of the path, trees and bushes of different kinds rose up and spread out. Ian didn't know much about trees. He could recognise a fir tree and a chestnut tree because of their cones and conkers, but mostly trees were just trees to him. There were a lot of them.

Surprisingly though, they weren't as thick and closely packed as they appeared from the balcony of the flats. Every now and then, they thinned out and there were clearings and open spaces. Other paths diverged from the main one and led away to the right. Ian explored some of them.

He came across a tennis court almost buried among the trees. Long grass and climbing plants had entwined themselves in the wire mesh and were reaching upwards. The surface of the court was crumbling in places and moss and weeds were taking over. The net was sagging, and it had more holes in it than it ought to have had. But it looked as though people still played tennis there.

Further on, Ian left the main path again and passed under a trellis-work archway smothered in flowers. He found himself in a paved area surrounded by beds of roses. Two garden benches were set out in the middle. Ian sat down on one of them and surveyed the scene.

Everything was neat and tidy. The roses were in full bloom — reds, yellows and whites. There were no weeds between the paving stones. It was clear that someone lavished a lot of time and care on the place.

It was clear too that it was private property. But who did it belong to? The big houses had their own gardens, so what did they need this for as well? Where he had lived, they had never had a garden. What would it be like to own a place like this? To be able to come here whenever you wanted to and know that you could be on your own and away from the noise of the traffic and the problems of other people.

The sun beat down sharply against his face. The scent from the roses and the other flowers was overwhelming. It was sweet and rich and heady. He hadn't realised flowers could smell so strongly. It was like the soap department in a big store. They hadn't had many flowers on the estate. Just a few weedy geraniums in pots.

What with the sun and the scent he felt himself becoming drowsy. It was like being drugged. Soon he would be drifting off to sleep.

He suddenly jerked his eyes open. Of course he was trespassing. If anyone found him, he would get into trouble. He glanced round quickly. There was no one about.

But then he thought why shouldn't he enjoy it? Why should he worry about these people whoever they were who wanted to keep everything to themselves? It was like that man at the Job Centre who told Jimmy off for trying to pinch his job. If the job was there, he had as much right to it as anyone else.

Ian got up and wandered on. Another side path led to a big wooden hut. It was bolted and padlocked. Beside the door was a tap. Ian turned it to see if it worked. There was a gurgling and a chugging and then water came gushing out. He quickly twisted the tap back until there was just a trickle and stooped to drink. The water ran down his chin before he could control it properly. It tasted cool and refreshing.

There was a window in the side of the hut. Through it, he could see garden tools neatly stacked. There was an old armchair with a cushion on it. A table held a small primus stove, a kettle, two mugs, a packet of sugar and a jar of coffee. Every mod. con. You could live there. He imagined what it would be like to be the hermit of the woods. The idea had its attractions.

He tore himself away and continued on the main path. Then he had the strange feeling of having been there before. The scenery seemed familiar. He recognised the crumbling wall. He was back where he started. He must have gone round in something like a circle.

He was pleased. He liked the place. It would be a great thing to show Andy and Maisie and Jean. They'd be sick with envy to know he had this whole place to himself.

But then the excitement ebbed away, and he felt empty inside. What was the point of having a place like this when you couldn't share it? He kicked at a turf of grass and wondered what to do next. He would go and have another look at that hut. You never knew when it might come in useful.

He had reached the hut and was just rounding the corner to examine the padlock again when the door was suddenly thrust open. Ian leapt backwards with shock. He was taken completely by surprise. A man stood in the doorway glaring at him. Ian gulped. He could make a run for it. But his feet were glued to the ground.

'What are you doing here?' the man demanded angrily.

He was quite old, much older than Dad. He was wearing old-fashioned dungarees and a flat cap. His shirt sleeves were rolled up, and he had wellingtons on his feet. He was carrying a pair of long-handled shears.

Ian tried to think of some excuse, but his brain wouldn't work. What could he say? The best he could manage was 'Nothing.'

'Nothing,' the man repeated contemptuously. 'Huh! You expect me to believe that? You council flat kids are always in here. Trampling down the flowers. Breaking off branches.'

'I've nivver been here afore,' Ian said in his defence.

The old man snorted. 'A likely story. I know you. I have to chase you out every week.'

Was the old man making it up? Or was he mistaking Ian for someone else? But there were no other children in the flats his age. Yet here he was being blamed for what they had done. The injustice of it stung him. He resented it.

'I wisny doing any harm,' he said stubbornly.

'Don't you give me none of your lip,' the old man responded. He brandished the shears in the air. 'Clear off.'

By now Ian's blood was up. 'Why should I?' he demanded.

'Because I say so.'

The old man advanced towards him, and they stood face to face glowering at each other. The old man was shaking with rage, but Ian stood his ground.

'You don't own the place,' he said.

'Don't you try that on with me,' said the old man. 'Do what you're told, you young hooligan.'

'I nivver seen no signs saying this place wis private,' Ian argued coolly.

The old man nearly burst. He waved his shears in front of Ian's face, nearly slicing his nose off. 'You know perfectly well it's private. Now, are you going? Or do I have to call the police?'

'Aye,' sneered Ian, 'that's always the way, intit?'

All the same, he decided he had better go. It wasn't just the threat of the police, though he didn't want anything to do with them. It was also the state the old man was getting into. He was shaking uncontrollably now. His mouth was dribbling. If he wasn't careful, he'd have a fit.

Ian turned away and began to walk along the path. He went as slowly as he reasonably could. He wasn't going to show the old man that he cared.

'And don't come back again,' the old man shouted after him.

32

Ian swung round. 'Go boil your heid,' he yelled.

He came to the gap in the wall and clambered over. It was a pity about the old man. Meeting him had quite spoiled the morning. He would have to keep an eye open for him next time.

He was suddenly aware that he was being watched. A girl was sitting on the steps of the back entrance to the flats. She was holding a baby on her lap. She was staring round-eyed at him, following his every move. He recognised her as one of the girls he had met on his first morning. She had got over her shyness or fright or whatever it was, and he had spoken to her a couple of times since then. Her name was Tracy.

Now her face broke into a cheeky grin. 'You been in the Park?' she asked.

Ian went and sat down beside her. 'Aye.'

The baby had round brown cheeks and large solemn eyes. It must have been one of Hyacinth's.

Tracy looked knowingly at Ian. 'I bet Old Bill caught you.'

'Is that the gardener? Aye.'

Tracy chortled gleefully. Ian wasn't sure he liked the sound of it. She seemed to be pleased he'd got into trouble.

She leaned towards him and became all confidential.

'You've got to watch it in the Park. Old Bill's always there. 'E's a terror.' She giggled mischievously. 'We quite enjoy gettin' 'im all worked up. 'E loses 'is temper easy as anythin'. You should 'ear the language 'e uses then. Even my dad don't use language like that.'

She thought about it for a while and then went on with relish. 'But the bit I like best is when 'e chases you. It's like playin' 'ide an' seek. It's good fun. Better than watchin' telly.'

Ian could imagine the dance Tracy and her friends would lead Old Bill. He almost felt sorry for him.

'Whit is the Park any road?' he asked.

'It belongs to the people what lives in the big 'ouses,' Tracy explained. 'It's their Park. They've all got keys to it through their back doors. We 'aven't got keys.' She cocked her head at the flats. 'This used to be a big 'ouse once. Then the council bought it up an' knocked it down an' built the flats. But they didn't give us a key to the Park. It don't seem fair, do it?'

'Right enough,' Ian agreed.

'That don't stop us goin' there though.' She giggled again.

The baby looked up into her face and imitated her.

'Ain't 'e sweet?' said Tracy, tickling the baby's chin.

'Aye,' agreed Ian, though he wasn't much interested in babies.

Tracy gave a sigh. 'School starts next week. I'm not lookin' forward to that. I 'ate school. All they do is boss you around an' tell you what to do.'

'I dinny much like it maself,' said Ian.

Tracy screwed up her nose. 'Don't you talk funny,' she said. 'When you first come 'ere, I couldn't understand what you was sayin'. But I suppose you get used to it.'

There was a call from above. Hyacinth was leaning over the balcony.

'Tracy, bring Paul up will you, love?'

She saw Ian and smiled. 'Hi! You settlin' in all right?'

'Aye,' said Ian. He had spoken to her before. Mum had been right. She was nice. Young and pretty as well.

'See you,' said Tracy as she gathered the baby into her arms and disappeared up the stairs.

'Aye,' Ian shouted after her.

He went on sitting there, his elbows on his thighs, and his head on his hands. School. Tracy had reminded him. He wasn't looking forward to it either.

What was the point of it? All you did was read books and copy down notes and sums. And then what did you find at the end of it? There were no jobs.

It was all a waste of time.

Still, there was a chance he might make some friends there. It might change everything. He hadn't met anyone yet. Tracy didn't really count.

If only Andy and Maisie and Jean were there. Perhaps he ought to write to them after all. But no. What was the use? They were miles away, and they wouldn't be interested in what he was doing any more. Besides, he wasn't sure he could tell them what it was really like.

In spite of himself though, words began to form themselves in his mind.

Dear Maisie, It's really great down here. There's that many places to go and that many things to do. At the end of the road there's a huge Common. Me and a gang of friends go there every day and play football. Then at the back of the flats there's a Park. Would you believe it? It's private and there's hardly ever anybody there. So me and my friends go and play in there. Nobody minds. It's got a real tennis court so we have a game of tennis. I've never played tennis before, but I'm getting quite good at it. When you come down, I'll teach you how to play. Sometimes we just sit in the sun and natter. I'm getting quite a sun tan. Jimmy and Bella both like it down here. They're looking for jobs, and I think there's a good chance they'll get them. There's all sorts of opportunities down here. Tell Andy I'll have lots to tell him when I see him. I hope you and Jean are keeping well. Love, Ian.

3

Ian trailed along the corridor searching for Room 19. That was where the school secretary told him to go. Room 19 — 4T — Mr Armstrong's class.

As he passed room after room, looking at the numbers on the doors, the noise of the pupils inside welled out and faded and welled out again. There might as well not have been any teachers there.

He had to double back twice and go up a flight of stairs before he eventually found Room 19. It was strangely quiet. He wondered if it was empty. Peering through the window in the door, he could see the teacher — presumably Mr Armstrong. He was perched on his desk talking to the class. He was swinging his legs and making sweeping gestures with his arms as he spoke. The pupils were listening. Well, that was something.

Ian knocked and went in.

Mr Armstrong turned his head and pulled a sour face at being interrupted. Then he seemed to remember. His expression relaxed and he gave a long 'Ah'. He jumped down from his desk and began to rummage among the papers on top of it.

While he waited anxiously, Ian took a quick squint at the class. They were a blur of black, brown and white faces out of which shone cool bright eyes. They were all staring at him. Curious. Indifferent. Hostile.

Then out of the blur, one of the faces sharpened into focus. It was a boy sitting in the front row. A black boy. Ian recognised him. It was the boy he had seen playing football on the Common. The goalkeeper. The boy who had snatched the ball out of his hands.

The boy was looking at him with raised eyebrows and pursed lips. Ian tried to make out what was going on being that mask. Was the boy amused? Mocking? Making fun? Ian scowled back at him.

'It's here somewhere,' Mr Armstrong was saying, scanning and scattering the papers on his desk. 'You're the new boy, aren't you?'

'Aye,' said Ian. 'Ma name's Ian McGloughlin.'

For a split second, there was an awed silence in the room, and then uproar broke out. They were falling about with laughter. The black boy in the front row was the worst. He was throwing himself backwards and forwards in his seat, practically falling off it. His face was creased up and his mouth wide open as sobs and guffaws shook his body. He had to wipe tears away from his eyes.

'Whit's up with you?' Ian demanded coldly.

'Yes, Vincent,' said Mr Armstrong. 'What's the matter?' Though Ian had a nasty suspicion that the teacher was only just able to restrain himself from joining in.

'Sir, sir,' Vincent replied, gasping for breath. 'I can't 'elp it. It the way 'e talk.'

He burst out into another fit of laughter, and the rest of the class joined in. Ian glowered darkly at him. Who did he think he was? Making fun of him like that. He wasn't anything special himself.

'Come on,' Mr Armstrong called. 'Settle down. You're not exactly giving our new friend a very good impression.'

There were still one or two last splutters and giggles, but the class finally subsided. Even Vincent managed to subdue his twitching lips and lower his eyes.

'There's a seat at the back for you,' Mr Armstrong pointed out. 'I'm just about to dictate the new timetable.'

Ian stumbled up the classroom to the empty desk and sat down. He could feel his face burning. But at least at the back he was out of vision for most of the other pupils, and he had time to recover.

No wonder he hated school when things like this happened. Just because the way he spoke was different from theirs. That had been no problem at his previous school. There they had all spoken the same. And anyway, they'd known each other all their lives. But he had still hated it. Now he had a double reason.

Mr Armstrong distributed timetable forms and began. He had only got two words out when someone shouted, 'Sir, I ain't got a pen.'

'Me neither,' came another voice.

The teacher felt in the pockets of his jacket. He drew out a couple of biros and threw them at the pupils.

Ian was amazed. They had it easy down here. Whenever he'd gone to his previous school without a pen, he'd had a clip round the ear to help improve his memory.

The dictation of the timetable went fairly smoothly, except when someone called out, 'Hey, sir, hang on. I'm still on Monday,' and Mr Armstrong had to pause and repeat things. There were occasional groans when they learned who was to take them that term — 'Oh, not him again!' — and enquiries about new teachers — 'Is she any good? D'you think she'll stay? Is she nice and young?'

The biggest groan of all came when Mr Armstrong announced that he would be taking 4T for English. He turned a look of injured pride on the class.

'Now you've really hurt me,' he pronounced in tragic tones.

'Aw!' went the class.

One of the pupils began to play an imaginary violin.

'Yes, you have,' the teacher insisted. Then he resigned himself to the situation. 'I might have known it, of course. You can't be expected to recognise quality when you see it.'

There were cries of protest at this.

'Who does he think he is?'

'Quality? He must be joking.'

'Come on,' said Mr Armstrong, returning to business. 'We've got no time for this badinage,' and he rattled off a whole string of subjects, teachers and rooms that left the class gasping to keep up.

38

He had just reached period 8 on Friday when the bell rang for morning break.

'How's that for timing?' he demanded triumphantly.

But there was already a stampede for the door, and half the class had disappeared.

'What's the matter?' the teacher asked. 'Did I say something wrong?' Though he didn't seem unduly upset.

Ian folded up his timetable as small as he could and shoved it into his pocket. He thought Mr Armstrong was soft. But he had to admit that the class appeared to like him.

Outside, the playground was swirling with people. Ian found a space for himself beside one of the mobile classrooms plonked down in the middle of the asphalt. He took out his timetable to check what he had next. Social studies in Room C. Where was that?

He was searching around for someone to ask when he saw Vincent approaching. He was laughing and joking with two other black boys. One of them was tall and lanky and had a silly grin on his face. The other was short and solid and had a sullen scowl. Vincent seemed to be making straight for him.

'Hi,' Vincent said, but he didn't sound friendly. He turned to his mates and gave them a wink. 'You should 'ear this guy talk. It really somet'in'. It's so — so —' — he hit on the word he was searching for — 'it's so bizarre.'

He had difficulty keeping his laughter in. It was one big joke to him. Ian couldn't see it himself.

Vincent was staring at him expectantly. So were the others. Ian looked from face to face. They were close to him, ranged round him, hedging him in. He had his back against the wall of the classroom. They were all waiting eagerly, bright-eyed, for him to entertain them. Well, he wasn't going to play.

'Go on,' Vincent urged. 'Say somet'in'.'

Ian gave him a cold stare. 'You talking to me? Or chewing a brick?'

Vincent and his mates fell about. They bent themselves double and danced backwards in circles, clicking their fingers in the air. Their shrieks of laughter drowned the shouts and bellows from the rest of the playground. Ian didn't think it was that funny.

Vincent tried to get a grip on himself. Still spluttering, he said to his friends, 'Didn' I tell you?'

'Yeah,' agreed the tall one, grinning widely. 'It's dread.'

They collapsed into another fit.

Vincent pulled himself together. 'You from Scotland, innit?' He glanced at his friends as though seeking praise for his superior knowledge.

'Whit's that to you?' Ian responded.

Vincent became all confidential. 'Tell me, ain't it true you lives on not'in' but porridge an' 'aggis?'

Ian couldn't be sure if he was being serious or not. His face looked serious enough, but Ian had a feeling he was being got at. He decided to play along with it.

'Aye,' he said. 'That's right enough.'

'What's 'aggis?' the short one asked. He sounded very suspicious.

Ian thought he might as well enjoy himself. 'You wouldny ken. It's only found in Scotland. It's a rarity. A wee beastie. They hunt it in the Highlands.'

The black boys exchanged doubtful glances. Even Vincent seemed uncertain for a moment. Then he recovered and started again.

'Is it true the Scotch can never open their wallets case the moths get out? That's what I 'ears.'

He watched Ian expectantly, awaiting a response.

But Ian had had enough. It was three to one, but why should he put up with this needling?

'Aye,' he said. 'The same way if they opened your heid a load of hot air wid pour oot.'

Vincent's friends were delighted by this, but Vincent wasn't. His face tightened, and he scowled with displeasure.

'You watch it,' he warned.

'Gonny make me?' Ian asked cheekily.

'Yeah.'

'Whit? You?'

'Yeah.'

'You and whose army?'

'I don' need no army.'

They glared at each other without blinking. It was stalemate. The other black boys were losing interest.

'Come on, Vince,' said the short one. 'You just wastin' you' time. Let's go play football.'

'Yeah,' echoed the other.

Vincent let his face relax into a sneering smile. 'Yeah. 'E ain't worth troublin' wit'. 'E ain't not'in' but a Scotch 'Aggis.' He laughed.

Ian sneered back. 'And you're nothing but a black ape.'

The effect was electric. The black boys became rigid. Their faces closed in hard and angry.

'What you say?' Vincent demanded, his eyes narrowed and glinting dangerously. He wasn't laughing now.

'You heard,' said Ian.

'Why don' you drill 'im up fo' that?' the short friend urged, full of indignation.

'Yeah,' echoed the tall one.

Ian stood his ground. He played it as cool as he could. 'Och, away you go,' he said wearily as though he was tired of their game, 'afore I thump you one.'

But it was Vincent who did the thumping. The blow caught Ian in the stomach and took his breath away. He just had time to feel a surge of anger before the black boy launched himself forward and grabbed him round the neck.

Ian struggled and tried to push him away. He caught a glimpse of Vincent's friends, excited and bright-eyed, urging Vincent on with shouts and squeals. Other boys were gathering round too, attracted by the prospect of blood. Vincent's face was close to his own, grim and breathing heavily. Ian got a hand free and pushed the black boy's face backwards hard. He kicked out and hooked his leg behind the black boy's knee. They lost their balance and toppled to the ground.

They rolled over and knocked aginst the legs of the spectators. Ian could hear the shouts and cheers. 'Come on, Vince.' 'You give 'im it.' 'Mash 'im up.' Vincent's friends were shoving the other pupils back, clearing a space so that the fight wouldn't be interrupted. You'd think they were promoters the way they were going on. They'd be charging admittance next.

Ian knew he was no match for Vincent. He went on struggling, but the black boy was bigger and heavier. It wasn't long before he found himself lying on his back, his arms held stretched out against the asphalt. He was practically smothered by Vincent's weight. He couldn't even move his legs.

'Take it back,' Vincent panted.

Ian could feel the hot breath against his face. He stared back defiantly at Vincent's piercing eyes.

'Why should I?' he retorted.

Vincent banged his arms against the asphalt. He gave a heave and landed with all his weight on Ian's stomach. The wind was knocked out of him. He gasped for breath.

'Take it back,' Vincent demanded again.

'Yeah, yeah,' called someone else.

Ian didn't like the idea. It went against the grain. But he couldn't see any way out. Vincent was too strong for him. He licked his lips and thought how he would put it. He didn't want to lose face completely.

But before the right words could come, he was distracted by something going on in the crowd around them. The shouts were different. 'Watch out!' 'Here comes old Hardwick.' The crowd was scattering and thinning out.

'Stop that,' came a voice. 'Get up at once.'

Vincent gave Ian a last withering stare and began to loosen his hold. The two boys got to their feet. Most of the crowd had dispersed, going back to their football, keeping clear of trouble, but Vincent's two friends were still there, lingering to see what was going to happen.

The teacher was grim and red-faced. 'On the first day, too. It's too much. I'm reporting you to your form teacher. Go to the office and stay there.'

Vincent tried to look hard done by, but he didn't protest. He gave Ian a glare that boded no good for the future, and then ambled across the playground towards the school. Ian dusted down his trousers.

'Well?' the teacher demanded impatiently.

Ian shrugged his shoulders and followed Vincent. From the back, the black boy seemed quite jaunty. He was walking with a kind of swaying motion of his shoulders and hips as if one leg was slightly shorter than the other. He seemed to have recovered his spirits.

Unless he was just putting on a show for his mates.

Outside the office, there was a row of chairs. Vincent plonked himself down on one of them. Ian watched him do it. The black boy's body just collapsed. He sat there sprawled out as though he had no bones at all. Ian sat down beside him. Neither of them spoke. Vincent just stared out into space without blinking. He had completely withdrawn into a world of his own.

Not that Ian cared. If Vincent didn't want to talk, that was his look-out. Even if he'd spoken, he'd probably only have said, 'Wait till I get you.'

Ian had enough on his plate to think about without that. How serious was fighting? What kind of punishments did this school have? Would he get the tawse or be sent home? It didn't really matter much. It wasn't as though it was the first time he'd been in trouble at school. It was something you got used to. It was just the first time at this school.

Mr Armstrong kept them waiting. It was nearly half an hour before he appeared. The bell for the end of break had gone. Teachers had hurried past them to their classrooms, giving them dirty looks on the way. The row of the pupils coming into school had subsided.

'In here, you two,' Mr Armstrong growled. He didn't sound pleased. Not like he had been in the form room earlier on.

He opened the door of one of the offices and held it ajar while Ian and Vincent went in. Ian noticed that Vincent rolled into the room with his shoulders held high and his chest puffed up as though he owned the place.

Mr Armstrong closed the door and stood against it with his arms folded. He blew out his breath and settled his face into a grim mask as he stared at them.

'Now what's all this about?' he asked.

' 'E start it,' said Vincent.

Ian turned on him in amazement. 'I did not. It wis you.'

'I were just tryin' to be friendly,' Vincent maintained.

'That's no the way it seemed to me,' retorted Ian.

'Man, you just can' take a joke.'

'Aye, mebbe I haveny got your sense of humour.'

'Stop,' cried Mr Armstrong, holding his hand up like a policeman halting the traffic. Ian and Vincent kept quiet, but they continued to glare at each other.

Mr Armstrong sighed. 'You're like a couple of old women the way you squabble.'

Vincent looked reproachfully at him. 'That's sexist, sir. You're always tellin' us.'

'That's rich, coming from you. You're the biggest male chauvinist pig of them all.'

'No I ain't.'

'Oh yes, you are.'

'No, I ain't,' Vincent protested again.

'Anyway,' said Mr Armstrong, 'don't change the subject. Mr Hardwick says you were fighting in the playground. I'm ashamed of you, Vincent. Ian here is a new boy, and what do you do on his first day here? Pick a fight with him.'

'I were just bein' friendly,' Vincent insisted.

'Huh,' exclaimed Mr Armstrong. 'You have a funny way of

showing it. The day you are friendly to a new boy will be the day pigs lay eggs.'

Vincent began to brood sulkily under this attack. He shot a murderous glance at Ian.

' 'E call me a black ape,' he said. 'I didn' like it.'

'You called me a Scotch haggis,' Ian retorted. 'I didny like that neither.'

' 'E probably t'inks we lives up trees.'

'Aye, I think you live up trees, the same way you think I live on porridge.'

'It ain't the first time I been called names. Insulted just 'cause I'm black.'

'You called me a name first.'

'Well then, perhaps you knows now what it like to be black.'

'Stop it, you two,' Mr Armstrong exploded. 'Really, haven't you anything better to do than sling insults at each other? You're like a couple of babies.' He rounded on Vincent before he could say anything. 'And don't accuse me of being ageist.'

Vincent didn't.

Then Mr Armstrong calmed down. 'Wait outside a minute, will you, Vincent?'

When they were alone, Mr Armstrong spoke quietly to Ian. 'A word of advice. Don't use the word black as an insult. There are a lot of black boys and girls at this school, and some of them are big. They don't like it, and I don't like it. Because if that comes tripping lightly off the tongue like that, it makes me wonder what other nasty racist thoughts are lurking inside your head.'

Sexist, ageist, racist? What kind of place was this, Ian wondered. If he'd wanted a sermon, he'd have gone to church. But he felt he had to make some reaction.

'I'm no racist,' he protested. Though he had to admit that he'd never asked himself whether he was or not. What he did know was that attack was the best form of defence. 'Whit aboot him then? He insulted me first.'

'Yes,' agreed Mr Armstrong, 'I'm not very happy about that

either. But you have to remember that Scots people have had centuries to build up their defences against insults like that. Blacks have only had a few generations.'

Ian wasn't sure that he understood.

Mr Armstrong called Vincent back in. 'Now, you two. I want no more of it. Is that clear?'

'Yes, sir.'

'Yes, sir.'

'Right, you'd better get to your lesson.'

Was that all? School did seem to be softer in England. Or at least this one was.

'Can you tell me where Room C is?' Ian asked.

'I should have thought of that,' said Mr Armstrong. He shouted to Vincent to come back. 'Now, I'm sure you'll agree it'll be a good idea if you take charge of Ian for the next few days. Show him round and make sure he doesn't get lost.'

Vincent stared at the teacher as if he'd gone mad. 'Me? You must be jokin'.'

'Oh no, I'm not,' said Mr Armstrong. 'And make sure you do a good job of it.'

'Bloody 'ell,' Vincent muttered, loud enough for the teacher to hear, but not loud enough to offend. He flicked his eyes contemptuously in Ian's direction and grunted, 'Come on.'

'How wis school?' Mum asked Ian when he got home.

'All right.'

There was no point in mentioning the fight.

For the rest of the day, Vincent had done what Mr Armstrong had told him to do. He had taken Ian to Room C, shown him the dining room at lunch time, told him what he had in the afternoon and how to get there. But it was clear he didn't enjoy it. For one thing, his friends — Terry and Les they were called — kept sending him up.

Terry — he was the tall one — came up to him all serious and

asked, 'Please can you tell me where the science lab is? I'm lost.'
Then he exploded with laughter, and he and Les went into a crazy
dance.

'Hey, man,' Les said when he had recovered, 'you found you'
vocation. You gets a job fo' sure when you leaves school. 'Elpin'
old people across the road.'

'Or lookin' after little babies,' Terry suggested.

'An' changin' their nappies.'

There was more mocking laughter. Vincent took it all with cool
disdain, but Ian could tell from the way his eyelids were half-
closed over brooding eyes and the way he pushed out his lips and
worked them about as if he was chewing his gums that he was
having to control himself. It didn't take much imagination to guess
who would be on the receiving end if and when he let go.

At the end of school, Ian had seen Vincent go striding down the
drive in front of him with Terry and Les. They were still joking and
jumping round him and slapping him on the back.

There was no point in telling Mum any of this either.

But she seemed satisfied with his vague reply. 'That's good,' she
said.

Then she burst out with her own news. 'I got that job.'

'Oh, aye?'

'It's at yin of they big hooses on the Common. I went along this
mornin', and they took me on straight away. Said they wis
desperate to get somebody. Is that no funny when you think how
many folks is oot of work? I start on Monday.'

'Oh, aye.'

'Awfie nice folk they seem. Least the lady I saw wis. Mrs Bentley.
Professional people. In the media, she said they wis. Though I'm
no sure whit that means. Is it television? They're oot a lot so
they've given me a key. Is that no awfie trusting of them? I must
have an honest face.'

Ian listened as Mum prattled on.

She was quite thrilled by her success. She'd never had a job like
that before. Nobody on the estate could afford to have cleaners.

They all did their own. Getting the job had given Mum quite a boost. It was quite an adventure. Here she was striking out on her own, finding a place for herself, getting a bit of independence. She'd be joining women's lib next. Good luck to her, Ian thought.

'My, but it's a grand hoose,' Mum was saying. 'I wis shown over it. Fitted carpets in every room. And you should see the kitchen. Freezer. Dish-washer. Two ovens. And lovely oak units. They didny get those frae the Cooperative.'

Mum went all dreamy-eyed as she thought about it. She would love a kitchen like that. A fat chance there was of her ever getting one.

She came back to earth. 'Ian, will you go a wee message fur me?'

'Aye, I don't mind.'

'I got that carried away, I quite forgot to get the sausages fur the night's tea. You'll need to go doon to that butcher's next the Junction. His sausages is the best.'

Mum got out her purse and gave him the money.

Tracy was playing in the forecourt with her two friends. One of them was crying, tears welling out and pouring down her cheeks, chest heaving and shaking.

'Whit's she greetin' fur?' Ian asked.

Tracy pulled her mouth down to show her contempt. 'She cries at anythin', she does. We was in the Park an' Old Bill chased us. That's all.'

At the mention of Old Bill, the little girl began to sob even louder. ' 'E said 'e was gonna tell me dad,' she managed to get out between convulsions.

'Yeah, an' if 'e does, she'll get a good 'idin',' Tracy confided to Ian. Then she turned to her friend. 'Don't you be so soft. 'E won't do that. An' if 'e does, I'll say 'e tried to rape me.' She grinned maliciously at Ian.

She would too. He'd have to be careful of her.

'Oh, aye,' he said.

The butcher's was in the pedestrian way leading up to the station. It was a crowded thoroughfare with people making a last-minute dash to catch trains or hurrying home from work.

Ian was just coming out of the shop with the sausages when he caught sight of Bella on the other side. She was standing in front of a shop window, but she didn't seem to be paying much attention to the goods on display. She kept looking first one way and then the other, watching the faces of the people going past as though searching for someone she knew. In her mouth was an unlit cigarette. That was strange. As far as Ian was aware, she didn't smoke. At least he'd never seen her smoke at home.

He forced his way across to her through the hurrying commuters.

'Hi, Bella.'

Her eyes narrowed to take in his face, and then widened as she recognised him. Her mouth opened and the cigarette dropped. She made a frantic grab at it before it reached the ground. She had a lot of make-up on. More like what she wore when she went to a disco.

'I wis just looking at the shops,' she explained.

She gave a casual nod at the window she was standing in front of. It was an ironmonger's. Ian was puzzled. Since when had she been interested in lawnmowers and power drills?

'Whit are you doing here anyway?' she asked. From the way she said it, you'd think she wasn't pleased to see him.

'I wis gettin' some sausages fur Mum,' Ian told her.

'Well, you'd better away,' said Bella. 'She'll be waiting fur them.' She kept looking up and down the alley as though afraid she might miss something. She made it plain she didn't want him there.

'I'll be off then,' he said.

'You do that,' said Bella.

She turned to face the window and became absorbed in comparing the prices of various chisels.

Ian could take a hint. He wandered back towards the main road. But he was curious. What was Bella doing just hanging around there? He stepped into a shop doorway and peeped round. Bella had put the cigarette in her mouth again and resumed her search of the crowd. She stopped a man. She took the cigarette out of her mouth and waved it about. She seemed to be asking for a light. The man shook his head and walked on.

Then she walked up to another man. They got into a long conversation. He lit her cigarette for her, and she blew out a billowy cloud of smoke. They chatted and smiled and laughed. They kept looking round as if worried someone might be watching them. Ian made sure he was well hidden in the doorway.

The man said something, and Bella pursed her lips and thought about it. Then she smiled and nodded her head. The man pointed down towards the main road, and they began to walk in that direction. Ian huddled back into the doorway as they passed. They were talking and laughing like old friends.

Ian emerged and stared after them until they were lost in the crowd. What a funny way to go on.

It was only when he was halfway home that the thought came to him. She wasn't —. No, she couldn't be. He'd heard of girls on the estate who'd been like that. Andy and the others were always on about them. They'd been well known. But not Bella. She liked men well enough, but she wouldn't stoop to that, would she? It wasn't possible.

His mind shied away from the idea. There was probably some perfectly ordinary explanation. The man was a friend, or a friend of a friend, or something like that.

He tried to concentrate on other things.

He thought back to his friends in Glasgow. He hadn't written to Maisie. He knew he never would. But the words of a letter began to form themselves in his mind.

Dear Maisie, I started school today. I think I'm going to like it there. Everybody is very friendly. They all want to help me and show me where the classrooms are and tell me what lessons I've got next. The special friend I have made is called Vincent. He's black. I don't know where he comes from, but he speaks just like a Londoner. Well, almost. He's very good at football. He's a goalkeeper. And he's very well-built for his age. I wouldn't like to be on the other side if he got into a fight.

Jimmy and Bella are still looking for jobs. There's a good chance they'll get them soon. Things are looking up down here. Mum has got a job. She's sort of housekeeper to these important people who live in a big house on the Common. She's dead chuffed about it.

I suppose you are back at school as well now. Tell Andy from me not to work too hard. As if that's likely!

Did you go bramble picking this year? I bet there was a super crop. Mum still has some bramble jelly left over from last year, but it's not going to last long. I wish I could have got her some brambles to make some more. Perhaps you'll send me some. Though I think they'd get a bit squashed in the post. There'd be no need to cook them. They'd be just like jam!

He turned in at the entrance to the flats and began to climb the stairs.

I'd better close now. I hope you are keeping well. Give my best wishes to Jean. Love, Ian.

4

It must have been the school dinner — spam fritters, beans and chips. But it was a bit surprising that it had worked its way through so fast.

It was halfway through lunch break. Ian was on the playground watching a game of football to try to take his mind off it. His stomach gave another rumble. It was no good. He hated using the school toilet, but he would have to go.

He peered into each cubicle in turn. There was no paper. Wasn't that just typical? There was no soap in the soap-dispensers either, and where the mirrors had been there were just squares of lighter coloured wall.

'Hey,' Ian called to a boy who had just unglued his lips from one of the taps — the water fountain didn't work either — and was wiping his mouth and chin with the back of his hand. 'Where d'you get paper here?'

The boy spluttered with laughter. 'You'll be lucky,' he said. 'You 'ave to ask Fred. You've got to 'ave a permit before 'e'll let you 'ave any.'

Ian went to the caretaker's office along the corridor. He knocked and pushed the door open. The caretaker was sitting in a battered armchair, a hand-rolled cigarette dangling from his mouth, the *Sun* lying on his lap, a steaming mug of tea on the cluttered table by his side. He didn't look pleased at being disturbed.

'I need some lavatory paper,' Ian explained.

'Why don't you wait till you get 'ome?' Fred asked gruffly. 'You're only tryin' to get out o' lessons. I don't know why the teachers let you get away with it.' He seemed to have forgotten it was lunch break.

Ian felt his bowels shift again. He wasn't sure how much longer he could hold out. 'I can't wait,' he pleaded.

Still grumbling, Fred leaned over and picked up a box of lavatory paper from the table. He drew out two sheets. You'd think they were pound notes the way he was handling them. Ian snatched them and rushed out.

'Don't bother to say thanks,' Fred called after him. 'I don't know. Kids today.'

Ian dashed into one of the cubicles and bolted the door. Whatever else was missing, at least they had locks. Not like his last school. They didn't even have doors there. All kicked down and never replaced.

Oh, the relief of it. He only hoped that two sheets of paper would be enough.

He heard voices outside. Some boys had come in. Ian looked up at the gap above the partition walls, first on one side and then the other. They wouldn't climb on the seats and peep over, would they? It was quite possible. It was one of the reasons why he hated using the school toilets.

But then his apprehensions were put at rest. He saw a cloud of smoke rising above the door. The boys had just come in for a crafty cigarette.

'You knows I don' like that kind o' t'ing,' one of the voices said.

The others teased and made fun of him.

Ian was suddenly alert. He recognised that voice. He was sure of it. He knew the others as well. It was Vincent with his two friends, Terry and Les.

'Come on, guy,' Les was saying. 'It time 'e get what comin' to 'im.'

'Yeah,' agreed Terry. 'It time you gets you' own back on 'im.'

' 'Avin' to show 'im round like you was 'is nursemaid or somet'in',' said Les.

'I calls that real shamin',' said Terry.

There was a moment's silence. They must have been thinking. But Ian was thinking too. He could imagine Vincent's face, hard and brooding. He remembered how much Vincent had resented having to show him where classrooms were and accompany him to lessons. He remembered how Terry and Les had danced up and down with delight at their friend's embarrassment. He was sure they were talking about him.

'I don' know,' Vincent said. 'I still don' like it. What if some teacher see?'

'But it so easy,' said Les. 'We waits fo' 'im outside school an' then gets 'im. No teacher gonna know.'

'Yeah,' said Terry. 'It 'bout time we 'ad a replay.'

There was silence again. They must have been puffing away at their cigarettes. A billow of smoke came over the top of Ian's cubicle and almost started him coughing.

'OK,' Vincent said. 'I t'ink I gonna enjoy it.'

Ian could see the slow smile of pleasure spreading across Vincent's face. Like a cat that had been given a mouse to play with.

There was a shouted warning. 'Watch it.' Ian could hear the flurried activity. Feet stamping out cigarette stubs. Breath and arms used to dispel the clouds of smoke. It went very quiet.

Ian pulled the chain and emerged.

What was he to do? The week had gone peacefully up till now. He didn't need Vincent to show him around any more. But it was clear the black boy still felt resentment, still felt he had a grudge at being humiliated like that. Or at least could have it stirred up by his friends. He was going to have his revenge.

Ian remembered the fight. Vincent's fists packed quite a punch. And there were Terry and Les too. They might not be content just to stand and organise the crowd this time.

Ian decided it wasn't the moment to be a hero. Self-preservation was more important. The best thing was not to be there when it happened. He would bunk off school for the afternoon.

It must have been near the end of lunch break. The playground was still a bawling whirling mass, but the bell would be going soon. He would have to hurry.

He edged his way to the corner of the building. A quick look round showed that the drive was clear. Since it was still break, there would be no one in the classrooms overlooking the drive. He could make it. He set off, head held low and legs working fast.

He had only gone a few yards when there was a shout. It didn't have to be for him, but he had a nasty suspicion it was. He thought of going on regardless, but the shout was repeated, more urgently this time. There was no mistaking it now. He came to a halt and turned round. Mr Armstrong was standing at the top of the drive. He had his hands on his hips, and even at that distance, Ian could see the sceptical expression on the teacher's face. He must have been on playground duty.

Ah well, that was that. He could have made a run for it, but that would only mean even more trouble. He slowly began to retrace his steps.

'Where were you off to?' Mr Armstrong asked when he was near enough.

Ian thought for a bit. From the way the teacher was eyeing him it would take a real whopper to convince him. He'd probably read the file on him from his previous school. There was bound to be something in there about him playing truant.

'I didny have ma maths book,' Ian said at last. 'I wis just going hame to get it.'

'But you don't have maths this afternoon,' Mr Armstrong pointed out.

'Don't I?' Ian said, playing the innocent.

'No,' said Mr Armstrong. 'You have the pleasure of a double period with me.'

'Oh.' Ian tried to show surprise. Then relief. 'That's all right then.'

55

He strolled casually up to the playground. He knew Mr Armstrong was watching every step he took.

The bell went. There was a drift of children into school. Ian wondered if he could slip away through the mass without being noticed. Mr Armstrong was chivvying the pupils, yelling at them to hurry up, but he was also covering the top of the drive. There was no way Ian could get past without him seeing. Reluctantly, he joined the crowds pushing into the building and cramming the stairs.

The classroom was already full of boys and girls, screaming at each other, chasing over desks, throwing books around. Ian threaded his way through them and found an empty place. Vincent and his friends were already in their seats.

When Mr Armstrong arrived, he gave a sharp bark, and the class gradually subsided. A kind of quiet descended.

Ian didn't pay much attention to the lesson. It was something to do with why people chose particular jobs. Mr Armstrong was going on about all the different reasons. The money. An open-air life. Working with people. Doing something socially useful. Things like that.

Ian couldn't see what it had to do with him. There didn't seem to be much chance of him getting any job, let alone one he wanted.

In any case, he had more pressing things to worry about.

There was no point in looking to anyone else in the class to help him. They hadn't deliberately cold-shouldered him. They spoke to him and said hello. They called him Scottie or Jock or Mac. But they weren't exactly friends. Maria and Bernadette, Xenephos and Ali, Pankaj and Sanjay — they had grown up together. Just as he had with Andy and Maisie and Jean. They didn't need to make new friends.

No, he was still an outsider. He would have to rely on himself.

Mr Armstrong dished out sheets of paper. They had to write an essay on 'The job I would like'. Ian had no idea how to begin. He chewed his biro and tried to concentrate. When the bell went for the end of the period, he had managed half a page.

Mr Armstrong asked Maria to collect the work and opened the register. He didn't have to call out the names. He knew who was there and who wasn't.

There was some coming and going as some pupils left and others arrived. Terry and Les went out — they had Mr Armstrong for English, but they weren't in his form. Ian was glad to see them go. That made the odds more even.

In theory, registration at the end of school lasted five minutes. Teachers weren't supposed to let their classes out early, before the final bell went, but Mr Armstrong sometimes did. Ian got himself ready to make a run for it just in case.

He checked the lay-out. He was sitting halfway back in the row of desks against the wall with the door in it. Vincent was on the other side of the room next to the window. He always sat there so that he could watch what was going on outside — except when Mr Armstrong remembered and ordered him down to the front where he could keep an eye on him. He had further to go to reach the door. At least that was something, Ian thought.

Would the bell never go? Time seemed to have stopped. Mr Armstrong had taken the register. He was having a joke with two of the black girls. Other pupils were searching their desks for books and packing their bags. Vincent was playfully trying to slap the face of another black boy sitting in front of him.

Ian crouched over his desk, his fingers gripping the top of the lid. He sat on the edge of his chair, his legs bent under it ready to kick it back and spring into flight. At the same time, he tried to give the impression that he was half-asleep in case Vincent was watching.

The bell shrilled out. Ian launched himself from his seat like a greyhound out of its box. He didn't think Mr Armstrong noticed because everyone else was on the move as well.

But Ian was first to reach the door. He wrenched it open and was out and down the stairs.

He was buffeted right and left as people pushed against him or tried to get round him. He didn't care. He bounced down the stairs two or three at a time and burst through the exit. Then he was off down the drive.

He couldn't move too fast because of the crowds of people, but he pressed forward with as much speed as he could. Looking back, he thought he could make out the heads of Vincent and Terry — Les would be too short to be visible — bobbing among the mass bearing down behind him. He put on a spurt.

At the main gates, the pupils thinned out as they went their various ways. Ian hesitated a second, uncertain what to do next. Then he made for the Common. He didn't exactly run. That would have drawn too much attention. It was more a kind of steady lope.

Where the road met the Common, he stopped again. A quick look showed Vincent and his friends advancing down on him. When they saw him turn to face them, they shouted and waved their arms at him.

Ian didn't wait to find out what they wanted. He took off across the road. A car shrieked to a halt inches from him, but he kept on, ignoring the curses of the angry driver.

Once on the Common, the going became tougher. The heavy clay dragged at his feet, and he stumbled over tufts of grass. He wondered if he was doing the right thing, but there seemed to be no alternative. Luckily, the three black boys appeared to be having the same difficulty. They were still in pursuit, clumping through the mud as clumsy as carthorses, larking about and barging into each other. It was a big joke to them. But not to Ian.

He reached the road again. He was running now, racing past the big houses to the flats. Clods of earth spattered out as his feet hit the pavement. As he turned in at the entrance, he looked round. Vincent and his friends had gained on him. They were only about twenty yards away. They would see where he was going. Well, it couldn't be helped.

He scooted into the doorway and straight through to the back. He took a flying leap at the wall and jumped over. He huddled down on his haunches and pressed himself against the wall. He was out of breath. His chest was heaving up and down. His jaw was stiff with the effort of dragging air into his lungs through his mouth without making a noise.

He ought to be safe. Vincent and the others probably didn't know the Park existed. They might see the broken-down wall and risk climbing over it. But he had the advantage of knowing the Park. He had explored it several times now. He was sure he could get away from them in time and hide some place where they would never find him. The only danger would be Old Bill.

He concentrated on listening. He could hear the boys. They must have come through to the back. They were gasping for breath. Ian got ready to make a run for it if necessary.

'Where 'e go?' Les asked. He sounded annoyed. Like someone done out of a bit of fun.

'I don' know,' said Vincent. He was in a bad temper too.

' 'E live 'ere, don' 'e?' said Terry.

' 'Ow you know?' demanded Vincent.

'I seen 'im come out o' 'ere a couple o' times. 'E got a sister too. She quite somet'in'.'

'Yeah? What would you know 'bout it?'

'I knows enough.'

'Maybe 'e gone 'ome,' Les suggested.

There was a thud next to Ian's head. He jerked back. One of them must have been kicking the wall.

'Why don' we pay 'im a visit?' Les asked.

'Yeah, get 'im out,' said Terry. He sounded enthusiastic again.

There was a pause before Vincent agreed. 'OK.'

Then there was silence.

Ian waited. Were they really going to knock at his front door? Probably. They had enough cheek for anything. It was a good job he'd decided to make for the Park and not the flat.

His legs were aching from crouching down. He stood up and straightened them out. There would be no point in going home yet. Vincent and his friends might hang around for ages. He might as well go for a walk.

He kicked through the piles of leaves that littered the ground.

They were crisp and dry like parchment and cracked under foot. More leaves came tumbling down in front of him, floating and curving backwards and forwards before landing. Only a few trees had lost their leaves so far. Others were turning gold and brown.

In the rose garden, many of the flowers were over-blown and petals strewed the ground. Some briars with ferocious thorns held up bloated hips. Ian wondered if they were the kind you made syrup out of. It all looked a bit neglected as though Old Bill hadn't been putting in as much time as usual.

'Clear off!'

Ian jumped in the air. Talk of the devil. The gardener was coming through the archway, brandishing his fist.

'I'll get the police onto you. Breaking in here. Trespassing.'

Old Bill's face was going purple, and his eyes were bulging fit to burst. It looked as though he might have a heart attack too. Ian didn't wait to see any more. He took off through the bushes. Creepers clawed at his feet. Branches whipped into his face. Curses and threats rang after him.

When he was clear, he slowed down and breathed a sigh of relief. Two chases in one day. It was beginning to get a habit. But at least he had got away both times. That was something. Old Bill and his angry words couldn't hurt him. And Vincent and his friends hadn't been able to get him. The Park had its uses, even if Old Bill was a hazard to be avoided.

They would be sure to have gone by now. He couldn't see Vincent and Terry and Les staying on where there was no hope of blood. He scraped the soles of his shoes against a turf of grass and tried to get rid of some of the mud caked there. It would be safe to go home.

'Whit a shame,' Mum said as he went into the kitchen. 'You just missed them.'

'Who?'

'They friends that called fur you.'

'Oh aye?'

60

'One of them said his name wis Vincent. They seemed awfie nice lads. Wanted you to go oot an' play.'

'Oh, aye.'

'Mind you, they left a bit of a mess on the balcony. Mud everywhere. I canny think where they'd been. Wading through ploughed fields by the look of it. I had to go oot and clear it up.'

Ian hoped he had done a decent job on his shoes. Perhaps he ought to go to his bedroom and check.

As he walked to the door, Mum smiled at him. 'I'm that glad you've found some friends.'

'Oh, aye,' Ian said.

With feeling.

He was sinking into the mud. With a tremendous effort, he dragged one foot out, raised it and pressed it forward. It was sucked back down into the soggy mire. At this rate, he would never escape.

He looked back. Vincent was gaining on him. He could see the black boy silhouetted against the sky, his arms held wide as he used his shoulders to urge his body onwards. Behind him was Old Bill, shouting and yelling. Who'd have thought he could move so fast?

Ian heaved his other foot out. It made a shlurp like water going down a plug-hole. He set it forward and felt it being caught and hauled under by the mud.

Leaves began to flutter down from the trees. More and more of them. They whirled round him, beating against him, blinding him. Like a snowstorm. They gathered thick on the ground, hemming his body in. He couldn't move for them. Soon they had engulfed him up to his neck. They were pressing against his mouth, his nose, his eyes. He was being buried alive.

He woke with a gasp and pushed the sheet away from his face. He couldn't breathe.

Then he relaxed and gave a sigh of relief. He was glad that was over. He opened his eyes. The orange glow of the street lighting shone through the thin curtains. He couldn't think what time it was, but it must have been late.

He raised himself on his elbow and looked across at the other bed. He could make out the hump of the pillow with the bedcover drawn over it. That was strange. Jimmy was usually in bed early. Often, he was there before Ian, snoring and grunting with the sheet pulled over his head, or grumbling and moaning at being disturbed.

Ian settled back against the pillow. He didn't want to close his eyes again just yet. He stared up at the ceiling and watched the pattern of light shimmering and changing. He hadn't thought about his Glasgow friends for a while. It must be nearly a week. It was time he wrote them another letter — even if it was only in his mind. He set about it. It would help to keep other thoughts from flooding in.

Dear Maisie. That was the easy bit. *I've been at school a week now, and it still seems OK. I think Mr Armstrong is my favourite teacher. His lessons are always interesting. Today we learned all about how to choose a job. I'm not sure what that has to do with English, but I'm sure it will be helpful when I leave school. I'm thinking of being a sports writer. They get to see football matches and car races free. Or maybe a football manager. That would be all right. How d'you fancy me as manager of Rangers? There'd be no stopping them then.*

Remember I told you about Vincent? I took him into the Park this afternoon. Old Bill – he's the gardener who looks after it – showed us all over. He said we could go there any time. He lent us some rackets and me and Vincent had a game of tennis. He's a good player. It was touch and go, but I beat him. He sure made me work for it. I was fair sweating by the end.

Mum's that pleased with her new job. She says the house is like a palace. The people there really like her. She says they treat her like one of the family. She even has her own key so she can come and go as she pleases. They pay well too. But Mum says the money's not important. It gives her an interest, she says.

I hope you and Jean are well. Tell Andy from me...

There was a creak. The door was opening. Ian saw Jimmy's head poking round before he shut his eyes and pretended to be asleep. But he opened them a few moments later. He hadn't heard the sound of the door being closed.

It was still ajar. Then Jimmy pushed through. He was carrying something. It seemed to be quite heavy and awkward from the way he was hunched over it. He was moving slowly across the room to his bed. He seemed to be taking care not to make any noise.

That was unusual. Normally he didn't bother, but banged about and cursed, whether his brother was in bed or not. He hadn't switched the light on either. He wasn't usually so considerate.

Jimmy had dumped whatever it was he'd been carrying on the bed. Now he was kneeling on the floor beside it. He couldn't be saying his prayers, could he? He lifted the thing and put it under the bed, shoving it to the far wall.

Ian couldn't think what it could be. He shut his eyes quickly as Jimmy stood up and turned round. The light went on. It burned through his eyelids, but he kept his eyes closed and continued his pretence of being asleep.

When Jimmy had undressed, knocking against a chair and swearing as he staggered trying to get out of his trousers, he switched the light off.

Simultaneously, Ian fell asleep.

'Ian, it's time,' Mum was whispering hoarsely. 'You're gonny be late.' She pulled at his shoulder.

Ian blinked open an eye and fixed it on her anxious face.

'OK,' he mumbled.

She took a quick look at Jimmy, curved into a ball and submerged beneath the blankets, and went out.

Ian yawned. He scratched his head and opened his other eye.

63

Then he remembered. Jimmy hadn't been disturbed. A gentle snoring came from the heap of bedclothes as they slowly rose up and down.

Ian threw back his blankets and sat on the edge of the bed. He leaned back and angled his head to try to make out what was under Jimmy's bed. But the bedcover was dangling over the side, and he couldn't see far enough under. There wasn't enough light coming through the curtains anyway.

He suddenly shot upright as Jimmy grumbled in his sleep and rolled over. His head was still wrapped up in the sheet and his face was invisible.

Cautiously, half his attention focused on his brother, Ian knelt down, lifted the edge of the bedcover and peered under. He made out a dark blur. Gradually, it took shape. He could see the press buttons and numbers on the front. It was a video recorder.

Now where could Jimmy have got that?

5

It was a bombshell. It dropped completely out of the blue. Nobody was expecting it. Dad just came out with it.

'We're getting the sack.'

His face was a grim mask.

At the words, everyone froze. Jimmy in mid-chew. Bella with her fork halfway to her mouth. Mum about to lift up her teacup. Ian slicing through his ham.

Mum was the first to recover and speak. 'Whit d'you mean?' Her voice was shaky and uncertain. So she must have had some idea.

'The sack,' Dad repeated. He became angry. 'The boot. Ma cards. On the scrap-heap. The dole. Don't you understand?'

Mum shook her head in bewilderment. 'I dinny get it,' she said, near tears.

'Whit did you do?' Jimmy asked. Even he sounded awed and subdued.

'You dinny have to do anything these days to get the sack,' Dad replied. He looked round the table from face to face. He took in a deep breath and let it out again slowly. 'They're gonny privatise the refuse department.'

They gazed at each other, trying to absorb the news.

'Whit does that mean?' Bella asked.

'It means all the borough employees is gonny get the boot.

They're gonny give the job of rubbish collection to a private firm. Put it oot to tender and give the contract to the lowest bid.'

'But that's no right,' Jimmy protested.

'Whit's right got to do with it?' asked Dad bitterly. 'They can do anything they want to.'

'It's this government,' said Bella. 'There's all they cut-backs they're making.'

'Aye,' agreed Dad. 'They want everything on the cheap. And that's whit they'll get. Cheap labour to give a second-rate service.'

Mum's face was filled with despair. 'Whit'll we do?'

'Whit we've always done,' said Dad. 'Manage somehow.'

'When's it gonny happen?' Bella asked.

'Oh no yet awhile,' said Dad. 'They've got to pass it through the council first.'

'Well, that's something,' said Bella. 'There's still a chance it won't happen.'

'Huh!' said Dad. 'No with this council. They're that mean they'd take the food oot the mouths of widows and orphans. Any chance they get of saving a penny here and cutting a service there they'll take. To hell with the consequences. They'd let old folks die of cold and close down hospitals if they could get away with it!'

Ian had heard Dad speak like this before, but never with such bitterness. When it affected you personally, it really struck home.

'Whit's the union doing aboot it?' Jimmy asked.

'There's a meeting after work the morrow,' Dad told him. 'They're talking of making a protest. Perhaps going on strike. Though I don't know whit good that'll do.'

'You nivver know,' said Mum, trying to look on the bright side.

'Naw, naw,' said Dad. 'It'll just give them an excuse to sack the lot of us.'

They went on with their tea, but somehow they had lost their appetites — even Bella.

She put down her fork and said, 'I wisht we'd nivver come.'

'Whit's the use of saying that?' Jimmy snapped at her.

'Well, if we're gonny be poor, I'd rather be poor somewheres I know. No this dump.'

'Don't you like it here then?' Mum asked anxiously.

Bella threw the question back at her. 'Do you?'

Mum thought. 'Well, I miss the old place. And the neighbours.' Then she became worried as a new idea struck her. 'Whit would they say if we went back? They think we've come to live the good life here in London. It wid be such a disgrace. Like going back with your tail atween your legs.' She turned to Dad. 'We'll no have to go back, will we?'

'I dinny ken,' he said. 'I don't see the point of it. Things is even worse up there. We might as well stick it oot doon here. Grin and bear it.'

'Aye,' Mum agreed. 'That's whit we'll have to do. Grin and bear it.' She cheered up and nodded at Bella. 'Besides, you've made friends doon here noo.'

'Oh, aye,' said Bella. She sounded unconvinced.

'And Ian's got his pals as well,' Mum went on. 'Ever such nice lads they are. Aren't they?'

'Aye,' said Ian.

'So things is no sae bad,' she concluded. 'It'll turn oot all right. You might no get the sack after all. And there's ma job anyways. That'll help. And Bella and Jimmy'll find something afore long. I just know it. We'll manage all right. It's no the end of the world. We're no finished yet.'

Nobody else said anything.

Ian didn't know what to think. Dad out of a job. Go back to Glasgow. It was all such a mess.

Dad hadn't lost his job yet, but it seemed quite likely. They'd held a union meeting and voted on some action. Lobbying councillors. Taking round a petition. They hoped that would have some effect on public opinion. The council meeting was in a month's time. It was then that they would decide whether or not to privatise refuse collection. In Dad's opinion, the council had already made up its mind. But he was out every night, attending meetings, talking to councillors, going round the houses getting signatures for the petition. They'd just have to wait and see.

And going back to Glasgow? Well, Ian quite fancied the idea, though it didn't look as though it was going to happen. As far as he was concerned, he didn't feel that coming to London had been much of a success. He hadn't made any friends. Mum went on about Vincent and Terry and Les and how nice they were and why didn't he ask them round. It was a joke.

He brooded over it as he walked along the path in the Park. He kicked a stone and watched it skitter through the grass and hit the trunk of a tree. He walked on.

Not that Vincent and his friends had been any bother. They seemed to have forgotten about their plan to get him. They just ignored him. Left him alone. Perhaps they had found something more interesting to take up their time. What was that expression Mr Armstrong used? A low boredom threshold. Perhaps they suffered from that. Or was it a high boredom quotient? Mr Armstrong was always saying things like that.

Though Ian had to admit he didn't take any risks. He kept out of their way and made sure he didn't give them any excuses. That was one reason why he was in the Park now and not on the Common. At least he was safe in the Park. Vincent and his friends were hardly likely to play football there. They didn't even know it existed.

The thought gave Ian a feeling of superiority. The Park was something he had that they didn't. He could go there any time he liked — Old Bill permitting — and be on his own. No one could get at him there.

And yet, there was a certain regret as well. It would be nice to have someone to share it with. Someone to take round and show it off to.

His thoughts were interrupted by a high-pitched squeal. It came from among the trees. It was probably Tracy playing with her friends. On the other hand, she might have seen Old Bill. Ian decided he had better retrace his steps.

He hadn't gone far when Tracy burst through the bushes onto the path in front of him. Her eyes were huge and round in her pale face.

'Whit's the matter?' Ian asked. 'Is Old Bill after you?'

'I've just seen 'im,' Tracy said. She sounded terrified. That wasn't like her.

'Well, we'd better clear out,' said Ian, 'afore he catches us.'

'No.'

'Whit d'you mean?'

' 'E wasn't chasin' me. 'E was lyin' on the ground. I think 'e's dead.'

Ian wondered if Tracy was having him on, but one look at her drawn face was enough to convince him that she wasn't.

'Come on,' he said. 'You'd better show me.'

Together, they pushed through the bushes and under the trees. The old man was lying not far from the hut. He was stretched out on the ground. His eyes were shut and he didn't seem to be breathing. His face was flushed and puckered up. For a moment, Ian was stunned. It was true. The old man did look as though he was dead.

Then he pulled himself together. He knelt down beside the body. Now, what was he supposed to do? He took one of Old Bill's hands between his own and began to pat it. It felt limp and dry. There was no reaction. The old man's face was as lifeless as ever.

'Oh, what are we gonna do?' Tracy cried with horror. She was pressing her knees together as though she needed to go to the lavatory.

Ian bent over the old man and put his ear to his chest. He wasn't sure, but there seemed to be some kind of beat there.

Didn't they use mouth to mouth resuscitation in cases like this? Ian glanced at the old man's face. Puffed up and creased the way it was, it looked more like a baby's than an old man's. Long scant grey hairs were stretched over his bald head to cover his scalp.

He didn't fancy the idea. Instead, he gave the cheek a timid slap. Then another.

Tracy yelped. 'You'll 'urt 'im.'

Ian grunted. It hardly mattered, if the old man was dead.

But he wasn't dead. His eyelids began to flutter. He let out a deep sigh. And then his eyes blinked and opened. He lifted his head and stared straight at Ian. He didn't seem to be seeing him. He gave a groan and fell back again, closing his eyes.

'Are you all right?' Ian asked anxiously.

Still with his eyes shut, the old man nodded his head. His tongue come out and he licked his lips. His chest began to heave heavily as he took in breath after breath.

'It's nothing,' he forced out. But it didn't look that way to Ian. 'I must have strained myself.'

He waved his hand feebly in the direction of a tree trunk lying on the ground nearby. 'I was carrying that back to the hut. It must have been too much for me.'

It certainly looked heavy.

The mention of the hut reminded Ian. There was a tap there. He could bring some water. That might help.

'Look after him,' he said to Tracy as he got up.

'What?' she cried, as if afraid she was going to be deserted.

'I'll be back,' Ian said.

Luckily, the door of the hut was open. He found a mug and filled it from the tap. The water spilled over the rim as he ran back.

Old Bill was sitting up. Tracy was staring at him goggle-eyed as if he was a ghost.

Ian held the mug to the old man's lips. He tried to steady it with a shaking hand and took a few sips.

'I just put it down to have a rest,' Old Bill said, 'and then I felt all dizzy.' His face was bewildered and frightened.

Ian didn't know what to do next. 'You'd best see a doctor,' was all he could suggest.

'Yes, you're right,' said the old man. 'Perhaps I should.'

He looked around him as if he had lost something. Then he

made grasping gestures towards his cap which was lying on the ground. But it was too far away for him to reach. Tracy ran over to it, picked it up and handed it to him.

Putting it on seemed to give the old man more confidence. He sniffed and said, 'Thanks. Now if you could just help me to the hut. I'll sit there a minute or two until I get my breath back.'

Tracy took hold of one of his hands. Ian took the other and put an arm round his shoulders. Together, they heaved and got the old man to his feet.

'That's it,' Old Bill said.

But his steps were still doddery. Ian supported him round the waist while Tracy drew him along by the hand. At the hut, the old man hung onto the door as though afraid he might fall.

'Off you go then,' he said. 'I'll manage now.'

Ian and Tracy watched as he groped his way inside and lowered himself into the battered armchair. He pushed his cap up on his forehead, let out a sigh and closed his eyes.

Tracy looked questioningly at Ian. He jerked his head at her to indicate that they'd better go.

'D'you think 'e'll be all right?' she asked when they had regained the path leading back to the flats.

'I don't know,' Ian replied. 'I think mebbe he's just had a shock.'

' 'Ow old is 'e?'

Ian considered it and then hazarded a guess. 'Mebbe seventy.'

'As old as that!' Tracy sounded shocked. ' 'E's too old to be lookin' after a place like this. My grandpa's sixty an' 'e never does any work. My nan's always complainin' about 'im.'

They walked on in silence for a while, but Tracy was obviously still worrying about the old man. 'D'you think we should tell someone?'

'Who is there to tell?' Ian asked.

And it was true. They didn't know anything about Old Bill. Where he lived. Whether he had any family. Who employed him and paid him. He was just the old man who looked after the Park and chased them away when he caught them in there.

'I tell you one thing,' said Tracy solemnly. 'I won't cheek 'im next time.'

Ian worried about the old man. The sight of him as he had last seen him, slumped in his chair, cap pushed back on his head, eyes closed, arms flopped at his sides, legs bent under him as though they were useless. Perhaps he should tell someone. Perhaps they should have got a doctor. Perhaps he should tell Mum. She might know what to do.

But when he reached home, he found that Mum had other things on her mind.

'Have you taken that key?' she demanded as soon as he went in.

Her face was grim and accusing. She didn't often get angry, but it was clear she was angry now.

'Whit key?' Ian asked.

'The key fur Mrs Bentley's house. It wis in ma purse. I had it yesterday. I know that because I used it to get in. And it's no there noo.'

She continued to scrutinise Ian steadily, searching for any sign of guilt.

'I don't know anything aboot any key,' Ian protested.

'I went to use it this afternoon and it wisny there. I wis fair put oot. I rang the bell, and lucky fur me, Mrs Bentley wis in. I said I'd forgotten to bring the key. Are you sure you haveny seen it?'

Again there was that hard suspicious stare.

'Naw, I haveny. Whit wid I want with it?'

At last, Mum believed him. Her face crumpled and the lines of worry showed round her mouth.

'I don't know whit Mrs Bentley'll say when I tell her I haveny got the key. She trusted me with it. I might even lose ma job.'

She grew fearful at the thought. 'First your dad, and then me. I don't know how we're gonny manage.'

'Mebbe you lost it,' Ian suggested. 'It might turn up.'

'Aye, I've been thinking aboot that. But I don't see how I could of. I've been going through it all in ma mind. I had it yesterday. I took it oot of ma purse to open the door. I had it when I left too. I know that. Because I had to use it to double lock the door behind me. I'm sure I put it back in ma purse. I couldny have dropped it. Then I put ma purse on the bureau where I always do. And I didny touch it again until I went to Mrs Bentley's this afternoon.'

She gave an exasperated sigh. 'I've been up and doon the road atween here and Mrs Bentley's looking fur it. People must have thought I wis demented. But there wis nae sign of it.'

She sighed again. 'It's a mystery,'

'You'd best tell Mrs Bentley you lost it,' Ian said.

'Aye, but whit'll she think of me? If it's lost anybody could of found it. They could use it to get in. The hoose is no safe.'

'But how will they know whit hoose it's fur?' Ian pointed out.

Mum thought about it. 'Aye, you're right there. It didny have a tag on it. I still don't know how I'm gonny tell her. I could still lose ma job.'

But she seemed to have calmed down and become resigned to the possibility. She recovered herself.

'Ah well, nivver mind. I can always get a cleaning job some-wheres else.'

She started humming to herself.

Ian went into his bedroom. That was just like her. Worrying herself sick one minute and then cheering up the next. But it was a bit much accusing him of stealing the key. He wouldn't do a thing like that.

Jimmy must have been out. It made a change to have the room to himself.

Then he remembered. Now was his chance. He could have a quick peep under the bed. He knelt down and lifted the bedcover. The video recorder had gone.

It was then that the shocked thought came to him. He knew someone who might have taken the key.

6

'Marshall! I've told you a dozen times already! Stop making so much noise!'

Vincent had been yapping ever since the period began. Mrs Summers allowed them to chat quietly while they worked. But the kind of din coming from Vincent's table was too much. He was taking advantage of her goodwill. She was beginning to lose her temper. She always did in the end.

Ian looked up from his drawing. Maria and Bernadette who were sharing his table looked up as well. Mrs Summers was standing over Vincent and glaring at him with deadly hatred. The black boy turned his eyes up at her with insolent coolness. She might have been a plane far away in the sky that had momentarily attracted his attention. Beside him, Terry and Les were covering their spluttering giggles behind their hands, delighted that their friend was in trouble again.

Mrs Summers moved on to another table and leaned across to inspect a drawing. As soon as her back was turned, Vincent started again. Ian couldn't hear the words, but he recognised Vincent's mocking voice. He was probably giving an imitation of Mrs Summers.

There was a sudden loud hoot from Terry, and the teacher swung round furiously.

'What did I tell you?' she shrieked. She rushed over to Vincent as though about to swipe him on the head.

'It weren't me,' said Vincent, his face hardening.

'Of course it was you!'

Mrs Summers managed to restrain herself. She gazed wildly round the studio, then gestured at an empty space at Ian's table.

'Go and sit over there.'

Vincent went on sitting where he was. He was clearly giving the matter a lot of thought. For a moment, it seemed as though he was going to refuse. Then he shrugged himself to his feet, picked up his drawing board and lazily ambled across to the other table. He put the drawing board down, dragged out the stool and stood for a while as if trying to summon up the energy to sit down. Finally, he sank onto the stool as if the effort had all been too much for him.

It was all done in slow motion, for maximum effect. Mrs Summers pretended not to notice, but the whole class knew that she was aware of Vincent's every move and was desperately having to hold herself in. But then, that was what Vincent wanted.

'Why d'you go on like that?' Maria asked him scornfully.

She wasn't exactly telling him off. It was more as though she was puzzled why someone should behave in such a childish way.

'Like what?' Vincent snapped.

'The big performance.'

'What big performance?'

'You know. You do it all the time.'

Vincent gave her one of his hard stares. But it had no effect on Maria. She just stared back — steady and unblinking.

Ian didn't want to get involved. He studied the potted geranium plonked down in the middle of the table and did a few tentative strokes on the paper. He was no good at art. He didn't know why he'd chosen the subject as an option. And Mrs Summers was no good as a teacher. She spent so much time keeping discipline, she never taught them anything.

But then, he'd had no choice. Because he was new to the school, he'd had to make do with what was left over. The subjects nobody else wanted.

Vincent soon recovered himself. He returned to the attack.

' 'Ow you know anyway? You watch me all the time or somet'in'? I bet you fancies me.'

He leered at Maria.

'No, I don't,' she said. She flashed her eyelashes at him for the merest second before adding scornfully, 'You fancy yourself.'

'Yeah,' agreed Bernadette. ' 'E's so arrogant.'

Vincent's face was blank with surprise. He was completely taken aback. It was as though nobody had dared to tell him a thing like that before. He couldn't believe it.

Mrs Summers was hovering near. Vincent ducked his head down to the paper and added a line to his drawing. When she had passed on, he seemed to have got over his shock.

'Anyway, what does it matter what you t'inks,' he said airily. 'Girls. They're only good fo' one t'ing.'

He laughed knowingly. Neither Maria nor Bernadette deigned to respond. They went on with their drawing as though he wasn't there.

Vincent seemed disappointed. Then he remembered something. He leaned over to Ian.

'Hey,' he said. 'I seen you sister the other day. Terry point 'er out to me. She's all right.'

'Oh, aye,' Ian said. He was immediately on his guard. He felt himself go tense. He didn't trust Vincent. The black boy was up to something.

'You can book me 'alf an' 'our any time,' Vincent went on. He pushed his lips out suggestively. 'I wouldn't mind that.'

'Whit d'you mean?' Ian demanded.

But he knew. His mouth was suddenly dry. The hair on the back of his neck was bristling. His hands were tightening into fists.

' 'S obvious,' said Vincent with a grin. 'She's a crow, innit? A pro. She's on the game.'

There were shocked stares from Maria and Bernadette. Ian felt his heart beating wildly in his chest. He wanted to speak out, but his tongue seemed to have swollen to fill his whole mouth. Vincent was still grinning. He wanted to knock that grin off his face, but he felt he couldn't move. He was fixed to his stool.

Then he acted. He threw the drawing board down on the table and stood up. He stumbled between the tables to the door. People were looking up enquiringly, but he didn't pay any attention to them. He pulled the door open and went out. Behind him, Mrs Summers was calling angrily, but he ignored her. He had to get away.

He didn't care who saw him going down the drive. If Mr Armstrong yelled at him to come back, he'd just carry straight on. He'd had enough.

But Mr Armstrong didn't yell. Ian reached the road without being stopped. He set off along it at a brisk pace.

Why did Vincent have to go and say a thing like that? What did it have to do with him? Why couldn't he mind his own business?

And those girls with their shocked faces. It would be all over the school by dinner time. It was bad enough being called Jock or Mac or Scottie — that was when anyone bothered to speak to him at all. Now they would have something else to talk about. Whisper about among themselves. Giggle over. Insult him with.

Perhaps he should have stood up and called Vincent a liar and punched him in the face. Why hadn't he? At least that would have given him some satisfaction. To have thumped a fist into that grinning face and see the smile disappear. But no, he had just run away. Upped and gone. He knew that didn't solve anything. It was like admitting what Vincent said was true.

And perhaps that was why he'd done it. Just run away. Because he had a sickening feeling that Vincent was right. There was that time when he'd seen Bella down the Junction. The way she'd been behaving. An unlit cigarette in her mouth. Going off with that man.

There were other things too. She was always out. She seemed to have plenty of money. She was forever buying new clothes and make-up and records. Mum didn't seem to notice, but he did.

She'd liked her boyfriends right enough in Glasgow. But this was something else altogether. To do it for money. With any man she picked up. That wasn't right. Was it?

Yet he knew it happened. There'd been girls on the estate who did it. And there were those stories in the *News of the World*. He'd read them and licked his lips. About women becoming strippers or going on the streets because they were out of work or had families to keep. And they'd justified themselves. How else could a woman make money, they'd said. They'd had no shame.

Bella couldn't be like that. Could she? He pushed the idea away. No, it wasn't possible. It must all just be a mistake.

By now, he had reached the flats. He wasn't sure if there would be anyone in. He'd have to take the risk. He could always say he wasn't feeling well.

He pushed open the door of the living room. There was a flurried movement on the settee. Two startled faces stared up at him. Wide eyes. Open mouths. Flushed cheeks. One was Bella's. The other was a man's.

Ian didn't take in any more. He blundered out of the room and into his bedroom. He closed the door and stood with his back to it. What he had seen had only been a blur, except for those two shocked faces. But he was sure all his fears had been confirmed. How could she? Using the flat when everyone else was out. What would Mum say if she knew? And how could he face those taunts at school, knowing that what they said was true?

He went and sat on the edge of his bed. Those faces were burning into his brain. Bella's hot and flushed with her hair mussed up and untidy. And the man's, surprised and anxious. He'd been older than Bella. His hair was fair, thinning on his forehead, and there were creases round his eyes.

Ian threw himself back on the bed. What was he going to do?

The door opened and Bella came in. She stood looking down at him. She'd tidied her hair up.

'Whit you doing hame?' she asked.

Ian didn't feel like speaking to her, but in the end he mumbled, 'I didny feel like school the day.'

'You'll get into trouble,' Bella told him.

'So what!' He didn't want any moral talk from her.

He glared at her. She was inspecting him like a doctor searching for symptoms. He was surprised at how much she resembled Mum. Younger, of course, but under the plump cheeks there was the same round face, and there were the same anxious appraising eyes. But he didn't want to think about that.

'Whit's up?' Bella asked.

She sounded concerned. Again like Mum. But she couldn't be. She was just worried because she'd been found out. Well, he wasn't going to say anything. He'd keep it to himself.

Then he found himself blurting out angrily, 'It's true, intit?'

'Whit?'

'Whit Vincent said.'

'And who's Vincent when he's at hame?'

'A boy at school.'

'And whit did he say?'

'He said you wis on the game.'

'Did he now?'

Bella's mouth shut like a grim trap. Her eyes widened with a brooding fury.

She turned and went out. Ian could hear her in the hall.

'Oot,' she was saying.

'But —,' the man began.

'Oot,' Bella said again. 'I'll see you later.'

There was the bang of the front door.

Bella was back.

'Come on, you,' she said to Ian.

'Whit fur?' he asked. He was suddenly apprehensive.

'Whit fur?' Bella cried, her eyes blazing. 'I want words with this Vincent. You don't think I'm gonny let him say things like that aboot me and get away with it, do you?'

'But —,' Ian began.

Bella bulldozed right over him. 'Don't you but me any buts. Up!'
It was an order Ian couldn't refuse.

As Bella's high heels clip-clopped furiously on the pavement, he had a hard job of it to keep up with her. She might have been on the big side, but she could certainly move when she put her mind to it. And there was no doubt at all that now she was on the warpath.

She kept her anger warm as she went along. 'I'll show him,' she muttered. And 'Wait till I get ma hands on him.' And 'Who does he think he is?'

It wasn't really intended for Ian's ear. In any case, he was only half listening. He was worrying about what he had started and what was going to happen next. She wasn't really going up to the school, was she? Well, it looked like it. And he knew that nothing he could say would stop her.

But what would people think? Getting his big sister in to sort them out. It would make things worse. They'd just think he was a big softy. Needing someone to fight his battles for him. He'd never be able to hold his head up again.

Besides, you couldn't just walk into a school. There'd be teachers and caretakers and people wanting to know what she was doing there. They had strict rules about things like that.

He would have to try.

'D'you think it's a good idea?' he asked tentatively.

Bella turned a hard eye on him. 'Whit?' she spat out.

'Going up to school.'

'I'm not letting him get away with it.'

'But I don't want you to.'

'Huh,' Bella snorted. 'I'm not doing it fur you. I'm doing it fur maself.'

The grim determination in her voice made any further appeal futile. Ian gave up.

They walked up the drive to the main entrance. Ian was relieved to see there was nobody about.

'Now, where can I find this Vincent?' Bella demanded.

Ian worked it out. Vincent would be doing history this period in Room 7.

'Show me,' Bella commanded.

When they were outside the door, Ian made one last attempt.

'You canny just go into a classroom,' he said. 'It's no allowed.'

'You get him then,' said Bella. 'I want to speak to him.'

Ian knew from the steely way her eye held his that she wasn't going to let him off the hook. He blew out his breath and surrendered to the inevitable. Through the glass in the door, he could see Miss Baxter writing notes on the blackboard. He would have to find some excuse.

'You keep oot of sight,' he warned Bella. He knocked at the door and went in.

'Why are you so late?' Miss Baxter asked as soon as she caught sight of him.

'I've been with Mr Armstrong,' Ian said. She would probably check up. She was that kind of teacher. But there was no help for it. 'He wants to see Marshall as well.'

Vincent's head shot up, his eyes wide with alarm. The class gave a roar of malicious glee.

'That's enough of that,' Miss Baxter cried. 'Vincent, you'd better go. But try not to be too long.'

Vincent shuffled to his feet and joined Ian at the door.

'What I done?' he asked, putting on an act of outraged innocence.

As soon as he saw Bella, it was clear from his face that he knew what it was all about.

'Come here, you,' said Bella, and she drew him down to the end of the corridor away from the door.

Vincent flicked a quick look at Ian, but he went with her.

Bella turned and fixed him with a cold stare.

'Now whit's all this I've bin hearing?' she demanded.

'What you on 'bout?' Vincent asked, still playing the innocent.

'You know.'

You could tell from her voice that she wasn't going to stand any nonsense.

Vincent licked his lips and made a great show of searching his memory. Then it seemed to come to him in a rush.

'Oh that!' He dismissed it. 'It were only a joke.'

You could see the anger rising right up through Bella's body into her face. She seemed to grow three inches taller. She exploded. 'A joke! Is that whit you call it? Well, I'm not laughing.'

Vincent tried again. 'It were not'in'.'

'Nothing!' Bella retorted. 'It might be nothing to you, but it's no nothing to me. Now you listen. I'm no having you nor anybody else going around saying things like that aboot me. And if I hear you've been doing it again, I'll come straight up here and give you a good belt round the heid. Understand?'

Vincent was gazing at her in a glazed sort of way as though he was in a trance. 'Yeah,' he mumbled like someone sleep-walking.

'I just don't get you,' Bella went on. 'Whit wis the big idea of spreading they stories around? I bet you wouldny like it if it wis your sister they wis said aboot.'

'No,' Vincent mumbled again.

'You think you're just great, don't you? You think you're a man. But you're just a baby. The way you go on, you'd think you were still in nappies. It's time you grew up.'

Vincent gulped and nodded.

'Right,' said Bella. 'You mind whit I said. If you mention anything like this aboot me again, I'll be up here like a shot and I'll have your guts fur garters.'

'Yeah,' murmured Vincent as though he was in a dream.

Bella gave emphasis to her words with a nod of her chin. She pushed past them and made for the stairs. They could hear her high heels clattering away into the distance.

'Wow!' Vincent breathed out.

Ian turned to look at him. He was expecting Vincent to be incensed by what Bella had said. But the black boy was gazing at the place where Bella had disappeared with an expression of rapt wonder and admiration glowing on his face.

'That's some woman,' he said to himself as much as to Ian.

There was nothing in what he said for Ian to take offence at. It was genuine. Vincent seemed quite overcome. He looked as though he had seen a vision. He went on staring into space with glassy eyes and a gaping mouth.

Ian felt he ought to make some kind of apology. 'It wisny ma idea,' he muttered.

Vincent slowly came back to himself. His eyes focused on Ian. 'What?'

'I didny mean fur Bella to come up here and tell you off.'

Vincent waved the apology aside with an air of great magnanimity. 'That's all right, man,' he said.

Then he breathed a deep sigh. 'It's been quite a day. I just don' seem to 'ave no luck. Summers. Maria. You' sister. They all gettin' at me.'

'That's because you're a male chauvinist pig,' said Ian. It was out before he realised it. He wished he could take it back, but it was too late. He shot an anxious glance at Vincent to see how he was reacting.

But Vincent didn't seem to mind. He was still lost in some private world of his own. 'She sure is a real woman,' he murmured.

Ian couldn't understand it.

'We'd better get back to the lesson,' he said, beginning to move. There was still going to be trouble with Mr Armstrong about leaving Mrs Summers' lesson without permission. And telling lies about him.

Vincent caught him by the arm. 'Hey, I'm sorry 'bout what I said. I didn' mean anyt'in' by it. I were just 'avin' you on.'

'That's all right,' said Ian.

Vincent stuck out his hand. 'Shake on it?'

'OK.'

Vincent's hand was firm in his.

Of course, Mr Armstrong hadn't been pleased. He'd given Ian two detentions for leaving Mrs Summers' lesson without permission and for taking his name in vain.

Not that Ian minded very much. Walking home across the Common, he felt happier than he had done a few hours before — in spite of the detentions. Things didn't seem to be so bad after all.

Then he remembered the Park and Old Bill. The picture of the old man slumped in his chair came back to him. It had haunted him since it had happened. Should he have done more to help? What more could he have done?

He had been in the Park a number of times since then, but there was no sign of the gardener, and the hut was locked. That meant that the old man had been able to get home, didn't it? That was something.

Unless someone else had found his body and carted it away. It was a possibility that crept into Ian's mind from time to time and which he resolutely ejected again. Old Bill hadn't exactly been the most friendly of people, but Ian had no wish to see him die like that.

There was no point in brooding over it though. He might never know one way or the other. Better to think of something more cheerful. His friends in Glasgow, for instance. How were they getting on? When he saw them again, he'd have quite a bit to tell them. Perhaps he ought to make the effort to write.

As he walked across the Common, he worked out what he might say.

Dear Maisie, I hope you are well. And Jean and Andy. I am keeping fine. The warm weather has finished down here now. We've had a lot of rain lately, and there's even been some fog. Of course, London is famous for its fogs. I don't remember anything like it in Glasgow. When it comes down, you can hardly see a hand in front of your face. You could easily get lost just trying to get across the Common.

Bella has got a new boyfriend. He seems very nice. He takes her out a lot and buys her clothes and things. I don't know whether it's

*serious or not. You know what Bella is like for having boyfriends! I
can't remember what his name is.*

*Vincent met Bella the other day. Fair smitten with her he was!
Vincent and me have become really friendly. I think you'd like
him. He's —*

Ian broke off. There was a police car parked outside the flats.
As he came alongside, he peered inside. It was empty. He gazed
up at the flats and wondered who the police could be visiting.
A sudden panic seized him, and he went up the stairs three at a
time.

He heard the voices as soon as he opened the front door. The
policemen were in the front room. There were two of them. Mum
and Jimmy were there too. It looked very crowded.

They were all standing up. Mum had her hands pressed to her
cheeks as though trying to hold in her horror. Jimmy was looking
sullen and hunted, like an animal that knows it is cornered and
resents it. One of the policemen was tall and thin. The other was
broad and beefy, bursting out of his uniform.

No one paid any attention to Ian.

'So you don't know anything about this key,' the tall policemen
was saying.

'Naw,' Jimmy replied defiantly.

'Well, that's very strange,' said the beefy policeman, all
sarcastic. 'It must just be a coincidence then, mustn't it? Mrs
Bentley gives your mum the key to the front door. The key goes
missing. And then a week later, Mrs Bentley gets broken into.
Except there's no breaking. Whoever got in came in through the
front door. With a key.'

'It wisny me,' Jimmy maintained, though he looked more
hunted and haunted than ever.

Mum came to his defence. 'It couldny have been Jimmy. The
key wis lost.'

'We don't know that, now do we?' the beefy policeman said. You
could see from his face he never believed anything anyone told
him. He turned to his colleague. 'What was it that went?'

'A video recorder and odd bits and pieces. A few ornaments. Some cash.'

Ian remembered the video under Jimmy's bed. Now here was another one. Jimmy seemed to be making a habit of it.

'I don't know,' the beefy policeman said. 'I sometimes think people deserve what they get. Leaving cash around.'

'But it's the video that's the big item,' the thin policeman pointed out. 'And it looks like a one man job. Otherwise they'd have taken a few more pieces of hardware.'

'Yes, videos are the things these days,' said the beefy policeman. They seemed to have forgotten the others were there. 'A lot of them's been nicked lately. Must be someone handling them. An easy market. Perhaps our friend here's had a hand in some of the others as well.'

'It wisny me,' Jimmy repeated.

The beefy policeman ignored him. 'Have you seen him with a video?' he asked Mum.

'Naw,' she replied. 'I've nivver seen him with anything like that.'

As if she would tell them if she had. Ian was glad the policemen didn't bother to ask him.

The thin policeman turned to Jimmy. 'You've been in trouble before, haven't you?'

Jimmy looked down without replying.

'Oh, don't worry,' the policeman continued. 'We've checked up. You've got form all right, haven't you, lad?'

'That doesny mean I did anything,' Jimmy retorted.

'We'll see about that,' the thin policeman said grimly.

'Yeah,' said the beefy policeman as if suddenly bored with the whole thing. 'It's cut and dried. There's no doubt about it.'

'Whit are you gonny do?' Mum asked anxiously.

'Well, Jimmy lad here had better come down to the station for questioning,' said the beefy policeman.

'That's terrible,' Mum cried. She clapped her hands to her cheeks again. 'Whit'll Dad say?'

But the policemen weren't interested in Mum's problems.

86

'Come on,' the beefy one said to Jimmy. 'Let's be going.'

Jimmy looked round desperately for a moment before giving a sigh of resignation. He had no option. He went through the door, and the two policemen followed him.

Mum ran after them to see them out and then came back. She clawed away the net curtain and peered out to catch a sight of them getting into the car. It drove off.

'Oh, the shame of it!' Mum cried.

From the way she spoke, you'd think she was taken completely by surprise — as if Jimmy had never been in trouble with the law before. But he had been. As the policemen said. He'd been to court twice when they lived in Glasgow. He'd been fined and had a suspended sentence. It was nothing unusual up there. Many of the people on the estate had been to court one time or another. It was a way of life. But Mum still found it shocking and worried about what the neighbours would say.

Not that Jimmy was a criminal exactly. Ian couldn't think of him like that. He'd kept clear of it for years. Nothing had gone wrong while he was at school. It was only when he left and found himself on the dole that he went astray. He was bored out of his mind. Frustrated. He wanted the things other people had, and the only way he could get them was to steal them.

Ian couldn't approve of what Jimmy had done. But he couldn't entirely blame his brother either. He was realistic about it. Who knew? He might end up doing the same thing himself.

'I'm sure Jimmy didny take the key from ma purse,' Mum said. 'I asked him maself and he said no.'

She seemed quite certain that Jimmy had told her the truth. Or else she was just trying to convince herself. Ian knew what he thought.

'It must all be a mistake,' she went on. 'I dinny believe whit they polismen said. Jimmy wouldny do anything like that.'

Then her face clouded over with doubt. 'Mind you, I have been wondering where he's been getting his money from latcly. There's things he's been buying. That leather jacket . . .'

She didn't go on.

Another worry assailed her. 'And whit's Mrs Bentley gonny say noo? She let me off aboot losing the key. But she's no gonny let this pass by. She'll give me the sack this time fur sure.'

There was nothing Ian could say. He left Mum pursing her lips and staring into space and went into his bedroom.

Mum's words had reminded him. He opened the battered rickety wardrobe he shared with his brother. There was the jacket. He stroked the black leather. It was smooth and supple, the finest quality. The jacket must have cost a fortune.

He slipped it off the hanger and put it on. He zipped up the front and thrust his hands into the slit side pockets. The jacket was too large for him, inflating his shoulders and coming down too low on his waist, but he was pleased with his reflection in the mirror. It made him look big and tough. He swung from side to side, admiring his image from different angles. He could see why Jimmy wanted something like this to wear. He wouldn't mind having one like it himself.

But would he be prepared to steal to get the money for it? Because how else could someone like him or Jimmy be able to afford it?

The feeling of pleasure suddenly evaporated. He felt a cold shiver of guilt run through him as though someone had walked over his grave. He unzipped the jacket and put it back on the hanger in the wardrobe.

7

The days that followed were miserable. There were nothing but rows. Jimmy and Bella were continually at each other's throats. The police were going to charge Jimmy and he would have to appear in court. Bella called him 'an eejit', said he was 'daft as a brush' and went on and on at him. Jimmy growled back at her and told her to mind her own business.

Mum was near to tears most of the time. Needless to say, she'd lost her job, and she worried about what they would do when Dad lost his as well — though the final decision wouldn't be made until the council meeting in four weeks' time.

As for Dad, he sought comfort in his whisky bottle.

The one bright spot, strangely enough, was school. Since Bella had told him off, Vincent had been quite friendly. He even spoke to Ian sometimes and asked after Bella. Terry and Les hadn't liked it much. Ian had overheard Les say to Vincent, 'What you want wit' that snowflake?' And Vincent put him down by retorting, 'That way I gets some intelligent talk.'

Yes, school was all right. It was home that was dire. He felt he wanted to get out as much as possible.

That Saturday morning, Bella and Jimmy were up early for once, and Bella started on him straightaway.

'Pinched any good videos lately?' she asked.

'Och, give it a rest,' Jimmy snapped back.

'You're no at it again, are you?' cried Mum with a look of despair.

Ian bolted down his cornflakes and got up. He made for the Park. At least it would be quiet there.

It was a clear morning. The sunlight slanted through the trees in shining arrows. More of the branches were bare now. Piles of leaves lay strewn on the ground.

Since it was Saturday, Ian half expected to find players in the tennis court. He approached with caution, but he heard no shouts, and there was no one there.

He was moving on along the path when a yell rang out. He looked round guiltily. On the other side of a clearing was Old Bill.

Ian's first feeling was one of relief. So the old man was all right. But then he remembered that he was trespassing. He prepared to make a run for it.

But the old man was waving to him. It wasn't his usual gesture of pushing him away. It was beckoning him to come nearer.

Ian was surprised. He almost turned round to look behind him to see if there was someone else there. But no, it seemed to be meant for him. He walked slowly across the clearing.

Old Bill had been gathering up leaves, and he was standing now with one hand resting on the handle of his rake. With his other hand he pushed back his cap. Ian couldn't work out the expression on his face. It could have been apologetic. But that didn't seem likely. It was certainly different from his usual ferocious glare.

'I was hoping I'd see you,' Old Bill said. That was a surprise for a start. 'I wanted to thank you for what you did the other week. Should have thanked you then but I forgot.'

'That's all right,' Ian said guardedly. He was still waiting for the gardener to tell him to clear off.

But instead, Old Bill put down his rake and said, 'Come and have a cup of coffee.'

Ian couldn't believe it. The old man's collapse or fit or whatever it was must have affected him more than he thought. Still with some apprehension, he fell in line with the old man, and they walked along the path towards the hut.

'Are you feeling better then?' Ian asked.

'Much better, thanks.'

'Whit did the doctor say?'

Old Bill gave a dry chuckle. 'I didn't bother about the doctor. I don't believe in them. Once you let them get their hands on you and send you to hospital, you're finished.'

'Oh,' said Ian. It didn't sound very sensible to him.

'It was nothing,' Old Bill continued. 'I'd just been overdoing it. That and old age.' He made an odd cackle at the back of his throat. 'There's no cure for old age.' Then he said more cheerfully. 'Still, I don't do too badly considering.'

Ian was forced to agree. 'D'you look after this place on your own?' he asked.

'That I do,' said Old Bill proudly. 'Have done for the past twenty years.' He sighed. 'Not that I'll be able to manage it much longer. It's beginning to get too much for me.'

By now, they had reached the hut. Old Bill opened the door. 'Sit yourself down,' he said.

'Naw,' said Ian. 'You have the chair. I'll be all right here.'

He squatted down on the floor and stretched out his legs. There was just enough room.

While Old Bill lit the primus stove and spooned out the coffee and boiled the kettle, Ian examined the hut and its contents. It was true that the armchair was old and battered, and the square of carpet on which it was sitting was worn and frayed, but everything was spotless. The garden tools were lined up and sparkling — not a speck of earth or mud on them. The old man had pulled off his wellingtons at the door and left them outside. He was padding about on stockinged feet. Ian wondered if he should have done the same.

'You sure keep the place clean,' he said.

'You learn that in the Navy,' Old Bill explained. 'When you live on a ship in a tiny space with lots of other men, you soon get that knocked into you. It becomes a kind of obsession. Scrubbing, washing, keeping things tidy. And old habits die hard as they say.'

'Were you in the Navy?' Ian asked. It was obvious that he had been. But it was a way of getting him to say more.

'I was that,' Old Bill said. 'All through the war. And I stayed on after. I liked the life. It suited me. Not that it was easy. There were times when I wondered if I would survive.'

He didn't go into any more details. His face suddenly looked gaunt and grim. Then he gave a shake of his head and came back to the present. 'Sugar?' he asked.

'Aye,' said Ian.

He watched as Old Bill heaped sugar into the mugs, poured on the boiling water and added milk from a carton. He stirred furiously and handed one of the mugs to Ian.

'Thanks.' It was hot, and Ian placed it carefully on the floor beside him.

Old Bill lowered himself into the armchair. He picked up his own mug from the table and sipped at it.

'How did you get this job then?' Ian asked, curious.

'It was after I left the Navy,' Old Bill told him. 'I had my pension, but I was too young just to sit about at home and twiddle my thumbs. I'd been an engineer in the Navy. I knew a thing or two about electrical work and repairs and that sort of thing. So I set up as a kind of odd-jobs man. People called me in when there were problems in the house. Blocked drains, slates off roofs, rotten woodwork — things like that.'

He chortled. 'I did quite a few jobs for people living in Trinity Park. Those old houses need a deal of looking after.'

'My mum works for someone in Trinity Park,' Ian said. 'Mrs Bentley.' Then he remembered. 'At least, she used to work fur her.'

'Mrs Bentley,' said Old Bill, mulling the name over in his head. 'I think she's one of the committee — the Trinity Park committee. You see, the people who live in Trinity Park have a committee to look after their interests. They pay an annual subscription to cover any work that has to be done. That's how I get paid. The old bloke who looked after the Park died, and they asked me if I would take it on. I didn't know anything about gardening. I'd never even had my own garden.'

He laughed as he remembered. He sipped at his coffee again. Then he resumed.

'But I thought about it. It was a healthy life. Out in the open air all day. Plenty of exercise. What I didn't know I could find out from books. And I would be more or less my own boss. I'd had enough of doing odd-jobs. Too many people telling you what to do and thinking they knew better than you did. So I said yes. And I've been doing it ever since.'

He shot a glance at Ian and then lowered his eyes. 'So you see. If I sometimes get carried away and yell at people to clear out, it's because I feel the place belongs to me. It's my park. I've looked after it and kept it up to scratch.'

'That's all right,' said Ian. He recognised an apology when it was made, and he accepted it. 'They don't seem to use the Park much.'

Old Bill gave a grunt of contempt. 'Well, isn't that just like people with money? They don't use it themselves, but they hang on to it to make sure no one else uses it.'

He changed the subject. 'Where are you from anyway?'

Ian presumed his accent had given him away. 'From Glasgow.'

Old Bill's face lit up. 'Are you now? I was stationed at the Gare Loch for quite a while during the war. We had some rare times in Glasgow. Saturday night in Sauchiehall Street. Going to all those clubs. The people were really friendly.' He became quite animated at the memory of it.

Ian too felt a sudden glow. To have met someone who knew Glasgow. Who remembered it with pleasure. It brought back a great flood of warm feelings and thoughts.

'What are you doing down here then?' Old Bill asked.

Ian returned to earth with a bump. 'Ma dad got a job down here, so we all came and joined him.'

'That's good,' Old Bill said.

'Aye, but my brother and sister haveny been able to get jobs, and it looks as if ma dad's gonny get the sack. He's a dustman, and the corporation's gonny privatise it.'

'I'm sorry to hear that,' said Old Bill.

'They're gonny make a protest at the council meeting. But I don't know if it'll do any good.'

'You tell me when it is. I might just turn up and give my support.'

'Would you? That would be great.'

Old Bill eyed him curiously. 'You wouldn't like a job, would you?' he asked. He sounded a bit uncertain.

'Whit d'you mean?' Ian asked.

'Like I said. It's all getting a bit too much for me. I could do with some help.'

It was like an appeal. Ian thought about it.

'But I don't know anything aboot gardens,' he said at last.

'Neither did I,' said Old Bill.

Since Ian still hesitated, he went on, 'I'll pay you.'

'All right,' said Ian.

But it wasn't just the promise of money that decided him. He was certain of that. It was something to do with the pleading tone of the old man's voice and the anxious look on his face. Anyway, it would give him something to do. It would be a way of passing the time.

They got down to work straightaway. While Old Bill scraped the fallen leaves into piles, Ian scooped them up and filled wheelbarrow after wheelbarrow with them. He carted them off and unloaded them into a dump that had been specially prepared for them.

'They'll be marvellous compost in a couple of years' time,' Old Bill said.

Ian was soon sweating. He stopped for a moment to wipe his forehead. Old Bill had the harder job to do — wielding the rake backwards and forwards as he gathered the leaves together — but he went at it unflinchingly. Ian was amazed at the old man's strength and perseverance. It made him feel ashamed for taking a rest. He piled more leaves into the wheelbarrow.

At last, even the old man had had enough.

'You'll be back this afternoon?' he asked.

Ian surprised himself by saying, 'Aye.'

'Good. I'll see you then.'

Ian went back home, tired but exhilarated. He was also ravenous.

Mum was doing fried eggs and chips for dinner. He didn't like fried eggs, but he gobbled them down. In any case, he knew what Mum would say if he complained — 'Eggs is good fur you. Anyways, they're cheap.'

'Can I have another slice of bread?' he asked.

Mum passed the loaf to him.

'I'm glad somebody's got an appetite,' said Jimmy. He pushed his plate away. There were still some chips on it.

'Can I have those?' Ian asked.

'Help yourself,' said Jimmy wearily.

Ian scraped them onto his plate and got stuck in. He needed to build up some energy for the afternoon.

'There you are,' said Old Bill when he returned.

Ian had a feeling the old man hadn't expected to see him. But if he was surprised, he quickly covered it up.

'I think we'll forget about the leaves for the moment. I can manage the rest of them on my own next week. What I really need some help with is these branches and bits of trees that are lying around.'

Armed with a saw, they went in search of them. Some of them had been torn off — by storms? — and lay dead on the ground. Others still hung precariously to the tree though it was clear they had been split from it and were slowly dying. Using the saw, Old Bill cut them into convenient lengths for Ian to carry away and store.

'I've got a market for them,' Old Bill said with a wink. 'Some of the people in the Park have wood stoves. It's some new-fangled thing. They pay me a bob or two for those.'

It was hard work. By the end of the afternoon, Ian's arms were aching. He wondered if he would ever be able to carry anything again. Not since the day they had moved had his body been put to such effort.

It had suddenly begun to get dark, and the cool November evening was coming down on them.

'We'd better stop there,' Old Bill said.

He stood for a moment looking around. He seemed to be sniffing the air.

'You know, I love this place,' he said.

He didn't seem to be speaking to Ian. It was more as though he was thinking aloud. He gave a quiet chortle.

'They pay me for looking after this place. Not that they pay much. But they hardly ever come here. I have the place to myself. It's like it was my own garden. I'd look after it for nothing if they did but know it.'

'Aye,' said Ian. 'It's great here. You could be miles from anywhere.'

His words surprised him. His words and his enthusiasm. If anyone had asked him about the Park, he would have said it was all right. But inside, he knew it was more than that to him. He could understand how Old Bill felt.

The old man was searching inside his dungarees. He brought out his wallet and opened it. He took out a five-pound note and held it out to Ian.

'Here,' he said. 'Is that all right?' He sounded gruff. More like his usual self.

'That's fine,' said Ian, taking the note. His heart gave a leap as his fingers closed on the money. He folded it up and put it in the pocket of his jeans. He hadn't expected so much.

'I'll see you next Saturday?' The old man's voice was a mixture of doubt and hope. 'There's a lot to be done.'

'Aye,' said Ian. 'I'll be here.'

'Off you go then,' said Old Bill. 'I'll clear these things away.'

Ian left the old man to it. It had been an exhausting day, but satisfying too. As he followed the path through the gathering dusk, he had the feeling of a job well done. And it was just the beginning. He would be back next Saturday, helping to keep the Park in order. Maintaining it as a pleasant place to be.

Tracy was playing ball in the entrance hall of the flats, bouncing the ball against the wall and catching it. She held the ball to her chest when she saw Ian.

'You been in the Park?' she asked.

'Aye.'

Her eyes widened. 'Did you see Old Bill?'

'Aye.'

'Is 'e all right?'

'Aye, he's as fit as rain.'

She seemed surprised. 'I thought 'e might be dead by now.'

'It'll take more than that to kill him.'

Ian hesitated for a moment and then said, 'I wis doing some work fur him. He gave me a fiver fur it.' He couldn't help boasting.

Tracy was suitably impressed. 'D'you think 'e'll let me work for 'im? I've never 'ad a fiver.'

Neither had Ian before. But he wasn't going to admit that.

He shrugged his shoulders and said, 'Mebbe.' Then he pounded up the stairs to the flat.

Mum was in the kitchen. Ian drew the note out of his pocket, unfolded it and held it out to her.

'Where did you get that?' she asked.

From the look of fear that flickered across her face, Ian knew that she suspected the worst.

'It's all right,' he said. 'Old Bill gave it me. Fur working in the Park. He wants me to go there again next week.'

Mum took the note and gazed at it with awe.

'My,' she said. 'Is that no wonderful?'

Then she pulled herself together and smiled. 'Well, son, thanks. We can do with the money right enough. But I canny take it all. You deserve something fur yourself.'

She fetched her purse and scrabbled about in it.

'Here's two pound fifty,' she said, handing him the money.

'Is that fair?'

'Aye, that's fine, Mum,' Ian said. He felt quite rich.

He went into the living room. Dad and Jimmy were there, watching the sports results. Ian joined them, but he didn't really notice what was being flashed up on the screen. His mind was miles away. He was thinking what a pity it was that tomorrow was Sunday. The library would be shut. He'd have to wait till Monday before he could go. But then he would be able to get out all those books on trees and flowers and gardening that he had a sudden urge to read.

Perhaps there was some point in books after all.

'Gerald's calling for me,' Bella announced later that evening as she got up from the table. 'If I'm no ready, tell him to wait.'

And with that, she bounced out of the kitchen and into her bedroom, leaving behind her a stunned silence.

'Who's Gerald?' Dad asked when he had got over his surprise.

'I don't know,' said Mum, equally puzzled.

'It must be her latest boyfriend,' said Jimmy. 'Though if it is, it'll be the first one we've actually seen.'

'Of course that's who it'll be,' said Dad irritably. 'But who is he?'

'She hasny said anything to me aboot him,' said Mum. 'I know she's had boyfriends doon here, but she's kept quiet aboot them.'

'Like I said,' Jimmy pointed out. 'It'll be the first one we've seen.'

Mum's eyes went misty as she thought back. 'I wonder whit happened to Fergus. He wis a nice lad. I always liked him.'

'He's in Glasgow,' Jimmy reminded her. 'So he's nae use to Bella. And any roads, she had ten boyfriends after Fergus.'

The pained expression on Mum's face suggested that she didn't wish to be told that.

The door-bell rang. Mum was startled. 'Oh,' she said in panic. 'That'll be him.'

'I'll go,' said Ian, jumping up before anyone else could move. He had a sudden curiosity to see what Bella's boyfriend was like.

He opened the door and found himself staring at the man who had been with Bella that day he had come home from school. He was sure it was the same one. There was the thinning fair hair and the wrinkles round the eyes.

Gerald was either shy or embarrassed. He opened his mouth a couple of times but nothing came out. At last, he found his tongue. 'Is Bella ready?' he asked.

'Naw,' said Ian. 'She said you wis to wait.'

He drew the door wider so that Gerald could come in, and then ushered him into the living room. Not that he needed to. He was sure Gerald could find his way there on his own.

'It's Gerald,' he told Mum and Dad.

'We'd better go and meet him,' said Mum.

'Whit fur?' Dad asked.

'It's only polite,' said Mum who was obviously dying to have a look at him. 'After all she doesny ask all her boyfriends to call.'

'You can say that again,' said Jimmy.

'It must be kinda serious,' Mum continued.

She got to her feet and straightened her skirt. Dad waited impatiently, and then they went into the living room. Jimmy didn't bother.

'Pleased to meet you,' Mum said, stretching out a hand. 'I'm Bella's mum.'

Gerald scrambled up from his seat and took the hand. He had that kind of fair skin that goes red easily. At that moment, his face was burning so hot it was surprising beads of sweat didn't break out all over it.

Dad shook his hand as well and mumbled something.

'Sit yourself doon,' said Mum. 'Bella'll no be long. Would you like a cup of tea?'

'No thanks, Mrs McGloughlin,' Gerald said. 'I've only just had one.'

He spoke with an English accent. He had a light voice. If he sang, he would be one of those tenors. Or perhaps he was just nervous.

'I'll see you then,' said Dad, and he went out.

But Mum sank onto the settee and settled herself comfortably as though preparing for a long chat while Ian watched Gerald. His face was still red.

'Have you known Bella long?' Mum asked. She could be inept at times.

'Just about a month,' Gerald told her.

'She's a good girl,' Mum went on as though giving a testimonial. 'Even if I do say so maself. It's an awfie shame she canny get a job. I'm sure if she could get started on something she'd be a great success.'

'Oh, I'm sure of it,' Gerald agreed. Ian noticed him take a quick look at his watch.

'Have you got a job?' Mum asked.

'Yes, I work in an office.'

'Oh, that's nice. I'm sure you're very good at your work.'

It wasn't possible for Gerald's face to get any redder, was it? Yes, it was.

'I do my best,' he managed to say.

The door opened, and Bella entered in a cloud of perfume.

'Oh, there you are,' she said as if it had been him who had been keeping her waiting. Her voice was gruffer and deeper than Gerald's. If they ever sang duets, Ian thought, she would have to take the lower part.

Gerald had got to his feet at Bella's arrival. He stood in the middle of the floor not knowing what to do next.

'Come on,' urged Bella. 'Or we're gonny be late.'

Gerald was prodded into action. He shook hands with Mum again. Ian thought he was going to shake hands with him as well, but he just nodded goodbye to him. Then they were out of the door and away.

'Have a good time,' Mum called after them.

Back in the kitchen, she was full of praise for Gerald.

'He seems awfie nice. A fine young man. And with a job as well. That's not to be sniffed at these days.'

100

Then doubts began to assail her. 'How old d'you think he is?' she asked Dad. 'Is he no a bit old fur her?'

Dad sighed with irritation. 'I don't know. Twenty-three or twenty-five mebbe.'

'Well, at least he ought to be dependable at that age,' said Mum, consoling herself. 'No like they flighty young gadabouts.'

Jimmy gave a contemptuous grunt. 'The way you talk you'd think they wis gonny get married or something.'

'Well, stranger things have happened.'

'I'll believe that when I see it,' said Jimmy. 'Bella's had more boyfriends than I've had hot dinners.'

Mum went on worrying. 'D'you no think she's too young?'

'Huh,' said Jimmy. 'Bella wis nivver young.'

Mum ignored him. 'It wid be nice to have her settled. It's a pity he's English though.'

'That's all they have doon here,' Jimmy put in.

Remembering school, Ian thought Jimmy hadn't got it quite right.

But Mum was not to be deflected from her dreams. 'I wid have liked to see her marry a guid Scots laddie, but it canny be helped. If they love each other, that's all that matters.'

And having settled it to her own satisfaction, Mum got up and began to clear away the plates.

But Ian was still confused. There was what he had seen down the Junction. There were the jibes Vincent had made. There was what he had seen when he came home that day from school.

Gerald couldn't be one of Bella's clients, could he? Surely he wouldn't call for Bella like that if he was?

And if he worked in an office, what had he been doing in the flat with Bella in the middle of the day? Unless he had slipped out on some excuse or other.

Perhaps it was his imagination. Perhaps Bella had been speaking the truth when she lammed into Vincent. But then he couldn't remember if she had actually denied the allegations Vincent had made.

It was a puzzle. Perhaps he would never know.

8

Mum was in a right state. The council meeting was at half-past seven. They had to be there by half-past six so they could canvass councillors as they arrived and make their protest. Ian was going with her.

'We're gonny be late,' Mum fussed. 'Now where did I put ma gloves? It's gonny be cold standing on they town hall steps. D'you think your dad remembered to take his muffler? I do hope we're gonny be able to make them change their minds. It'll be a crying shame if they don't. I don't know whit we're gonny do.'

'Come on, Mum,' said Ian impatiently. At this rate, the vote would have been taken before they even arrived.

At last she seemed to be ready, but then she dithered again.

'Are you no coming?' she asked Jimmy who was slumped in front of the television. Bella was out with Gerald.

'Whit's the point?' Jimmy responded glumly. 'They've already made up their minds.'

He was probably worrying about his court case. It came up in two days' time. Though it didn't need anything like that to put him into a miserable mood.

'But they have to listen to public opinion,' said Mum. 'Whit the people say.'

'Why should they? The only time they're interested in whit the people say is when there's an election.'

'At least we've got to try,' said Mum. She sounded more as though she was trying to convince herself than persuade Jimmy.

'Well, I wish you luck,' Jimmy said. His words didn't have a very encouraging ring to them.

They had to wait for a bus. Ian read the graffiti scratched into the paintwork of the bus-shelter. He knew what KBW meant now. A cold wind whirled round his legs and scattered the litter in the gutter. It looked as though the corporation needed more cleaners not less.

Mum didn't know where the town hall was. The housing department was in a different building. They had to ask the bus conductor to let them know when they got there. Not that they need have bothered. It was obvious from the way the building was floodlit and the crowds massed on the steps, banners waving.

As soon as they got off the bus they could hear the commotion. Chants of 'No cuts! No cuts! No cuts!' ballooned into the night air, rising to a crescendo and then falling away in a ragged mumble.

'Whit a lot of people,' said Mum in amazement. 'We'll nivver be able to find your dad. Still, it's good they've all turned out. It makes you feel a bit more cheerful.'

Strangely enough, 'cheerful' seemed to be the word for it. The crowd might have been there fighting for their jobs and worried about being made redundant, but the mood was more like that of people on a holiday outing. There was laughter and jokes, teasing and larking about, playful pushing and shoving. They seemed to be having a good time.

Or else they were just trying to keep their spirits up.

There must have been about two hundred of them, packing the steps of the town hall and spilling out onto the forecourt. Most of them had placards which they held up high and brandished about. Ian read SAY NO TO CUTS, NO PRIVATISATION, SAVE OUR JOBS, SERVICE NOT PROFIT.

Whenever anyone approached who might have been a

councillor, the people surged forward towards him and the chanting began. A passage was formed so that he could get through the crowd to the entrance, but he was urged on all sides to oppose the cuts and save the jobs. Some councillors stopped and listened and argued or gave their support. Others pushed through stony-faced as though they weren't even aware there were other people there.

Mum searched through the crowd until she eventually found Dad. He was talking to a NUPE official, judging by the badge pinned to the man's sweater.

'Aye, we've got them on the run,' Dad was saying.

'But we've got to keep up the attack,' the official said.

Dad saw Mum.

'This is ma wife,' he said. 'This is Jack Wilson. He's our shop steward.'

'Pleased to meet you,' Mum said, and they shook hands. 'My, there's a lot of people here.'

'We need all the support we can get,' Jack said. 'It's going to be a tough fight.'

'I hope we win,' said Mum.

'So do I,' said Jack with a grim smile. 'I'd better go and see the others. Rally the troops.'

'Aye,' said Dad. 'You do that.'

Jack slapped him on the back and pushed his way through the crowd.

'I've kept seats fur you in the public gallery,' Dad said. 'You'll be able to see everything from there.'

'That's fine,' said Mum. Then she tutted. 'Och, you haveny got your scarf on. You'll catch cold.'

'I'm all right,' Dad retorted. 'Stop fussing.'

Someone was coming across the forecourt towards the entrance. Dad pushed forward to accost him. 'Whit aboot oor jobs?' he yelled. The man was surrounded by people clamouring to know which side he was on. Mum joined in.

The crowd didn't seem so cheerful now. Ian saw anger and

bitterness and despair. These were people fearful for their jobs, desperate to avoid the emptiness and deprivation of unemployment and redundancy.

Then Ian spotted a face he knew. It was the cap he recognised first and then the worn face and the dungarees. So Old Bill had come to give his support after all. He said he might. He was carrying a placard on which was printed the slogan COAL NOT DOLE. Perhaps it was one left over from another protest. Not that it mattered. They were all in the same fight. It was good of him to turn up like this.

Ian was just about to ease his way through the throng to greet him when he felt a tug at his arm. He swung round and was surprised to see another familiar face.

'Hi,' said Vincent. He was grinning from ear to ear.

'Whit are you doing here?' Ian asked.

'I'm 'ere wit' my dad.' Vincent nodded in the direction of a large black man with a beard who was deep in conversation with the NUPE official they had met earlier.

'I didny know you wis interested in this kind of thing,' said Ian.

'Why not?' said Vincent. His face suddenly became serious. 'My dad were made redundant six month ago. When the cannin' factory close down. Six hundred people lost their jobs. Just like that.'

He snapped his fingers in the air. His eyes were burning angrily.

'My dad were somet'in' big in the union,' he went on. 'So 'e keen to 'elp the workers whenever 'e can. I comes along sometimes an' lends 'im moral support.'

He pursed his lips and gave a mocking smile as though sending himself up.

'What 'bout you?' he asked.

Ian explained.

'That's grim, man,' Vincent said, 'I sure 'opes the council makes the right decision.'

They looked at each other for a moment. Ian had the feeling they were both thinking the same thing. It was strange how they were in the same class as each other day after day and yet knew so little about each other's lives.

'Is you' sister 'ere?' Vincent asked. He searched round hopefully.

'Naw,' said Ian.

Mum came back up the steps.

'Hello, Vincent,' she said, her face lighting up.

Ian was amazed. She'd only met Vincent once as far as he knew, and yet she remembered his name and was greeting him as though she'd known him all his life.

'Hi, Mrs McGloughlin,' said Vincent. Ian wasn't sure, but the black boy seemed to be almost blushing. He'd never have thought of Vincent as being shy. Unless he was remembering the last time he met Mum.

There was a commotion at the entrance. The doors were open, and the attendants were letting people in.

'Come on,' Mum cried, and she grabbed Ian by the arm.

There was a blockage as people pushed to get in and others pushed to get out. The attendants wouldn't let them take their placards inside, and they had to dump them on the steps.

Then they were through. Vincent was still with them. Ian had never been inside a building like this before. The entrance hall was vast. The walls and floor seemed to be made of marble. Not that he had much time to take it all in. People were making for the stairs. Mum followed them, dragging Ian along with her.

'It's a guid job I've had plenty of practice at the sales,' she panted as she clattered up.

Dad caught up with them. 'The seats is in the front row,' he told them. 'I put a newspaper doon to reserve them.'

They hurtled up the next flight of stairs and came to the door of the public gallery. It was a kind of balcony. It was already more than half full. But there was still a gap in the front row, though it looked as though it was scarcely big enough for three, let alone four.

'You go on, son,' Dad said to Vincent. 'I'll stand at the back.'

'But —' Vincent began. He looked as though he was suddenly embarrassed.

'It's all right,' said Mum. 'You're Ian's friend.'

Vincent raised his eyebrows in question, but there was no time to go into it then. Mum was already shuffling along the row. Ian and Vincent followed. They squeezed into the vacant seats. People edged over to make room for them.

The council chamber was impressive. Ian and Vincent gazed down at the wood panelling and the horseshoe of solid dark red leather armchairs. Wood and leather glowed with polish. On a dais at the far end was a huge chair like a throne and above it hung the borough's coat of arms.

'I could make a cabinet out o' that,' said Vincent, eyeing the walls.

Some of the seats below were already occupied. People — councillors presumably — were poring over thick piles of paper or wandering about chatting to each other.

'My, it's a big place,' said Mum with awe in her voice. She unloosened her scarf and opened her coat. 'It's hot in here. It's well seen where all the money goes.'

'That's Councillor Stanley,' said the woman sitting next to her, pointing down. 'He's on our side.'

'D'you think we're gonny win?' Mum asked.

'It'll be pretty close,' the woman said. 'They've got a majority, but one or two of them are wavering. Worried about what'll happen when they come round for election again.'

'But all they people oot of work.'

'They're not interested in that. All they do is pay lip-service to it. If they can cut the rates by a penny, that's all they care about. They think it might win them a few votes. To hell with how many more have to go on the dole. To hell with the kind of public service they provide.'

The woman sounded angry and bitter. Mum listened earnestly and nodded her head despairingly. It was as though the full horror of the situation was only just beginning to sink in.

There was more activity down below. The seats were rapidly being filled. The mayor entered, the massive chain of office round his neck resting on his paunch, and took his seat. An expectant hush settled over the public gallery.

Ian didn't really follow what happened next. People stood up and said one thing and then another. There were arguments about procedure, about whether or not to discuss the items as they appeared on the agenda or whether to take other items first. The mayor looked up at the gallery and said that since there was so much public interest in that issue, they would take it first. He sounded smug and insincere to Ian. He wouldn't have voted for him.

The debate dragged on and on. One side talked about the need to reduce waste and overmanning, the need to cut rates and make savings. The other side talked about service to the community and the rise in unemployment. Some of them just seemed to like the sound of their own voices. It grew quite heated at times with people shouting each other down. The audience in the public gallery joined in with cheers and cat-calls until the mayor banged his gavel and warned them that he would have the gallery cleared if they didn't behave themselves. Ian couldn't see that the argument was getting anywhere. It was just going round and round in circles.

Another thought hesitated at the back of his mind. He remembered what Jimmy had said. They'd probably already made up their minds. They were just going through the motions of discussing it for the benefit of the public. To make it look good.

Beside him, he was aware of Mum getting more and more agitated. She was shifting about in her seat, gasping to herself at some of the things being said, making grunts of satisfaction at others.

Then someone below said, 'All this talk about unemployment is nonsense. There are plenty of jobs around. The dole's too generous, that's the trouble. People are just work-shy. They'd rather sit around doing nothing on the dole than do an honest day's work.'

Mum let out a great breath of indignation. She was on her feet.

What was she doing? Ian looked round with embarrassment. He tugged at her coat to get her to sit down. But she pulled her coat away from him. It was too late anyway. She had started.

'That's rubbish,' she was saying.

Her voice was loud. It cut right across what was going on below. Ian had no idea she could make such a noise. Heads were turning to look up at her.

'You don't know whit you're talking aboot,' she went on.

'Madam, will you sit down?' the mayor said. He was looking disconcerted.

Mum paid no attention. 'I know all aboot unemployment. Ma son hasny had a job the three years he's been oot of school. Ma girl's been left school fur two years and still no steady job. And ma youngest boy, whit chance is there fur him?'

Cries came from below. 'Madam, you have no right to speak.' 'This is disgraceful.' 'Turn her out.'

But Mum rode over them all. 'You don't know whit it's like to be unemployed. Searching fur a job day after day. Turning up fur interviews and finding fifty other applicants fur one vacancy. Looking at the future and seeing nothing, nothing but emptiness and despair.'

Down below, there was something like panic. The mayor was making wild gestures at the attendants. People were rising from their seats, waving papers around, talking to each other. In the gallery, there were cries of approval. 'You go it, girl.' 'You tell 'em.' 'That's right.'

Ian's embarrassement had evaporated. He was filled with an awed pride. Who'd have thought she had it in her? That was his mum speaking. Who'd have thought she had that kind of courage?

And she wasn't finished yet.

'Ma man wis oot of work fur years,' she cried, her voice filling the hall. 'So whit did he do? He got on his bike. He found a job doon here. And now whit are you gonny do? You're gonny give him the push. A guid man like that. He's forty-five, and you're putting him on the scrap-heap. That's whit you're doing. You ought to be ashamed.'

Two attendants were clattering down the central aisle towards her. Dad was behind them.

'Get out, you,' one of the attendants barked. He tried to push his way along the row and make a grab at her, but people stuck out their legs and arms and wouldn't let him pass.

'Leave her alone,' Dad yelled.

'It's all right, Joe,' Mum said. 'I'm coming. I've said ma piece.'

She edged along the row towards the aisle. Ian and Vincent followed her. People patted her arm and clapped her on the back. 'Well done,' they said. 'They need a bit o' the truth.'

When she reached the aisle, the attendants tried to take hold of her arms as though they were going to drag her up the stairs.

Mum drew back and pulled her coat about her. 'There's nae need fur that,' she said quietly. 'I'm going.'

The attendants let her pass in front of them. It was just as well. If they hadn't, Dad would have knocked them down if the look on his face was anything to go by.

Nobody said anything on the way down. The attendants were close behind them to make sure they really left and didn't try to slip back. Their footsteps rang out hollowly on the marble stairs.

Once outside, Mum started to shiver. She hugged her arms round herself.

'I don't know whit got into me,' she said.

Dad put his arm round her waist and held her hand. 'You did well, lass,' he said.

'Yeah,' agreed Vincent. 'You really tell 'em.' His eyes were shining with admiration.

Ian's eyes were shining too. He felt he couldn't speak.

Someone else had come out of the town hall and was standing close by. Ian recognised the black face and the beard. It was Vincent's dad.

'You all right, boy?' Mr Marshall asked.

'Sure, Dad,' Vincent replied.

'I saw what 'appen,' Mr Marshall went on, turning to Mum. 'You done the right t'ing. I were proud.'

He stuck out his hand. It was big and hard. Mum's hand was swallowed up in it. Mr Marshall pumped it up and down. From the way Mum's face flinched, it was a good strong handshake. But she managed an appreciative smile.

'That's awfie good of you,' she said.

Then it was Dad's turn to have his hand crushed.

'Thanks, Wesley,' Dad said. 'You've been a real help.'

Ian looked with surprise, first at Dad's face and then at Mr Marshall's. He thought Dad didn't like blacks. He was always saying things about them. It was news too that Dad knew Vincent's father. It was certainly a small world. They probably knew each other through their union.

Mr Marshall's face had grown angry. He seemed to be going over again in his mind what had occurred at the meeting.

'Can' nobody speak the truth these days,' he burst out. 'It's like they afraid to 'ear it. An' when that 'appen, this country finish. This ain't no free country no more.'

'Aye, you're right there,' agreed Dad with a sigh.

'I don' know if there anyt'in' left 'ere fo' me,' said Mr Marshall. He sounded suddenly very depressed. His face was bleak and empty.

'Aye, times is hard.'

'You nivver know,' Mum put in, trying to perk them up. 'They might still decide no to go ahead with this privatisation.'

'Aye,' said Dad. 'I suppose whiles there's life, there's hope. We'll go back and see how it's getting on. You better go hame though. I doubt they'll let you back in after whit you done.'

They were smiling again.

'I'll wait,' said Mum.

'Naw, it's too cold oot here. You'd best see your mum hame, son. I'll tell you whit happens.'

'OK, Dad.'

'See you,' said Vincent as he and the two men went back into the building.

111

'Sure,' said Ian.

He took a last look round. There were still a few people about standing in bunches on the steps, stamping their feet to keep warm and waiting for news of the outcome. They probably hadn't been able to get into the public gallery. The discarded banners were stacked against the wall or lying on the ground. Some of them were turned the wrong way round so you couldn't see the slogans. Others were upside down. Somehow it didn't seem a hopeful omen.

When they got home, they found Bella in the living room. She was alone. She wasn't even watching television.

'Whit are you doing at hame at this hour?' Mum asked.

Bella glared at her. She looked as if she was in a bad temper.

'We had a row,' she said.

'Is that no awfie,' said Mum. 'Whit aboot?'

'Oh, nothing.'

Ian couldn't tell whether she meant it or just didn't want to talk about it.

Mum tutted. 'On top of everything else too.'

Then she pulled herself together. 'You'll soon get over it. You see. Gerald'll be round the morrow night and everything'll be back to normal. Young people always have little tiffs, but it doesny amount to anything. It wid be peculiar if you didny have the odd disagreement.'

'It's no that I'm worried aboot,' said Bella.

Mum's face suddenly went ashen. 'You don't mean — ' she began falteringly.

'Naw,' said Bella impatiently. 'It's nothing like that. It's Jimmy.'

'Jimmy?' Mum said. She said it as if she was completely confused. As if she had no idea who Jimmy was.

'Aye,' said Bella. 'He's gone.'

'Gone?' Mum cried. It was almost a shriek. 'Whit d'you mean?'

Bella explained. 'He packed a bag and went. He wis just leaving when I got back. He said he wis gonny hitch a lift to Glasgow.'

Mum sank down into a chair as if her knees had given way.

112

'Is that no terrible,' she said. 'How's he gonny manage?'

'He said some of his friends wid put him up.'

Then Mum remembered. 'But whit aboot the court? He's supposed to appear there on Friday. He'll only get into more trouble noo. Could you no stop him?'

'I tried,' said Bella. 'I told him all that. But you know whit Jimmy's like once he gets an idea into his heid. He said he just couldny face it.'

'Whit are we gonny do?'

'There's no much we can do.'

'But they'll be after him. The polis. He canny just run away. He canny hide fur ever.'

'That's whit I said. But he wouldny listen.'

Mum stared despondently into space.

'As if we didny have enough worries,' she said. 'And your dad won't be hame till late.'

'How wis the meeting?' Bella asked.

'I don't know. It isny over yet.'

'Mum made a speech,' Ian boasted.

'Och, away with you,' said Mum.

'Did you?' Bella asked. 'I thought you wereny allowed to.'

'I just got carried away.'

'She wouldny stop,' said Ian. 'They had to throw her oot.'

'My, you are coming on in the world,' said Bella. 'You'll be standing fur Parliament next.'

Her words were half mocking, but there was surprise there too and pride.

'Och, it wis nothing,' said Mum modestly.

She went back to brooding about her worries. She gave a sigh. 'But whit are we gonny do aboot Jimmy?'

Ian had no idea. His brother had certainly made a mess of things this time and no mistake. The magistrate wasn't exactly going to be pleased when he didn't show up.

It would probably be quite easy to get a lift up the motorway. Jimmy had friends in Glasgow — on the estate and elsewhere. Ian didn't know all of them. Some of those he did know he wouldn't trust an inch. In crime up to their necks. They would just help Jimmy while it suited them and then they would ditch him.

Ian wondered about his own friends — Andy, Maisie, Jean. What would they do if he just turned up on their doorstep? The idea had crossed his mind in the early days. It was so simple. Pack a bag. Hitch a lift. Knock at the door. Do what Jimmy had done.

But he hadn't thought about it lately. Things seemed to have settled down in spite of the problems the rest of the family were having. There was his job in the Park. School hadn't turned out to be too bad. He might even have found a friend.

Yet he still missed the old crowd on the estate. If he arrived out of the blue, he was sure they'd be glad to see him and would want to help him.

On the other hand, they might have forgotten all about him. He still hadn't written to them. He hadn't even written a letter to Maisie in his mind for weeks. But then, none of them had written to him either.

He thought about letters he might write. He could tell them about the Park and his job there. He could tell them about Vincent. But what about Jimmy? Would he tell them his brother had gone back to Glasgow for a holiday? And what about Dad? Would he say his father could be getting promotion and more pay?

It wasn't on. Even in his head, it didn't make sense any more. Some things were so grim you couldn't disguise the fact and pretend otherwise. You just had to face reality and accept it. This was no time to be making up stupid letters.

9

Terry was showing off the gold chain that hung round his neck over the top of his sweater. It was made up of a sequence of tiny links and shone bright yellow. Les and Vincent were examining it enviously. Ian stood and watched. The black boys didn't mind. They'd got used to having him around.

'That ain't solid gold,' Les said contemptuously, though his eyes were still glued to the chain.

'Yeah, it is,' Terry protested.

'It's plated,' said Les.

'Brass more like,' Vincent put in.

'Naw, naw, man,' Terry maintained. 'It's solid gold.'

Les and Vincent went on fingering and studying it.

'Where d'you get it?' Les asked.

'Up the West End,' Terry told him.

'Down the market, you mean,' said Les.

'Or Woolworth's,' added Vincent.

Ian listened. He couldn't help smiling to himself. It was funny the way Terry, Les and Vincent were the best of friends and yet were always trying to put each other down. It didn't mean anything. It was just a kind of game they played.

'Naw, naw, man,' Terry came back. 'Up the West End. Oxford Street.'

'When you ever up the West End?' Les asked.

'I goes up there all the time,' Terry boasted.

Les gave a scornful snort. 'The only time you was up there were in the second year when they take us to the Science Museum.'

'An' then you got lost,' Vincent pointed out. 'The coach 'ave to wait a 'ole 'our while old 'Ardwick scoot round tryin' to find you.'

Terry dismissed the accusation. 'That were years ago. I been up there 'undreds o' times since then.'

Neither Vincent nor Les believed him. Les threw the chain back against Terry's chest. He curled his lips disdainfully, but you could see he fancied it.

Terry arranged it in a curve so that it could be shown to its best advantage.

'You the ones ain't never been up the West End,' he sneered.

'Course I 'ave,' protested Les and Vincent, both at the same time.

The bell rang for the end of break.

As Ian and Vincent walked across the playground to their next lesson, Ian said. 'I've nivver been up the West End.'

Vincent turned and stared at him in amazement. 'Ain't you? 'Ow long you been 'ere now?'

'About four months.'

'An' you ain't never been up the West End.' Vincent shook his head. 'Man, you' education sure 'ave been neglected.'

Then he pursed his lips and became thoughtful. He gave Ian a quick glance. 'We could go up there Saturday,' he said casually.

'I work on Saturdays,' Ian told him. The sudden prospect of going to the West End with Vincent as his guide was tempting, but he couldn't let Old Bill down. And anyway, they needed the money.

Vincent mulled this over. They had come to a halt in the middle of the playground. There were still lots of other pupils milling about so there was no rush. They wouldn't be last in.

Some idea was beginning to form itself in Vincent's mind. There was a gleam in his eye, and his face broke into a sly smile. 'Say, why don' we go now?'

Ian felt a quick surge of excitement. His friends in Glasgow had all talked about the sights of London. He'd never seen them. This was his chance. It meant bunking off school. But it wouldn't be the first time.

'OK,' he said.

' 'Ow much money you got?' Vincent asked.

Ian checked. He had nearly five pounds. Mum let him keep half the money Old Bill gave him each week, and he never seemed to find much to spend it on. The odd packet of crisps or bar of chocolate, that was all.

'I've got 'bout the same,' said Vincent. 'That should be enough.'

He hurriedly looked round the playground. It was practically deserted now. The teacher on duty had gone, and there were only a few stragglers left. They must have been quite conspicuous standing there in the middle.

'Come on,' said Vincent. 'We'll go the back way.'

He sounded excited too. They scurried past the art block, heads down, as though that would somehow make them invisible. Ian felt his heart beating against his chest. It was a big adventure. And it had come right out of the blue, totally unexpected. They would probably be reported for missing lessons, but that didn't matter. It would be worth it.

They reached the back gate safely. Nobody saw them. Or if they did, they didn't shout after them or try to stop them.

They legged it down to the Junction. Ian assumed they would be getting a train, but Vincent turned his nose up at that idea.

'Naw,' he said. 'A bus is better. You can see t'ings from a bus.'

They waited at a bus stop. Several buses came and went. Vincent let them go.

'Which bus d'we get?' Ian asked at last, afraid they were going to stand there all day.

'Don' worry,' Vincent reassured him. 'I knows it when it come.'

Another bus hurtled towards them and shrieked to a halt.

'This is it,' Vincent cried excitedly.

Ian just had time to notice the name Piccadilly Circus on the front before he scrambled after Vincent onto the bus.

There weren't many people on it. Ian and Vincent clambered up the stairs as the bus took off again. The front seats were empty. They sprawled out on them, taking a seat each.

Ian had a momentary worry when the conductor came to collect their fares. Would he wonder what they were doing out of school at this time of day? But the conductor didn't say anything. He just took their money. The look on his face was probably just annoyance at having to come all that way to collect it.

Ian relaxed. He forgot about the conductor. He forgot about the trouble there would be when their absence was discovered. He watched the houses and shops fly past and grew excited at the thought that he was on his way to the West End. After living in London for four months, he was actually going to see what it was like.

They came to the river. It looked cold and murky. There were some houseboats moored on the other side. Ian didn't fancy the idea of living there.

'Which bridge is this?' he asked.

Vincent peered from side to side. 'I ain't sure. Waterloo. Blackfriars. Somet'in' like that.'

The bus was filling up. Ian went and sat next to Vincent. The bus turned into a busy road clogged with traffic and crawled its way along it in fits and starts.

'Where are we now?' Ian asked.

Vincent didn't answer straightaway. He kept his eyes peeled on the street outside. Then he suddenly said, 'Yeah, I thought it were. It's King's Road. Where they 'as all the boutiques an' trendy clothes. Though I don' rate 'em much myself. It ain't my style.'

Watching the pedestrians, Ian could see what Vincent meant. He'd never seen so many peculiar clothes and hair styles. All the clothes in the boutiques seemed to be on the streets. He wouldn't have been seen dead wearing some of that gear. And if he did, Mum would have a fit.

'Most o' them's tourists anyway,' Vincent said airily. 'They ain't real Londoners.'

Ian wondered what a real Londoner was. He wasn't one himself. How could he be? He'd only been there for four months. Perhaps he would grow into one. Whereas Vincent, he supposed, was a real Londoner. After all, he had been born there.

The bus inched forward or came to a standstill as the traffic allowed. It ground to a halt at traffic-lights or hurled itself forward to shoot through just as the lights were changing. It was making slow progress.

'That's Regent's Park,' Vincent volunteered, pointing to an area of green open space on their right. 'They've got a zoo there.'

Ian looked, but there wasn't much to see.

They passed a tube station which said Green Park.

Vincent squinted round to see whether or not Ian had noticed. He had.

'I guess I got it wrong,' Vincent said. 'It must be Green Park.'

It was beginning to dawn on Ian that Vincent was not exactly the most experienced guide he could have chosen. That big show he'd put on in front of Terry and Les had been sheer bravado. It wouldn't have surprised Ian if this was Vincent's first visit to the West End.

He felt like asking, but Vincent was back at it, studying the street signs.

'This is it,' he suddenly announced. 'This is Piccadilly.'

He beat the conductor by a couple of seconds. 'All change' came the call from below.

They clattered down the stairs and jumped off. The pavement was crowded with people, strolling along, dawdling, window-shopping. They were flashily dressed and prosperous looking. Americans, Ian guessed. But then a group of Arabs passed, the women covered up except for their eyes. And after them a collection of Orientals in smart shiny suits and raincoats. Japanese? It wasn't what he expected London to be like at all.

'It's this way,' said Vincent, plunging ahead through the mob, though he didn't exactly sound confident.

Ian followed, and they came to an open area. In the middle were some steps leading up to a boarded-off section. Cars and buses zoomed round it. Ian wasn't sure what he hoped to see, but this didn't look anything special.

Vincent must have registered Ian's disappointment. 'Yeah, well,' he said. 'They've taken Eros away to be cleaned or somet'in'. I seen it in the news. It ain't the same wit'out Eros.'

Ian took Vincent's word for it.

He suddenly remembered what Andy had said when he was leaving Glasgow. All about Soho and the goings-on there.

'D'you know where Soho is?' he asked Vincent.

There was a pause before Vincent replied. He seemed to be thinking. 'It's round 'ere somewheres,' he said at last.

They wandered up and down the streets off Piccadilly Circus for a while, looking at the shops, threading their way through the crowds. It was Ian who noticed the sign above the shop.

'Look,' he cried and pointed.

It said Soho Fashions.

'Yeah,' said Vincent. 'I knew this were Soho.'

They stared in at the window of the shop. It was full of pieces of women's underwear. They were so frilly and flimsy Ian couldn't imagine how they could cover anything.

Further along, they came across a strip club. It was open even at that hour. But there were no pictures on display, just the sign. It didn't look very exciting to Ian.

A man sitting in the doorway noticed them.

'Fancy the show?' he asked. 'Best show in town.' He winked at them. 'Real saucy. It'll make your hair curl.'

Ian had a feeling he was sending them up, though his face was dead serious as he added, 'I'll let you in for half price.'

Now he was sure of it. Vincent was moistening his lips and

showing interest. Any second and he would be taking the man up on his offer.

Ian gave his friend a push and they moved on with Vincent protesting. The man's loud laughter came echoing after them.

Anyway, even at half price, they wouldn't have had enough money.

There were more sex shops and strip clubs further on, but all of them concealed their wares behind drawn blinds and empty display windows. A lot of the shops were just ordinary grocer's and newsagent's and restaurants.

'They cleaned it all up,' Vincent explained. 'My brother Fitzroy said it use to be wild. Sex shops an' strip clubs everywhere. Perhaps it's different at night.'

Then he added defensively, 'Not that my brother needed to go to places like that.'

'I didny know you had a brother,' Ian said.

'Yeah, well . . .' For once, Vincent was lost for words. 'I don' talk 'bout 'im much,' he said in a way that didn't invite further questioning.

It was all very disappointing really. Ian couldn't think what he could write and tell Andy about Soho — if he ever wrote. It certainly didn't live up to the vivid picture in Andy's imagination.

The one moment when his heart lifted was when they came upon a street that seemed to be filled with Chinese. There was Chinese lettering everywhere and lanterns and bronzed flattened ducks hanging in shop windows. He was suddenly transported back to Glasgow. Wee Lin would have loved it.

They found a McDonald's and had a hamburger and a Coke. It was expensive eating out. They would just about have enough for their fare back home.

They walked back to Piccadilly Circus and up Regent Street to Oxford Street. The Christmas decorations were out, arching across the street. But they weren't lit up yet, and you could have walked past them without even noticing.

The crowds were thicker here, people out doing their Christmas shopping. The windows of big stores were filled with Christmas scenes and tinsel and presents. They pressed their noses against the glass.

'I fancy that,' Vincent said again and again as he pointed out one thing after another — transistor radios, track suits, computer games.

But they both knew there wasn't a cat's chance in hell that they would ever get them.

It was when they got to Oxford Street that Vincent came out with it. They had decided it was about time they went back. But Vincent didn't seem to know which bus to take. He studied the bus stops on both sides of the road, but he couldn't make sense of them. Ian had visions of them being stranded there for the night.

'I don' even know which direction we're suppose to be goin',' Vincent cried in exasperation.

Then his face puckered up into a slow smile. 'Truth is,' he admitted, 'I ain't never been 'ere before.'

'But whit you said to Terry and Les,' Ian exclaimed.

'Oh that,' said Vincent dismissively. 'That didn' mean not'in'. I didn' want 'em to be one up on me.'

Although he had suspected it, Ian was still amazed. Did saving face mean so much to Vincent? Apparently it did.

'We could always walk back to Piccadilly Circus,' Ian suggested, 'and catch the bus there.'

Not that the idea appealed to him much. He felt as if he'd been walked off his legs already.

''Ang on a minute,' said Vincent. 'One o' these buses is sure to go to the Junction.'

He went back to one of the bus stops and frowned furiously at the timetable that was fixed to it as if the force of his stare would produce the information he required. Ian was sure the people standing in the queue thought Vincent was trying to push in. They were giving him odd looks.

It was a waste of time. Vincent had already examined that bus

122

stop and the ones across the road. They would just have to walk back to Piccadilly Circus.

Ian was just about to go across to Vincent and tell him when a policeman emerged from the crowd. He went up to Vincent and said something. Vincent's mouth dropped open and his eyes went round with alarm. The policeman took him by the arm and led him to an alleyway between two shops.

Ian watched horrified. What did the policeman want with Vincent? He wondered what he should do. Make a run for it? But why should he? He hadn't done anything wrong. And anyway, he couldn't leave Vincent in the lurch. Vincent hadn't done anything wrong either.

Summoning up his courage, Ian approached the alleyway.

'You'd better come clean,' the policeman was saying. 'I know your sort. Just waiting for the right moment to snatch someone's bag.' He was glaring fiercely at Vincent.

'But I weren't,' Vincent protested. His face was shiny with sweat in spite of the cold.

'Don't come that,' the policeman said scornfully. 'I've been watching you for the last quarter of an hour.'

With an effort, Ian made himself speak. 'I'm with him.' His voice was shaky.

The policeman turned to him. 'You what?' he demanded. He seemed put out.

'I'm with him,' Ian repeated, more firmly this time. Vincent flashed him a quick look of gratitude.

'So there are two of you at the game, are there?' the policeman said. 'One keeps watch while the other does the snitching.'

But somehow all the puff and fury had gone out of him. His face had a disappointed droop to it. The sudden appearance of Ian had spoilt his fun.

'Naw, it wisny like that at all,' said Ian, gaining confidence. 'We wis just trying to find the bus hame.'

'A likely story,' said the policeman, but without much conviction. He looked from one face to the other, and then decided on

123

a different approach. 'What are you doing here anyway? Shouldn't you be in school?'

A host of excuses scurried across Ian's mind. It was half-term. They had a day off for Christmas shopping. They were working on a project. But he decided honesty was the best policy. If he told a lie and was found out, the policeman might think again about what they were doing there.

'We bunked off school,' Ian admitted.

'Yeah, to look at the Christmas decorations,' Vincent added.

'What school d'you go to?' the policeman asked.

Vincent gave the name.

'I think I'd better let them know where you are,' the policeman said. 'They might be worried about you.'

He seemed to be enjoying himself again. If he couldn't get them one way, he'd get them another.

He took out his notebook and wrote down their names and addresses. Then he flicked his walkie-talkie on and got through to the station.

'I have two lads here. Get through to the school, will you, and say they've been found wandering around in Oxford Street.' He gave the particulars.

'Now then,' he said to Ian and Vincent. 'You'd better hop it back to school. They'll be expecting you.' The idea seemed to amuse him. Then he became stern again. 'And don't let me find you here again. You won't get off so lightly next time.'

Ian and Vincent pushed back into the throng surging down Oxford Street.

Vincent blew out a stream of air in relief. 'That were close.'

'But why did he pick on you?' Ian asked.

'Pick on me's right,' said Vincent bitterly. 'There one good reason why 'e pick on me. 'Cause I'm black. See? Soon as you turns up, 'e change 'is tune quick enough.'

'And he couldny have been watching you fur quarter of an hour.'

'Course not. 'E were just tryin' it on. The bull tells more lies than a cuckoo clock. I 'ates 'em. They done my brother fo' somet'in' 'e never do. 'E spend six month in jail.'

Ian suddenly thought of Jimmy. Was that what would happen to him when the police caught up with him? Though, unlike Vincent's brother, there was no doubt that Jimmy had done something. Perhaps Vincent's brother had as well. Ian only had Vincent's word for it that he hadn't, though there was no reason why he shouldn't believe him. And there could be no mistake about what had happened just now. Vincent had been accused, and he had been innocent. Perhaps it was because he was black. He certainly had a right to feel indignant.

They found their way down Regent Street to Piccadilly Circus and waited on the right side of the road for the bus to the Junction.

'Thanks fo' stickin' by me back there,' Vincent said. 'Some people would just 'ave scarpered. Terry an' Les fo' instance.'

'That's OK,' said Ian. He thought it better to keep quiet about his own moment of panic.

'Not that they would 'ave been much 'elp. They're black too. The bullman wouldn't 'ave believed 'em the way 'e believed you.'

'Nivver mind. At least we've been up the West End. I wouldny have managed it if it hadny been fur you.'

'Yeah,' agreed Vincent, cheering up. 'It were great, weren't it?' He grinned. 'But don' tell Terry an' Les it were my first time.'

'I won't,' Ian promised.

A bus with the Junction on the front came along and they got on. It was packed with Christmas shoppers, and they had to stand most of the way.

'Whit's Mr Armstrong gonny say?' Ian asked as they neared the end of their journey.

'I don' suppose 'e be pleased,' said Vincent. 'But 'e better than the bullstation.'

Ian had to agree.

As luck would have it, they arrived at school just as the pupils came charging down the drive. They had to push against the tide. People looked at them as though they were mad. Others shouted

out, 'You're too early. It's closed.' Or 'You're going the wrong way.'
Then they spied Terry and Les bouncing towards them. It was too
late to avoid them.

Terry slapped Vincent on the back. 'Old Armstrong's wild. You
in a 'ole 'eap o' trouble.' He sounded delighted and had a big grin
on his face.

'Where you been?' Les demanded. It came out like an
accusation.

'We been up the West End,' Vincent told them casually.

'Yeah?' said Les. You could hear the envy in his voice. 'What you
go up there fo'?'

'We just felt like it,' Vincent explained. 'Like I said, I goes up
there all the time.'

From his face, it was clear that Les didn't know whether to
believe him or not. He looked suspiciously at Ian, but he didn't say
anything.

Terry returned to his gloating. 'Armstrong know you been
bunkin'. You in fo' a lashin', boy.' He gave a giggle and then
became puzzled. 'What you goin' up to school fo' now? You gonna
confess or somet'in'?'

Vincent explained about the police.

'That's grim, man,' said Terry.

'They does that all the time,' said Les.

Then Terry was grinning again. 'That'll learn you not to bunk off
school. You better go an' take you' punishment like a man.'

Vincent and Ian continued up the drive with Terry's mocking
laughter ringing in their ears.

Mr Armstrong was in the form room. He seemed surprised to
see them.

'Well, if it isn't the prodigal sons come back home,' he said. Then
he became serious. 'You must be daft to think you can bunk off
school and nobody will notice.'

Vincent put on his repentant look. 'Sorry, sir.'

'It's no good being sorry,' Mr Armstrong went on. 'Missing your
education. Putting people to all this inconvenience.'

126

'It weren't my fault the police pick me up,' Vincent pointed out.

'The police?' Mr Armstrong asked, his face suddenly alert.

Vincent realised he had blundered. Perhaps the policeman had been bluffing about telling the school. Perhaps nobody had bothered to pass on the message. But it was too late now. Vincent had to explain what had happened.

Mr Armstrong's reaction was the same as Terry's. 'That'll teach you not to bunk off school.' Though he wasn't smiling. 'That makes the whole thing much more serious.'

'But it weren't my fault,' Vincent protested. 'I 'adn't done not'in'. I ain't no criminal.'

Mr Armstrong was staring at him steadily as though trying to make up his mind how much to believe.

Vincent looked as though he was becoming embarrassed, though there was a twitch of a smile on his lips. 'Well, maybe I take a chocolate bar when I small. Ain't you never done not'in' like that?'

'We're not discussing my private life,' Mr Armstrong said coolly, but he wasn't offended. He let out a sigh. 'You know the word for you, Vincent? Incorrigible.'

Vincent grinned with pleasure. 'Thank you, sir.'

Mr Armstrong turned to Ian. 'And what about you? You're making a habit of bunking off.'

'It's only the second time,' Ian pointed out. 'I used to bunk off much more at my other school.'

'Well, that's something,' said Mr Armstrong. 'I suppose we must count ourselves a success.'

Ian couldn't tell if Mr Armstrong was being sarcastic or not.

'I still think it's serious,' the teacher went on to both of them. 'Especially with the police being involved. I ought to let your parents know.'

'Aw, sir,' Vincent exclaimed in protest. 'My dad'll go spare. 'E 'ad enough o' the police when they send my brother to jail. An' my mum's sick.' He looked close to tears.

'You certainly know how to put on the sob stuff,' said Mr Armstrong admiringly.

'Me too,' said Ian.

Mr Armstrong showed his surprise. 'My, you are learning fast. So you've got a cop-hating dad and a sick mum as well?'

'No. It's ma brother. He's due up in court. If you tell ma mum and dad aboot this, they'll just get more upset. It's bad enough as it is.'

'I see,' Mr Armstrong said slowly. He looked from one face to the other as he thought about it. Then he decided. 'All right. Two detentions each. And I won't tell your parents.'

'Thanks, sir.'

'Thanks, sir.'

'Now off you go.'

As Ian was leaving the room, Mr Armstrong called him back.

'I see you've made a friend at last,' he said.

Ian smiled back. Yes, he thought he had. There wasn't much Mr Armstrong missed.

'Good,' the teacher added. 'I'm glad to see it. Vincent's all right.'

As they were going down the stairs, Vincent said, 'I didn' know you 'ad a brother.'

'You didny ask.'

Vincent considered this and then admitted, 'That's true. What's 'e up fo'?'

'Stealing,' Ian told him.

'What are 'is chances?'

'No very good.' Ian felt an urge to confide in Vincent, to have someone who could share the family's worries. 'You see, he didny turn up at court. He ran away. Nobody knows where he is.'

Vincent was all sympathy. 'That's bad. Makes 'im look guilty.'

'Och, he's guilty all right,' said Ian. 'Nae doubt aboot that.'

'Well, I 'opes 'e ain't sent to jail,' said Vincent. 'It did fo' my brother. It finish 'im. 'E were only there fo' six month fo' somet'in' 'e never do, an' 'e come out a changed man. 'E 'ardly speak. 'E never go out the 'ouse. 'E afraid o' everyt'in'. I don' know what they do to 'im in there, but they sure mess up 'is mind. My dad ain't never gonna forgive 'em fo' that.'

128

Ian had never heard Vincent speak with such bitterness before. It made him worry again about what would happen to Jimmy.

'Whit did your brother do?' he asked.

'I told you,' Vincent retorted. ' 'E didn' do not'in'. They fix up some charge 'bout 'im dealin' in drugs, but it weren't true. Where would 'e get the money to buy drugs from? 'E were unemployed. It were all a put-up job. An' it finish 'im. 'E'll never be the same. That's why I 'ates the police.'

Vincent went into one of his brooding moods. When he came out of it, he gave a grunt and said, 'One t'ing though. It mean we 'as somet'in' in common.'

'Aye,' Ian agreed.

They stood at the school gate for a moment before going their separate ways.

'See you in detention,' Vincent said with a grin.

'Aye,' said Ian. 'Thanks fur taking me up the West End. It wis worth it.'

'Any time,' said Vincent with an airy flourish of his hand. And then he walked off down the road.

As he walked across the Common, Ian decided it hadn't really been worth it. He was grateful to Vincent for taking the trouble, but it had all been rather disappointing. Soho wasn't the den of sin it was painted as. Regent Street and Oxford Street were just shopping streets with crowds of people. Piccadilly Circus was nothing when there was no Eros there. He hadn't even seen Big Ben or the Houses of Parliament, the Tower of London or Buckingham Palace, Trafalgar Square or St Paul's. There didn't seem to be much there to write home to his friends in Glasgow about.

He remembered that he'd decided not even to think about writing any more. And hadn't he said he'd seen all those sights in the first letter he'd written — or rather hadn't written? Well, if he did write, what would he say?

Dear Maisie, I bunked off school today with my friend Vincent, and we went up the West End. We saw Piccadilly Circus, but there

129

was no Eros there because it's away being repaired. We saw the Christmas decorations in Regent's Street and Oxford Street, but they weren't lit up yet. The shops were full of marvellous Christmas presents, but we couldn't buy anything because we didn't have any money. We didn't know how to get a bus back home, and a policeman accused us of trying to pinch purses instead of helping us. When we got back to school, we got two detentions for bunking off.

No, that wouldn't do at all. He screwed up the letter he had written in his mind.

It was later that evening when the police arrived. Ian was watching television with Mum and Dad. Bella was out with Gerald. The row — whatever it had been about — had been patched up.

For one awful moment, Ian thought they'd come about him. Come to tell Mum and Dad and accuse him of stealing handbags in Oxford Street. But it wasn't that.

It was the same policeman as before — the tall thin one. The beefy one was probably sitting in the car outside, too lazy to come up.

Mum and Dad were horrified at the sight of him. They feared the worst. They ushered him into the living room and waited anxiously to hear what he had to say. The policeman seemed strangely apologetic.

'It's about your son Jimmy,' he said. 'He's been arrested in Glasgow for stealing cars.'

Mum gasped and clapped her hands to her face. Dad cursed and ground his teeth. Ian almost wished it had been about him after all.

Then Dad looked up suspiciously. 'But he cannny drive.'

'You can say that again,' the policeman commented grimly. 'He crashed the car.'

'Is he all right?' Mum asked anxiously.

'As far as I know. But he was lucky. You should see the car. I'm told it's a write-off.'

Mum stared at the policeman in horror.

He went on. 'Because your son didn't appear in court down here, he's been remanded in custody until the case comes up.'

'In prison?' Mum cried. 'Oh, that's dreadful.'

'We thought you ought to be informed,' the policeman said like somebody doing his duty.

Mum remembered her manners. 'Thanks fur letting us know, officer. We're very grateful.'

She showed him out.

'Grateful!' Dad burst out passionately as soon as the policeman had gone. 'I could of kicked his heid in.'

When Mum returned, she was tearful and upset. 'Whit are we gonny do?' she asked. 'Jimmy's that far away. We canny go and visit him or anything.'

'Whit can we do?' Dad shot back at her. 'Jimmy's made his own bed, and he'll just have to lie on it. There's nothing we can do.'

Mum began to sniff at this, but she knew Dad was right. 'At least we know where Jimmy is,' she said at last. 'At least he's getting his meals regular.'

It seemed poor consolation. Even Dad thought so. 'I'm going oot,' he announced abruptly and was through the door.

Mum and Ian exchanged glances. They knew he was off to the pub. He wouldn't be back now until closing time.

Mum sighed and switched the television on again. She made a pretence of watching, but it was obvious her mind was elsewhere.

Ian slumped down in his seat. Here was something else he wouldn't be able to tell Maisie and Andy and Jean and all the others. Though, being in Glasgow, it was quite likely they knew more about it than Ian did himself.

10

Christmas came and went. It was pretty miserable. No one felt much like celebrating. For a start, money was short. Ian didn't get the transistor radio he wanted. He had to make do with a pair of jeans. He needed some new ones, but it wasn't exactly what you would call an exciting present.

There hadn't been many Christmas cards either. None from his friends in Glasgow. But then he hadn't sent them any. How could he when he hadn't bothered to write?

Mum did her best to pretend it was the festive season. She roasted a chicken with all the trimmings, and there was Christmas pudding and mince pies and trifle. But you could tell her heart wasn't in it and she was grieving that Jimmy wasn't there to share it.

Dad was low too. A few days before Christmas, he'd been informed that a private firm was taking over refuse collection in the borough at the end of January. He'd be paid off then.

'Whit a Christmas present,' he said bitterly when he told them.

'It's no the end of the world,' Mum coaxed, trying to cheer him up. 'We've been through as bad as this afore.'

But the bleak look on Dad's face didn't go away. It stayed there for days. He went around like a man haunted.

There were only three of them for Christmas dinner — Mum,

Dad and Ian. Bella spent the day with Gerald's parents. It looked as though she and Gerald might be getting married after all. So that was something to be cheerful about. But it meant that Christmas in the flat was very quiet — not to say funereal. They just sat around eating and drinking and watching television. It wasn't like the old days in Glasgow when neighbours and friends had popped in and out all day long.

It was a relief for all of them when it was time to switch the television off and go to bed.

Next morning, Ian went for a walk in the Park. He needed to get away from that atmosphere of gloom. He needed to clear his head and get some fresh air.

It was strange how familiar the Park had become to him. What was it? Four and a half months. Yet he felt that he knew every corner of it, every bush and tree. He felt it was his. Wasn't that how Old Bill felt about it too? And there was still so much to look forward to. He had seen it in late summer and autumn and now winter. But there was still spring to come, and the whole place would be transformed.

Old Bill had taught him a lot. About pruning and transplanting and keeping weeds down. And he had learned a lot from books. There were whole shelves of books on gardening in the library, and he was steadily working his way through them. Well, it was something to do.

As usual, there was no one about. Still sleeping off their Christmas excesses, Ian thought. Or getting ready for the next bout. Above his head, bare branches formed an intricate network against the sky. Conifers and cypresses loomed up, dark and forbidding. Everything was very still. It was cold but there was no wind. The trees looked as though they were frozen into shape. There were no birds singing.

'Boo!'

Ian nearly jumped out of his skin. He swung round to find Old Bill grinning at him.

'Och, it's you.'

'I thought I'd give you a fright,' Old Bill said gleefully. 'You were standing there as if you were in a dream. So I crept up on you.'

He went on grinning. He was delighted with himself, like a little boy who had found a new game. Well, Ian thought, it was nice somebody was happy. The old man didn't smile all that often.

'I wis just looking at the trees,' Ian explained.

Old Bill raised his eyes and let them wander over the tree tops. 'I like this time of year,' he said. 'You can see the way they grow and the different shapes they make.'

'Aye.'

'But then I like them all the year round.'

The old man stood and gazed, lost in wonder.

'I didny think you'd be here the day,' Ian said.

'I like to keep an eye on things,' Old Bill said. 'Make sure everything's all right.' He chuckled. 'Make sure nobody from the council flats has broken in. Eh?'

'Aye,' Ian agreed.

The old man was in a jovial mood. Ian hadn't seen him like this before. Perhaps he'd been celebrating Christmas too and was still under the influence.

'Come and have a cup of coffee,' Old Bill suggested.

'OK.'

Another explanation came to Ian. Perhaps the old man was just glad to see him. Perhaps he had spent a lonely Christmas and was glad now of the company. Any company. He was full of stories about things he had done and places he had been to, but he had never mentioned any family. Ian had the feeling that the old man lived on his own, but he had never asked. He didn't want to appear nosey.

It was snug in the hut with the primus stove going.

'We'll have to get you a chair,' Old Bill said when they were settled with their mugs of coffee, he squeezed into the old armchair and Ian squatting on the floor.

'I'm fine,' said Ian.

It was the fourth or fifth time the old man had suggested it.

Though where they would find room for it in that crowded space Ian couldn't imagine.

Then Old Bill asked, 'Has your dad heard anything yet?'

The old worries returned with a rush.

'Aye,' Ian said. 'He heard about a week ago. He'll be oot of a job by the end of January.'

Old Bill's face creased with concern. 'I'm sorry to hear that. It's a crying shame.'

They were silent for a moment.

'What's he going to do?' Old Bill asked.

'He's started looking fur another job,' Ian told him. 'But I doubt he'll find one.'

'To think of someone his age being put on the scrap heap. It's criminal.'

'Aye. That's whit Mum says.'

'I suppose I ought to consider myself lucky,' Old Bill went on. 'I'll be sixty-eight next birthday and I'm still working. And doing something I want to do, what's more.'

'Aye.'

'Though I won't be able to go on forever.'

They were silent again. And then Ian became aware that the old man was staring at him as though trying to solve some difficult problem and yet at the same time not knowing where to begin.

'Have you thought what you're going to do when you leave school?' Old Bill asked.

'Naw,' said Ian despondently. 'There doesny seem to be much point. I guess I'll be like Jimmy and Bella. On the dole.'

'How long have you got to go?'

'Another year and a half.'

Old Bill thought about it for a while. It was clear from his face that there was something he wanted to say.

'How about working here?' he got out at last.

Ian shot him a puzzled glance.

'In the Park,' Old Bill explained. 'You could take over.'

He said it casually, but his eyes were watching anxiously.

135

It was a moment before Ian could take it in. Then a surge of hope swept through him. He was being offered a job. And a job in the place where he most wanted it. He could hardly believe it.

He checked his excitement and asked cautiously, 'D'you think I can do it?'

'You've been fine these last few months,' Old Bill told him. 'You're a quick learner and a hard worker. And you'll have plenty of time to learn more before you take charge.' He chuckled. 'Anyway, I'll still be here to keep an eye on things. You won't get rid of me that easily.'

Ian sat and thought about it. To look after the Park. To be responsible for keeping it in shape and seeing it grow. To have a purpose in life.

It suddenly seemed everything he had ever wanted, and at the same time it suddenly seemed too good to be true. He began to search for the snags.

'Am I no too young?' he asked.

'You'll be sixteen when you leave school,' said Old Bill. 'That's old enough. And you'll have had plenty of practice with me. A kind of apprenticeship. And like I said, I'll still be around to help out.'

'Whit aboot the people who own the Park?'

'The committee'll take my word for it. They'll be only too glad to be saved the bother of looking for someone.'

Ian didn't say anything. He let the idea grow warm inside him.

'Mind you, they don't pay much. But it's better than the dole. And you'd be your own boss. There'd be nobody to order you about and tell you what to do. Except for me now and then.'

Old Bill looked at Ian expectantly. He seemed a little disappointed at the lack of response.

'You don't have to decide now. Think about it.'

'Aye,' said Ian. 'I'll do that. Thanks.'

He thought about it walking along the path to the flats. Four months before, he didn't know places like the Park existed. He couldn't have imagined that one day he would be asked to look after it.

136

He gazed up at the tracery of bare branches, at the cypress trees pointing to the sky. He took in a deep breath. He was filled with a sense of well-being and contentment. Now it really did feel as though the Park belonged to him.

If Christmas Day had been miserable, it looked as though New Year's Eve was going to be even worse.

Again, there were just the three of them — Mum, Dad and Ian — sitting round the television set, waiting for midnight to come so they could bring in the New Year. Bella was out with Gerald again. There was a variety programme on the screen, but nobody was really concentrating on it.

'D'you think they'll let Jimmy see the New Year in?' Mum asked.

'Naw,' said Dad scornfully. 'They'll have locked them in their cells at six o'clock and thrown away the key.' He took another sip at his whisky. He'd been going at it steadily all evening.

'My, we've seen some changes this year,' said Mum. 'I nivver thought a year ago I'd be living in London. Remember last Hogmanay when you came up and we had all the neighbours in? My, that wis a great night. I wonder whit they're all doing the noo.'

'The same as us,' said Dad. 'Watching telly.'

'I miss all they friends we had,' Mum went on. 'Ellen and Mary and Patrick and all the others.'

'Well, you'll have to go on missing them,' said Dad. ''Cause we're no gonny be seeing them fur some time.'

Ian thought about his own friends back in Glasgow. They would be having a party. They would be having a great time. They wouldn't even notice he wasn't there.

Mum went off on another train of thought. 'D'you think Gerald's gonny ask Bella to marry him?'

'How should I know?'

'Well, I think it's possible. That would be nice. At least we could see her settled.'

Dad didn't comment.

137

There was a New Year's party on television now. Some dancers had just finished a Scottish reel, and the announcer was getting all worked up. It was only five minutes till midnight.

'A fine New Year we've got to look forward to,' muttered Dad.

'Och, it'll no be sae bad,' said Mum. 'You know I've got a new job starting next week. At a hoose on the other side of the Common. We'll manage.'

'Aye,' said Dad with a sigh. 'I suppose we will. We always have done.'

The people in the television studio were going hysterical. The announcer was counting off the seconds. When midnight struck, there was a great cheer. Balloons came raining down. People threw streamers at each other.

Mum raised her glass. 'Happy New Year,' she beamed.

'Happy New Year,' said Dad. He lifted his glass wearily and clinked it against Mum's.

'And you, Ian,' said Mum.

She got up out of her seat and kissed Dad and gave Ian a hug. 'It'll be all right. You see.'

She had hardly sat down again when the door bell rang. She stared in alarm at Dad and Ian. 'Who can that be?'

'Mebbe it's Bella and Gerald,' said Dad.

'Och, aye,' said Mum, relieved. 'That'll be it. Go and let them in, son,' she said to Ian.

As he went out of the room, he heard Mum say, 'But she's got a key. Whit's she ringing the bell fur?'

When he opened the door, Ian was astonished by what he saw. Standing in front of him was Vincent. There was a big grin on his face. He was holding out his hand. In his palm was a huge lump of coal.

' 'Appy New Year,' he cried.

Ian was lost for words. 'Whit are you doing here?' he managed to stammer at last.

'I'm first footin' you,' said Vincent. 'What you t'ink I'm doin'?'

'Oh, is that whit it is?'

Mum called out, 'Who is it?'

'You'd better come in,' said Ian.

In the living room, Vincent was a sensation. Mum and Dad stared at him open-mouthed.

'I've come to wish you a 'appy New Year,' Vincent announced. And then he explained. 'You see, I found this book in the school library all about Scottish customs. 'Bout Hogmanay an' all that. An' it said 'bout first footin', an' 'bout 'ow the first person across the threshold 'as to be dark. An' they don't come much darker than me.'

'Well,' exclaimed Mum. 'Isn't that lovely?'

'Oh,' Vincent went on, suddenly remembering something else. 'An' it said you 'ad to bring a piece o' coal. So that's what I bring.'

He held the coal out for their inspection.

Mum gazed at it with admiration. 'My,' she said. 'I haveny seen a lump of coal like that fur years.'

She took it from him as if it was a holy relic and placed it on the hearth in front of the gas fire.

'Here,' said Dad. 'Have a dram.' And he slopped a great dollop of whisky into a glass.

'Sit yourself doon,' said Mum.

Vincent took the glass and sank onto the scttce next to Ian. He sipped the whisky and gasped. 'Wow! This is strong, man.'

Dad laughed. 'It ought to be. It's the real stuff.'

'Ah,' said Vincent. 'But it ain't as strong as rum.'

'Rum!' cried Dad contemptuously. 'There's nae comparison.'

'You better not let my dad 'ear you say that.'

'Who is your dad?'

'Wesley Marshall,' said Vincent. His voice was proud.

'Oh,' said Dad. 'So you're Wesley's boy. I thought I'd seen you afore. He's a fine fella, your dad.'

'Tell me,' said Mum, all puzzled. 'Where did you get that piece of coal from?'

'Aw, well,' Vincent began. He was suddenly embarrassed. 'I'm not sure I should tell you. You see, when I read in this book that the first footer was suppose to bring a lump o' coal as a present, I racked my brains where I could get it from. Nobody what I knows use coal any more. An' then I remembers they still burns coal at my junior school. They 'aven't got round to gas or oil yet. So one night I goes up there an' pinch a piece.'

Mum laughed. 'Is that no wonderful?'

Even Dad was relaxed and smiling.

When they weren't looking, Ian gave Vincent a punch. Vincent turned and gave him a wink. He knew perfectly well what he was doing. He had brought a bit of brightness into their lives.

'It minds me of the old days,' Mum was saying. 'When we wis kids. That's whit we used to do. Go first footing.'

'Aye,' Dad admitted, 'it's nice to be reminded of it.'

'Mebbe you'll bring us luck after all,' said Mum.

'I sure 'opes so,' said Vincent.

There was a noise at the front door. Bella and Gerald burst in. Bella was flushed and excited. Gerald was flushed too — but then he usually was.

'Happy New Year,' Bella announced.

'Happy New Year,' everyone answered.

Then Bella went round kissing them all. That wasn't like her. Ian didn't care for it much, but he was aware that Vincent enjoyed it.

'Wow,' he whispered. 'She's some woman.'

Then Bella just came out with it. 'We're gonny get married.'

Mum clapped her hands with joy. Dad opened his mouth and looked as though he'd had too much to drink. Gerald got redder and redder.

'Is that no marvellous?' Mum cried.

She jumped up and kissed Bella and then Gerald. Then Dad was kissing Bella and pumping Gerald's hand. And Bella was kissing Ian and Vincent again. Vincent didn't object.

'That's the best news I've heard in a long time,' said Mum. 'I hope you'll be very happy.'

'If you're as happy as me and your mum,' said Dad, 'you'll no do sae badly.'

140

Mum stared at him in amazement. 'Good Lord, whit's got into him. It must be the drink talking.'

'Och, wheesht, woman,' said Dad.

It was suddenly very crowded in the room. Gerald curled up on the floor, looking uncomfortable, while Bella perched on the arm of the settee near to Vincent. Ian noticed that his friend was gazing at her with awe in his eyes. The announcement of her engagement didn't seem to have cooled his ardour.

Dad filled some glasses, and Mum handed round the shortbread.

'Well, when's it gonny be?' Mum asked.

'I don't know,' said Bella. 'We haveny decided yet. But soon.'

'The sooner the better, eh?' said Dad.

Gerald grinned feebly and went an even darker shade of puce. Perhaps it was the whisky. He looked like Dad when he came back from the pub.

'We're gonny start looking fur a flat,' Bella told them. 'Put doon a deposit and get a mortgage. Gerald's been saving up.'

'Is that no grand?' Mum said, sounding impressed. 'Your own place.'

'We canny afford a big wedding, you know,' Dad warned. 'There just isny the money.'

'I know that,' said Bella. 'That doesny worry me. At least you'll have one less mouth to feed.'

'Och, don't say that,' Mum protested.

'Well, it's true,' said Bella.

'Aye,' said Dad grimly. 'Every bit counts.'

'Two mouths less in fact,' Bella went on. 'There's Jimmy as well.'

'Och, don't remind me,' said Mum. 'The poor laddie. I wonder whit kind of New Year he's having.'

'Don't fret yourself, lass,' said Dad. 'He's probably all right. Tucked up and fast asleep in his bed.'

'Aye,' said Mum. She began to smile again. 'We've got to stay cheerful. If it wisny fur Jimmy, I'd say this wis the best New Year we've ever had.'

141

'I'll drink to that,' said Dad, and he took a good gulp.

Then Mum was struck by another thought. 'Who'll give you away?' she asked. Her voice faltered. 'If Jimmy's no back, I mean.'

'There's always Ian,' said Bella. 'That is, if he's no too young. You'd do that fur your sister, wouldn't you?'

'Oh, aye,' said Ian.

Perhaps it was the talk of Bella being given away, or else the fact of Bella's marriage had finally got through to him, but Vincent was suddenly looking despondent. He put his glass down on the table.

'I better be goin',' he said, though he seemed reluctant.

'Naw, naw,' said Dad. 'Bide awhile.'

'Thanks, but my mum'll be worryin' where I am. She's not well.' He stood up.

'It wis good of you to come,' said Mum. 'And see, you've brought us guid luck already.'

'That's right enough,' said Dad.

Vincent shook hands all round. Bella gave him another kiss. Ian peeped across at Gerald to see if he was getting jealous, but he didn't seem to mind. He was beaming away happily.

Ian went to the door with Vincent.

'Whit's this Scottish customs bit fur?' he asked when they were alone.

'Like I said,' Vincent replied. 'I read it in a book.' Then he gave an embarrassed squirm the way he did sometimes. 'Actually I were rememberin' 'ow we treats you when you first come 'ere. Man, that were bad. I got to thinkin' 'bout it. It weren't right we should treat you that way just 'cause you speak different. It remind me the way some people treat me just 'cause my skin's a different colour. I don' like that, an' I reckon you didn' like it either. So I thought I'd try an' make it up to you.'

It was Ian's turn to feel embarrassed. 'Well, thanks. You certainly cheered Mum and Dad up.'

Vincent grinned. 'That were the idea.'

He opened the front door and stepped out. When he turned

142

round, he was looking serious again, as though he had something to say and didn't know how to say it.

'Well then,' Ian said. 'I'll see you next week at school.'

'That's just it,' Vincent said. 'You won't.'

'Whit d'you mean?'

'I were gonna tell you.' Vincent stopped. For once, he seemed lost for words. Then he came out with it. 'We're goin' back to Jamaica.'

Ian couldn't believe it. It had come so suddenly. And Vincent was looking so unhappy too. Ian felt a pang of pity for him.

'D'you want to go?' he asked.

'Yes. No. I don' know.' Vincent shook his head with bewilderment. 'My mind's just so mix up I don' know what I think.'

They were silent for a moment. Vincent was staring gloomily into space. Then he said, 'I gotta go,' but he didn't move.

'Come round the morrow,' Ian suggested. 'We can talk aboot it.'

Vincent's face lightened. 'Yeah. OK. I'll do that.'

He gave a quick smile. 'See you.' Then he was off, padding lightly down the stairs.

11

How could he ever have thought Vincent's face was like a mask, Ian wondered as he waited for his friend next morning. Vincent showed every change of thought and feeling in his face and his body. And he showed them off to the full. When he was happy, his whole being glowed with it. When he was miserable, it was as though the end of the world had come. When he was angry, then he bristled with it all over, and you had to watch out. Even when he was acting, giving a performance, you knew it was only an act.

He was so different from Ian. Ian knew that he rarely showed his emotions or revealed in his face what was in his mind. He hardly ever smiled. It was strange.

Was it because Vincent was black and he was white? Or because Vincent was a Londoner, and he was from Glasgow? Probably neither. That was just like those funny ideas he'd had about English people before he came to London — that they all lived in big houses and thought they were superior.

But he and Vincent were certainly different. Perhaps that was why he liked Vincent. The difference between them.

And yet they had so much in common as well. Fathers out of work. Brothers in trouble. Pulling up roots and having to start again. Leaving friends behind.

He was certainly going to miss him.

144

When Vincent arrived, Ian took him down to the back of the flats. He was going to show him the Park. It seemed the only kind of goodbye present he had to give him.

'I never knew this place were 'ere,' Vincent said as they clambered over the wall. 'You sure keeps t'ings to yourself.'

Wasn't that just what Ian had been thinking? The difference between them.

They came to the path and began to walk along it. Vincent gazed around him in wonder.

'That's an oak tree,' Ian told him. He indicated a huge tree whose naked branches spread out in a great arc.

'Is it?' said Vincent with interest. And then he asked with suspicion, ' 'Ow you know?'

'I read books too,' Ian said, and he almost smiled.

Vincent got the reference and gave a chuckle.

'You can tell by the shape,' Ian explained.

Vincent was looking at him with a sudden understanding. 'Say, this were where you went. That day when we was chasin' you after school.'

'That's right.'

'And we thought you'd vanished by magic.'

'Well, it wis a kind of magic.'

It seemed so long ago.

They walked on along the path past the tennis court.

'Hey,' Vincent exclaimed. 'I wish I'd known 'bout that. I could 'ave polish up my backhand.'

'I didny know you played tennis,' said Ian.

'I don't.'

'Neither do I.'

'But we could 'ave learned 'ow to play on that court.'

It was too late for that now, Ian thought.

He had explained to Vincent who owned the Park and had the use of it, but his friend was still surprised at how large it was.

'An' nobody else 'ere,' he said.

'There hardly ever is,' said Ian.

'It's so quiet. I ain't sure I would like that.' He thought for a bit. 'I dunno though. It could grow on you. I guess where I'm goin' in Jamaica is a bit like this. It's in the country.'

They walked on in silence.

'That's the hut where Old Bill keeps his equipment,' Ian pointed out. 'I wonder if he's there. He usually comes here every day and potters aboot. I think he'd be dead if he didny have this place.'

The idea hadn't occurred to Ian before, but he knew it was true. The hut was empty. There was no sign of the old man.

'What are those birds?' Vincent asked.

Two large birds with black and white bodies and long black tails were waddling clumsily across the grass in a clearing, occasionally waggling their tails and pecking at the ground.

'They're magpies,' said Ian. 'Old Bill told me. He doesny like them. He says they steal other birds' eggs and eat them.'

'Sounds nasty,' Vincent agreed. 'I never knew t'ings like that went on.'

'I used to think they looked like parrots.'

'I wonder if they 'as parrots in Jamaica. I ain't sure. I ain't never been there.'

Vincent was plunged into a mood of gloom.

Then they saw Old Bill. He was stooping over a flowerbed and seemed to be examining it intently. When he caught sight of Ian, he raised himself, pressed one hand into the small of his back and pushed his cap up on his forehead with the other.

'I was just seeing if the snowdrops were up yet,' he said. 'They're coming through, but it'll be a while before they're in flower.' Then he grunted. 'That dratted ground elder's spreading already. I thought I'd given it a good going over.' He glanced across at Vincent. 'Who's this then?'

'It's a friend of mine,' Ian said. 'Vincent.'

Old Bill stared steadily at the black boy for a moment or two with his sharp blue eyes. Ian could tell that Vincent was getting nervous under the scrutiny, worried about what kind of welcome he was going to get. But it was all right. Vincent must have been approved. The old man put out his hand and said, 'Pleased to meet you.' Ian sensed Vincent's relief.

'So you're a friend of Ian's,' Old Bill went on.

'Yeah,' said Vincent. 'We go to the same school.'

'There are a lot of black kids round here,' Old Bill said.

Vincent tensed. It wasn't clear from the old man's words whether he was expressing disapproval or just making a statement. He had this dry way of speaking. Even Ian couldn't always be sure, and he was used to it.

'One of my best mates in the Navy, my oppo, was black,' Old Bill said. 'From Barbados, he was. We had some grand times together. I wonder where he is now. We lost touch after the war. A pity. I said I'd write, but I never did. There's times now I wish I had.'

Old Bill hadn't mentioned that before. He was full of surprises.

Vincent was clearly impressed. He started asking the old man about his time in the Navy, and Old Bill seemed pleased to talk about it. Ian had heard most of the yarns before, but Vincent listened wide-eyed. He and Old Bill seemed to have taken to each other.

A chill wind was cutting through the trees. Old Bill gave a shudder.

'It's a bit nippy for me out here talking,' he said. 'I think I'd better get back home now.'

Then he had a thought. 'Why don't you go and make Vincent a cup of coffee? You can be warm in the hut.'

He pulled out a bunch of keys and peeled one off.

'I'll give you the spare key. You can let me have it back on Saturday.'

Ian took the key and said thanks.

There was something else he wanted to say if he could find the right words.

'Aboot the Park,' he began.

Old Bill was watching him warily.

'I've been thinking aboot whit you said. I'd like to look after it.'

The old man's face relaxed. 'Good. I was hoping you would.' He

147

gave a contented sigh. 'Right. I'll be off then. Make sure you bring your friend again.'

'Aye, I will,' said Ian.

But it didn't seem likely.

'Don't forget to lock up after you,' Old Bill warned. Then he had another thought. 'You'd better keep the key. You'll be needing it.'

He pulled his cap down over his forehead and made his way back to the path. They watched him go. Then Vincent suddenly seemed to remember something.

' 'Appy New Year,' he shouted.

Old Bill turned round, raised his cap in the air and twirled it round. 'And to you!'

Vincent talked excitedly as they walked back to the hut. 'That were nice o' 'im. Fancy 'im 'avin' a black friend. I never knew there was black people fightin' in the war. You sees 'ow they keeps those t'ings quiet? Well, you learn somet'in' new every day.'

The primus stove soon heated the hut up. Ian boiled a kettle and made two mugs of coffee. They helped themselves to sugar and powdered milk.

'This is a great place,' said Vincent as he sank into the old armchair and gazed around. Ian had insisted. After all, Vincent was the guest.

'What were all that 'bout lookin' after the Park?' Vincent asked.

Ian explained.

'So this'll all be yours?'

'Sort of.'

'Wow! That's quite somet'in'.' Vincent sounded really impressed. 'You gonna be all right.'

Yes, it did look that way. But it had been a sheer fluke. Being in the right place at the right time. Not everyone was as lucky as that.

They sipped away at their coffee for a while. It was too hot to take more than tiny mouthfuls.

'So when are you going?' Ian asked at last.

'Next week,' Vincent told him. His face had gone flat and depressed again.

148

'As soon as that?'

'Yeah. Dad's sold the 'ouse. We've been gettin' ready fo' months. I just 'aven't told nobody 'bout it.'

'Why are you going though?'

'Oh, there's a 'ole 'eap o' reasons.'

Vincent's eyes searched about, bewildered where to begin. 'My dad say this country finish. He say it were bad enough when 'e first come 'ere, what wit' racial discrimination an' prejudice. But now 'e say it worse. Ain't no free country no more. An' 'e ain't gonna get another job 'ere now 'e been made redundant.'

He thought for a while. 'I don' know if it any better in Jamaica. They got unemployment there too. An' violence an' crime. They say the badmen in Kingston'll shoot you dead fo' two dollars.'

'Mebbe it's exaggerated,' Ian suggested. 'Or a myth. Like the razor boys in Glasgow. They wis supposed to cut you up just fur looking at them. But I nivver seen any.'

'I dunno. Anyway, we'll be livin' in the country. St Anne's. My uncle got a farm or a planatation or somet'in' there. 'E want my dad to 'elp 'im run it. Well, it's a job, innit? It more than 'e 'ave 'ere.'

'Aye, that's something,' said Ian, thinking of his own father.

'Then there's Fitzroy,' Vincent went on. 'Dad t'ink 'e be better in Jamaica. Get back 'is confidence. Like I said, 'e ain't been the same since they done that to 'im.'

Ian couldn't help wondering again about Jimmy. What would he be like after he'd been to jail?

'An' Mum want to go. She never like it 'ere. The climate. The damp get in 'er chest. She been sick a lot wit' that.'

'But whit aboot you?' Ian asked.

Vincent gave a snort. 'They don' bother consult me. I'm the youngest. It don' matter what I t'inks. I don' count. My dad t'inks I gets a better education there, but I dunno.'

He brooded over it for a while. 'I don' know not'in' 'bout Jamaica. It all right fo' my mum an' dad. They born there. But I were born 'ere. I don' feel not'in' fo' Jamaica.'

Then his face relaxed, and his eyes began to dance with mischief. 'You the one what's the foreigner,' he said.

Ian grinned. 'Oh, aye,' he said.

Things had changed a lot since their first meeting.

He sighed. 'It sure is a long way to go.'

'Yeah,' Vincent agreed. 'Six t'ousand mile. It take ten 'ours in the plane.'

'Is that all?' It had taken them longer to get down the motorway from Glasgow, and that was only four hundred miles.

'I suppose I don' really 'ave no option,' Vincent said gloomily. Then his voice hardened with determination. 'But I knows one t'ing. I won' be stayin' in Jamaica forever. I were born 'ere. This is my country. An' I'll be back. I don' care if there are people like that policeman who t'ink I don' belong.'

He certainly meant what he said.

'You know, I been t'inkin' a lot these last months. 'Ad to wit' my 'ole world 'bout to change. I looks round my friends an' I sees they's all black. Course I were friendly wit' white kids in my junior school. But as I gets older I some'ow didn' want to be wit' 'em nomore. I suppose I feels safer wit' my black friends. I suppose I were afraid 'ow white folks would react. Like wit' Old Bill just now. But I ain't afraid nomore. I don' care 'ow they reacts. They'll just 'ave to take me or leave me. It's their problem, not mine.'

Had he helped, Ian wondered. He couldn't think how. Perhaps just listening helped.

But Vincent hadn't finished yet. He had a sort of faraway look in his eyes as though trying to get things straight in his mind. 'I don' know if it's the same wit' everyone, but it come to me in one day. It change my 'ole way o' t'inkin'.'

He became almost excited as he remembered. 'It were that day in art when old Summers kept on at me, an' then Maria got at me as well. 'Bout me givin' a big performance. I didn' like it at the time, but I t'ink 'bout it, an' it were true. I were always givin' a big performance. What d'I need to do that fo', I ax myself. I don' need to give no big performance. I can just be myself.'

Then he went on with even more fervour. 'An' then later you' sister come an' give me a real earful. Why don' you grow up, she say. An' I t'ink 'bout that as well. I don' resent it 'cause I know she were right. So I decided it's time I grows up.'

He gave a quiet chuckle. 'Funny 'ow somet'in' like that can change you' life.'

Ian tried to think if anything like that had happened to him. He wasn't sure. Unless it was when Old Bill asked him to help with the Park. Yes, that had changed his life.

They had finished their coffee. It was time to go back. Ian rinsed the mugs out under the tap outside. The water was icy. He put the padlock on the door and locked it carefully. It was good of Old Bill to trust him with the key.

Back at the flats, they found Tracy sitting by herself on the steps. She was looking miserable.

'Where's your friends?' Ian asked.

Tracy pouted and dismissed them with contempt. 'I ain't playin' with them no more. They're just little babies.'

She examined Vincent with interest. 'Who are you?'

'I'm Vincent. Ian's friend.'

She gave him a bold smile. 'You look nice,' she said. 'Perhaps I'll marry you when I grow up.'

'Yeah,' said Vincent with a look of mock horror on his face. 'An' perhaps you won't.' But you could see he was flattered.

'Oh well,' said Tracy. She sighed. 'I'll just 'ave to find someone else then.'

In the entrance way, Vincent turned to Ian and said, 'I'll see you.' And then added with a smile, 'When I gets back from Jamaica.'

'Aye,' said Ian.

Vincent had another thought. 'I'll write to you an' let you know 'ow I gets on.'

'Aye,' said Ian. 'Do that.'

They shook hands.

Ian remembered there was something else after all that he could give Vincent as a goodbye present.

'Wait a minute,' he cried and began racing up the stairs, leaving Vincent looking puzzled.

Mum was just coming out of the kitchen, wiping her hands on her apron.

'Whit's the matter?' she asked, surprised by the way he burst through the door.

'Nothing,' said Ian.

He didn't stop. He carried on past her into his bedroom.

It was still there in the drawer where he had put it that first evening. It was squashed flat. The flowers had faded a bit. But it was still all right. He hurried back to Vincent with it.

'Here,' he said, handing Vincent the white heather. 'You're the great one fur Scottish customs. You'd best have this. It might bring you luck.'

'Thanks,' said Vincent. He looked really pleased.

'It'll be a wee bit of Scotland in Jamaica,' Ian said.

It seemed fitting somehow. It was like handing on some kind of token.

'Oh, aye,' said Vincent.

'Yeah, man,' said Ian.

Vincent was grinning. And Ian found he was grinning back.

'Give my love to Bella,' Vincent said.

And then he was gone.

Next morning, when Ian sat down at the kitchen table, he found a letter beside his plate. He never received letters. Just the odd Christmas card and birthday card. He picked it up and examined it curiously. The postmark said Glasgow.

Mum was obviously dying to know who it was from.

'It doesny look like Aunt Sarah's writing,' she said, hovering over him.

Ian tore the envelope open and looked at the signature. He was surprised.

'It's from Jean,' he said.

'Oh aye,' said Mum. 'I mind her well. An awfie nice girl.'

Her curiosity satisfied, she lifted the teapot, poured Ian a cup of tea and got on with the washing up.

While he spooned cornflakes into his mouth, Ian read the letter.

Dear Ian, it said, *A Happy New Year to you! I hope you are well and settling down in London. I heard about Jimmy from my brother. Is that not awful? I hope everything goes all right for him. The weather here has been dreadful. We've had snow. It's all right for you down in sunny London! How are you getting on at school? We go back next week. I'm not looking forward to it.*

We were disappointed when you didn't write. Especially after you promised. I hope you don't mind me writing to you now. But I've got something to tell you that I think you ought to know. Maisie's going out with Andy now. I told her it was wrong, just because you were away, but she wouldn't listen to me. I'm not speaking to her at the moment because of it. Perhaps if you'd written like you promised, it wouldn't have happened.

I'm sorry to be the bearer of bad tidings, as they say, but I thought you ought to know.

Yours sincerely,

Jean

P.S. You can write to me if you like.

Ian went on chewing his cornflakes. Was it bad news? He didn't feel particularly upset. It was the kind of thing that was bound to happen. He'd never been very keen on Maisie anyway. She was the one who kept saying he was her boyfriend.

It was good of Jean to write and let him know. It couldn't have been easy for her.

And now that he came to think about it, he'd always preferred her anyway. She was more serious, more sensible, less flirty, less of a show-off. She was better-looking too. Ian remembered her strong square face and dark brown hair. And she was always cheerful. Maisie always had a sulky pout on her fit to turn milk sour. He wished Andy luck with her.

Of course, he should have written. That was bad of him. He'd

153

always meant to. He'd just never got round to it — except in his mind. Well, it was too late now.

Unless . . .

He helped Mum dry up the breakfast things. Dad was at work — he wouldn't have many more days of that. Bella was still in bed. She wouldn't be up for another hour at least.

He went to his bedroom. Jimmy's case hadn't come up yet, but it was a fair bet Ian would have the room to himself for quite a while.

He tore a page out of an exercise book, took up his science book to lean on, and went and sat on the bed. He wondered for a while what to write. He didn't know how to begin.

He found his thoughts wandering to Vincent. In a sense, Vincent was about to set out on the same kind of journey Ian himself had had five months or so before. Only he was going further. He wondered if Vincent would have the same difficulty making new friends. Probably not. Vincent was the sort of person who would make friends anywhere.

Ah well, Ian sighed. Wasn't that just like life? No sooner did you make friends than they went away. He would have to start all over again. And so would Vincent.

But he had survived. And Vincent was a fighter. He would survive too.

Ian looked at the sheet in front of him. It was still blank. Vincent had said he would write and let him know how he got on. Ian wondered if he would. He hoped so. He didn't want to lose touch with him the way Old Bill had with his mate in the Navy.

But then, what guarantee was there that Vincent would write? He himself had said he would write to Maisie, but he hadn't.

His mind wandered on again. It was funny to think of that white heather going all the way to Jamaica. Being handed on like that.

Then it suddenly came to him. Why hadn't he realised it before? It was Jean who had given him the white heather, not Maisie. The memory of it brought with it hope. It could be a lucky omen.

154

Perhaps if he wrote, it would somehow ensure that Vincent wrote to him. That they didn't lose touch.

That settled it. He took up his biro.

Dear Jean, he began. *Thank you for writing to me . . .*

Managing Teaching Assistants

A guide for headteachers, managers
and teachers

Anne Watkinson

RoutledgeFalmer
Taylor & Francis Group

LONDON AND NEW YORK

First published 2003
by RoutledgeFalmer
I I New Fetter Lane, London EC4P 4EE

Simultaneously published in the USA and Canada
by RoutledgeFalmer
29 West 35th Street, New York, NY 10001

RoutledgeFalmer is an imprint of the Taylor & Francis Group

© 2003 Anne Watkinson

Typeset in Times New Roman by
RefineCatch Limited, Bungay, Suffolk
Printed and bound in Great Britain by
MPG Books, Bodmin, Cornwall

British Library Cataloguing in Publication Data
A catalogue record for this book is available from the British Library

Library of Congress Cataloging in Publication Data
A catalog record for this book has been requested

ISBN 0–415–26994–6

To John and Viv
Thank you

Contents

Illustrations

FIGURES

TABLES

Preface

In starting to run courses for teaching assistants (TAs) and give advice to schools as a newly appointed consultant to the local education authority (LEA) in 1994, I needed to find out what TAs really did. I knew, from my experience of TAs in the schools where I had worked for nine years as a primary and nursery teacher and twelve years as a headteacher of two schools, that TAs no longer just supported the work of teachers, or the environment of the classroom, but were also increasingly working directly with children and young people. I decided to undertake some research of my own, encouraged by both my line manager and my future research supervisor. While still a consultant, later an adviser and senior adviser in the LEA, I undertook a survey of provision in the county and some in-depth case study research in two primary schools. I kept a diary, or more correctly a file of jottings, notes, reflections and evaluations over the late 1990s, and delved into the literature. I worked closely with over fifty schools for several years, and must have visited over two hundred more in various capacities as an inspector, adviser, tutor, facilitator and friend. Much of this book is based on my findings and experiences in my own schools and the many others I had the privilege to visit. The research material is scattered through the book in separate frames and shaded. My findings are backed by an increasing level of published work from others.

When I retired in 2000, my knowledge and understanding were used by the then Department for Education and Employment (DfEE) TA team to help in the preparation and delivery of TA induction materials in England. This meant I was able to meet, share ideas and attempt to understand a wide perspective of views and experiences of TAs across the country. In 2001, I was able to share the picture found in England with our European colleagues at a human resource conference in Barcelona. It was interesting to find how advanced the UK is, in having tapped this wonderful resource.

It is my hope that sharing my experiences, findings and ideas with a wider audience will enable the varied expertise of TAs to be understood and utilised to its maximum potential. In doing so, I hope also to celebrate the achievements of TAs to date, hoping for their recognition as a profession in their own right. All schools and members of staff are different, there is no one pattern that fits all, but I have put forward further suggestions for action, based on ideas I have used over the past few years with the various schools in which I have had the privilege to work.

Acknowledgements

I wish to express my grateful thanks to those who have contributed to the completion of this book:

- Professor Barbara MacGilchrist for encouraging me to study for a higher degree in the first place and for her continuous encouragement, patience and training in the research process which she provided, and her help with my writing
- Essex County Council Learning Services Directorate for facilitating the use of my time and the resources of the authority to support the research work
- the headteachers, teachers and particularly the teaching assistants of all the schools I have visited, especially the two study schools, who gave so generously of their time and the rich data they so willingly provided
- the children and parents of the two study schools who allowed me to observe, video, photograph and write about the staff who work in their classes
- my work colleagues in Essex County Council Learning Services Directorate, Essex schools and more recently the DfEE and Department for Education and Skills (DfES), for the opportunity to enter into informed critical debate on the subject matter
- Anna Clarkson of RoutledgeFalmer for continuing to have faith that I could write a useful book and pointing the ways forward
- the headteachers and staff of Beehive Lane Community Primary School, Chelmsford, Essex, Our Lady of Peace Junior School, Slough, Berkshire and its former headteacher Geraldine Lindsay, Maldon Primary School, Essex, and Stewards School, Harlow, Essex for permission to reproduce their documentation
- David Fulton Publishers for permission to reproduce the material found on pages 30, 126, 133 and 134.
- my husband Frank for his support and encouragement throughout, including his never-ending patience with my ICT system.

Abbreviations

A level	Advanced level
ALS	Additional Literacy Support
CA	Classroom assistant
DES	Department of Education and Science
DfE	Department for Education
DfEE	Department for Education and Employment
DfES	Department for Education and Skills
DHT	deputy headteacher
EAL	English as an additional language
EP	educational psychologist
EY	early years
EYNTO	Early Years National Training Organisation
FAS	Funding Agency for Schools
FE	further education
FEFC	Further Education Funding Council
FTE	full-time equivalent
GCSE	General Certificate of Secondary Education
GEST	Grants for Education Support and Training
HE	higher education
HEFC	Higher Education Funding Council
HMCI	Her Majesty's Chief Inspector
HMI	Her Majesty's Inspectorate
HT	headteacher
ICT	information and communication technology
IEP	individual education plan
IiP	Investors in People
INSET	in-service education and training
KS	key stage
LEA	local education authority
LGMB	Local Government Management Board
LGNTO	Local Government National Training Organisation
LMS	local management of schools

LSA	learning support assistant
MDA	midday assistant
NAS	National Association of Schoolmasters
NASUWT	National Association of Schoolmasters and Union of Women Teachers
NC	National Curriculum
NLNS	National Literacy and Numeracy Strategies
NLS	National Literacy Strategy
NNEB	National Nursery Examination Board
NNS	National Numeracy Strategy
NOS	National Occupational Standards
NTO	National Training Organisation
NUT	National Union of Teachers
NVQ	National Vocational Qualification
OECD	Organisation for Economic Cooperation and Development
Ofsted	Office for Standards in Education
O level	Ordinary level
OU	Open University
PDR	professional development review
PE	physical education
PGCE	postgraduate certificate of education
QCA	Qualifications and Curriculum Authority
QTS	qualified teacher status
SAT	standard assessment task
SDP	school development plan
SEN	special educational needs
SENCO	special educational needs co-ordinator
SNTA	special needs teaching assistant
STA	specialist teacher assistant
STAC	Specialist Teacher Assistant Certificate
SWOT	strengths, weaknesses, opportunities and threats
TA	teaching assistant
TEACCH	Treatment and Education of Autistic and related Communication Handicapped Children
TEC	Training and Enterprise Council
TTA	Teacher Training Agency

Chapter 1

Introduction

I absolutely love the job I do and have given 100% time and effort to it. Unfortunately this is frowned upon by some members of staff who, I feel, think TAs should be there to sharpen pencils and wash paintbrushes. I feel the opinion of TAs needs to be raised so that they are of more benefit to the children, staff and school.

(A teaching assistant in a response to the 1998 Essex LEA survey, quoted in Watkinson 1999a)

This chapter identifies the group of people about whom this book is written and briefly outlines their status and the need for interest in their role. Their relative invisibility yet continued growth is described along with the importance of management in their effective use. The complexity of their role and context is explained. The way in which the book is structured to aid managers and teachers to realise the full potential of TAs is outlined.

Who and what are teaching assistants?

Background

Teaching assistants are adults who are paid to work in school classrooms in the UK, usually directly with pupils. There are many names currently in use for these people. For the purposes of this book, they will be referred to as teaching assistants. The DfEE (2000a) *Good Practice Guide* defines TAs as follows:

The term 'teaching assistant' is the Government's preferred term of reference for all those in paid employment in support of teachers in primary, special and secondary schools. That includes those with a general role and others with specific responsibilities for a child, subject area or age group.

(DfEE 2000a p. 4)

Whether they are washing paintpots, making materials or working one-to-one with a child, they are supporting the learning of students of the institution in which they work, either directly, or indirectly through supporting the teaching. Enhancing learning is usually a main aim of schools. The label *learning support assistant* (LSA) largely signifies supporting the learning of a child with special educational needs (SEN) especially in secondary schools. *Classroom assistant* (CA) appears to put more emphasis on the 'paintpot' role, and *teacher assistant* appears to assume the TA is an aide to a specific teacher. The word *ancillary* means 'subservient', and *paraprofessional* could refer to any professional.

As a teacher, head, adviser, researcher and consultant I have been privileged to work with and for this group of people since the early 1970s. In that time they have become recognised. The above quotation goes on:

> The term [TA] captures the essential 'active ingredient' of their work; in particular it acknowledges the contribution which well-trained and well-managed assistants can make to the teaching and learning process and to pupil achievement.
>
> (DfEE 2000a p. 4)

This book aims to share my experiences with senior managers in schools so that they can have well-trained and managed assistants, who support not only teaching and learning, but also the whole school community, and become more successful and fulfilled people in their own right.

The title TA is established only in England, Wales and Northern Ireland. Scotland refers to this group as CAs. While other countries have aides or assistants, they have different titles. In the USA, the 1960s job creation scheme saw an expansion of assistants in schools and the role of *paraprofessional* was recognised. In *Paraprofessionals Today*, Gartner *et al.* (1977) described a movement in the USA in the development of educational and human services following the anti-poverty programme of that time. They also saw the role as something beyond just helping in schools:

> Paraprofessionals have achieved prominence in a role to patch up an unworkable system. They must become a force in developing the education of the future – an education that prepares people for peace, social equality and human organisation.
>
> (Gartner *et al.* 1977 p. 244)

In the USA, the term *paraprofessional* has persisted although *teacher aide* is also common. *Teacher assistants* or *teaching assistants* are the graduates who help out teaching staff in universities for extra money while they themselves are taking postgraduate courses. Kerry (2001) gives the role of the *para-educator* from a 1977 Kansas State Department of Education document. In

Canada, TAs form part of the trainee teacher programme, again in higher education (HE).

Many European countries have only a limited range of associate staff as defined by the National Union of Teachers (NUT 1998), although some have staff who act as supervisors or have welfare responsibility. The Netherlands has the nearest equivalent to the British teaching assistants. Kerry (2001) made attempts to contact embassies throughout Europe, with few results.

In 1994, when I started as an adviser to run courses for TAs, many issues were already being raised. Schools had started to seek advice from the LEA about assessing the effectiveness of TAs and their value for money, as well as their management and deployment. Questions were being asked particularly about effective teaching and learning and the use of additional adults in the classroom. The TAs themselves began to ask about training and qualifications. The climate of school management had radically changed following the Education Reform Act 1988, bringing the National Curriculum (NC), accountability through assessment and inspection and local financial management. Schools and the people in them had become more responsible for their own destinies and those of their pupils.

Status

When I first investigated the subject of TAs, as I was about to tutor them, rather than just use them or employ them, the role of TAs was diffuse as well as invisible, even their name was often 'non-teaching assistants', as though they were 'non' people, the 'forgotten staff' (Burnham 1988 p. 31). Swann and Loxley (1997 p. 1) still talked of an 'historical invisibility as far as local or national policy making is concerned'. Despite this, I knew they performed a wide variety of jobs for which they needed various skills, and were a group with an apparent fund of goodwill, enthusiasm and growing expertise. At that time there were minimal opportunities for TAs to gain any training and few felt valued, yet they had a great deal of job satisfaction. When I had worked in schools, I had seen how useful the TAs were in all sorts of ways, but also had a sense of the problems associated with their employment, as well as their desire to learn for themselves more about teaching and learning.

TAs have had little status. Administrative, caretaking and cleaning staff have had clearer roles and foreign language assistants, technicians and librarians more recognition. TAs are not yet organised as a group and not unionised. Even now, a rough estimate is that only some 10–20 per cent of TAs belong to Unison, the public sector workers' union. Even nursery nurses, a group much more generally recognised, were called *Invisible Professionals* by Robins (1998). Yet nursery nurses at least have a recognised professional body, a recognised qualification and a contractual status. These do not apply to TAs, who perform a similar role in mainstream school to nursery nurses in a nursery school. Teenagers may voice their desire to be a nursery nurse when they leave school, but few young people express the wish to be a TA and only a very small minority of men join their number, although I sense changes in attitudes from the general public as well as the media, showing an increased recognition of a distinct TA role.

While TAs have come to the fore in the early 2000s following the recognition by the government of their value in 'making an enhanced contribution to the learning process in schools' (DfEE 1997a p. 51), it is still too often as a resource to fill a gap, such as providing cover, or a quick route to entry to the teaching profession or a support to teachers to offset their career rather than for what they can do as themselves. Status is still a problem: TAs are not recognised as a profession in their own right.

What we know

Numerical increase

We know that numbers of assistants increased steadily during the 1990s although the numbers are difficult to judge accurately. Form 7, completed by headteachers every January for the then Department for Education and Employment had outdated headings which are ambiguous with regards to nomenclature, and defining full-time and part-time staff. The returns to the DfEE until January 2001 were made in terms of hours worked, and then calculated to a nominal full-time equivalent (FTE). Education support staff includes nursery nurses, those employed to support pupils with SEN and ethnic minorities, and those working in a more general capacity. The figures in Table 1.1 for 1992 to 1994 come from an report on class size by the Office for Standards in Education (Ofsted 1996), and those for 1995 to 2000 from the DfEE statistics office (personal communication by email; electronic data were not available prior to that date). They showed a constant year by year increase (see Figure 1.1).

From 2000 onwards the nomenclature of Form 7 changed to reflect the increased visibility of TAs in schools and reports indicate a further increase in numbers since 2001. The DfES provisional data for 2002 (statistics obtained from the DfES website www.dfes.gov.uk) indicates a total of 103,624 FTE posts for TAs in schools. This total includes special needs

Table 1.1 Education support staff in English primary schools from 1992 and English secondary schools from 1995 to 2000 with a total for 2002

Year of January count	1992	1993	1994	1995	1996	1997	1998	1999	2000	2001	2002
Total primary	32,483	36,441	41,117	46,324	50,644	54,143	58,056	61,729	68,694		
Total secondary				21,464	23,105	24,887	26,550	28,174	31,765		
Total				67,688	73,749	79,030	84,606	89,903	100,459		103,624

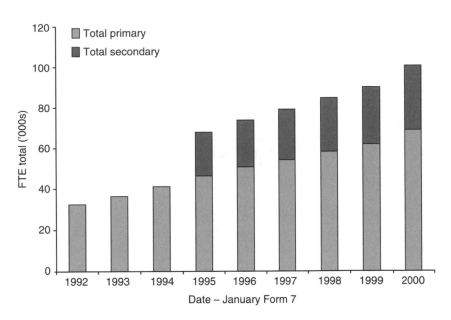

Figure 1.1 Graphical display of Table 1.1 showing education support staff in English primary schools from 1992 and English secondary schools from 1995

support staff and minority ethnic staff; 213,012 FTE support staff as a whole were employed in schools in January 2002. It is therefore likely that over 200,000 people were employed in classrooms to support the teaching and learning processes at the time of the census.

The literature

In 1994, I started to look for not only information to support my TA courses but also ideas to pass onto school managers. I found there was little published research, and little recognition by the educational hierarchies, national or local. Gradually, over the last few years the volume has increased but the field is still new. Loxley and Swann (1997) argued that the difficulty lay in

> accepting responsibility [and] Until this issue is resolved, primarily at national level with the DfEE giving a policy lead, the result will be disillusionment and frustration with the initiative, particularly for the students ... they are probably the richest untapped resource in our education service. They deserve recognition.
>
> (Loxley and Swann 1997 p. 21)

Teachers' unions, such as the NUT and the National Association of Schoolmasters (NAS), later the National Association of Schoolmasters and Union of Women Teachers (NAS/UWT), were openly antagonistic towards TAs in the 1960s, fearing a dilution of the status of teachers. They are now less strongly opposed and are more open to debate, but rightly protective of the status of teachers and they still voice concerns about the growth in numbers of TAs and the possible inappropriate responsibilities being given to them.

There had been a general lack of attention paid to support staff as a whole, and particularly to TAs. Most literature on human resource management for schools still focuses on the teachers. Staff development for schools still frequently means only professional development for teachers, although Grants for Education Support and Training (GEST) have been, and Standards Fund budgets are, clearly for the training and development of all staff and governors. The class size debate largely revolved round the teacher:pupil ratio not the adult:pupil ratio until the report by Blatchford *et al.* (2002).

Management theories, epitomised by authors such as Senge (1990), along with ideas of Total Quality Management have supported the practice of recognition of all people who work in an establishment contributing to its effectiveness. School effectiveness research endorses this. The philosophy of Investors in People (IiP) recognises that the training and development of *all* staff is important to the healthy growth of an organisation, but schools had been slow to commit themselves to the IiP process. Texts supporting staff development or human resource development in schools rarely mentioned support staff except in passing, 'staff' meant 'teachers', and 'staff meetings' meant 'meetings of teaching staff'. Appraisal and performance review work for schools even in 2000 still related only to teaching staff (DfEE 2000b), although professional development 'should also be available to teaching assistants' (DfEE 2000c p. 5).

By 1992 the Ofsted inspection process was beginning; Her Majesty's Inspectorate (HMI) published one of their last pamphlets in the Education Observed series on *Non-teaching Staff in Schools* (HMI 1992). It predicted a likely increase in numbers, and pointed to an increasing diversity of role. Until the late 1990s, there was a lack of work published on TAs and few major texts or projects to which to refer. Mortimore and colleagues commented on the 'relatively few studies' and 'few education reports or books' (Mortimore *et al.* 1992 p. 5) in their research report on non-teaching staff for the then Department for Education (DfE), which was published later in book form (Mortimore *et al.* 1994). Mortimore's report also recognises that this omission is surprising given 'the influence of management theory and its emphasis on team approaches to institutional management . . . HMI . . . researchers and educational writers have failed to emphasise sufficiently the potential of these roles' (Mortimore *et al.* 1992 p. 5).

By 1995, the Local Government Management Board (LGMB) undertook a survey into the work of assistants working in the classroom. They considered there were 87,061 TAs employed in the autumn of 1995 (LGMB 1996). The numbers have continued to rise. Further surveys have been done.

The Unison *Survey of Classroom Assistants* (Lee and Mawson 1998) showed similar results, and the NUT study *Associate Staff: Support for teachers* (NUT 1998) had similar recommendations. The latest survey commissioned by the DfEE (Local Government National Training Organisation (LGNTO) *et al.* 2000) showed an increase of 39.4 per cent from 1995 to 1999 in schools with children at Key Stage (KS) 1 and KS2, excluding middle schools. This survey calculated that 121,500 people were working in infant, junior and primary schools in England in 1999. Their figures included the independent sector.

Effectiveness

More recently, the role itself has received attention: not enough was known about how TAs can enhance teaching and learning by what they do, rather than by just being an extra pair of hands. The findings and those of my own research all point towards the potential for such assistants; if properly trained and selected for particular purposes they can help raise standards of teaching and learning, and can provide a welcome additional dimension to school life. Until very recently, literature has talked of TAs as if they were a material resource, like any other piece of equipment, to be used or discarded as the needs of the school dictated.

The research does show that the effectiveness of TAs is only as good as their use, deployment and management. There is a great need for teachers and managers to be aware of the potential of the team they already have within their own establishment, to deal with them as full members of staff, to understand how best to use them and to both value and evaluate what they do. It is hoped that this book will not be seen as a patronising 'manual for a useful household tool' (O'Brien and Garner 2001 p. 2). While I cannot speak as a TA, although I have often helped a group in a teacher's class, and so will have to refer to 'them', readers must remember that TAs are people who can change, grow and develop depending on the opportunities around them.

Complexity

The role of TAs is not simply defined. They work with children and young people of all abilities, not just those with SEN throughout the phases of education. Some individuals have three or even more different contracts, and perform a multitude of tasks in each one. They can work with several different teachers within a morning, let alone a week. They themselves have had diverse educational histories, and their pay and conditions of service are varied. This has to be set in the complicated contexts of classroom, school, local authority and country, at a time of rapid changes in education as well as social, economic and technological changes, all of which affect their work.

The context of the TA is one where various adults, working largely in a classroom environment determined by the teacher, assist the pupil learner. The learner could be seen at the centre of what schools are about. The classroom is not an isolated area; the teacher works in a school with policies, practices, management structures and systems. Even in circumstances of high autonomy, the school must conform to certain national and local requirements, and will seek support from various agencies for the pupils and with professional development for the staff. Local authorities vary considerably in their funding and support mechanisms for state schools, and all schools have to adhere to a legal framework and national accountability of some kind. This context can be shown diagrammatically by putting the learner – the pupil or student – as the centre of concentric circles of various influences (Figure 1.2). TAs assist learning and support the teacher and the teaching in

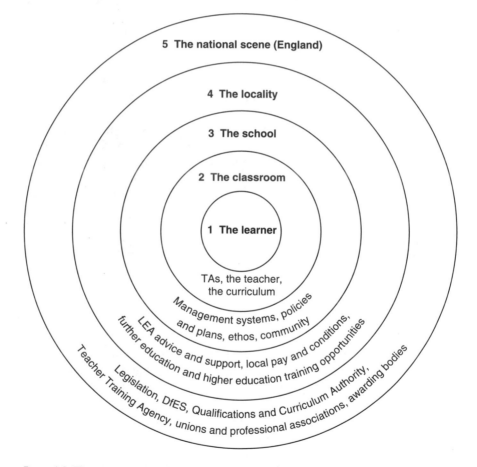

Figure 1.2 The context of the learner and the TA
Source: Adapted from Watkinson 1998a

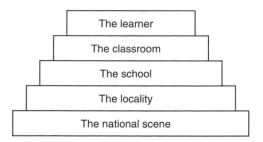

Figure 1.3 The support constituents for a school

the classroom, so it could be possible to consider the place of the TA in relationship to the learner, the classroom, the school, the locality and community influences and national initiatives.

The TA could also be considered as a support to the learner, themselves supported by the teacher, school, locality and national initiatives; the influences can be seen as helpful as well as possibly interfering. The concentric circles could be considered as a child's tower of building blocks as seen in Figure 1.3.

However, it is not as simple as these figures imply. The components of each circle are not even, the influences can be helpful or can hinder. Nor does the hypothetical structure just consist of building blocks of uneven size; their juxtaposition is also always changing, rather like the computer-generated pictures of the inside of Hogwarts in the Harry Potter films, sometimes supporting and sometimes adding to the pressure on the pupil learner or the TA. In addition to this, the 'structure' or context will differ for each TA, as there is little consistency of approach throughout even England let alone the UK. The definitions of teaching and learning are also constantly changing; public accountability is demanding numerical measures of attainment and achievement, alongside a recognition of the value of stimulating curiosity and creativity.

Also, while it is possible to consider these various layers of the education system, the relationships between them and the people who constitute them are what actually 'cements' the whole organisation. Schools are organic, living, changing places, which work because the people in them make them work – or not. Relationships constitute the medium which hold the building blocks together, maintaining the strength of the building. For schools, relationships between the learner and teacher, classroom and management, documentation and practice, the school and its community, the local and national authorities and their responsibilities enable the organisation to become effective. It is the relationship between the TA and all these elements which enable them to assist in the provision of a coherent and effective learning environment for pupils.

The structure of the book

It was not easy to produce a linear structure for this book, and at all times each chapter will need to be related to the others, more like a network. It will look at the processes involved as well as the constituent parts. Figure 1.4 gives a simplified network model which will be used to underpin the work described in the book.

As it is possible for senior managers to be responsible for TAs without ever having had one in their class when teaching, and certainly without having had any training in their management, it is important for managers to find out how many TAs are in their school in order that their usefulness be properly utilised. Chapter 2 looks at the TAs themselves, the kinds of jobs they have done and are doing, the people they are and the skills, knowledge and understanding they can bring to the job. TAs come from a varied background of education and experience. The arrival of nationally accepted descriptions of TAs in the form of standards is described and the implications for appropriate school procedures are examined.

Chapter 3 looks at ways for managers to find out what is going on in their school. Inappropriate deployment of TAs, lack of understanding of their knowledge, skills and competencies and ineffective management by teachers can result in some negative results, for the pupils, teachers, TAs and the school. The school therefore needs to review the qualities of its TAs and their deployment in order to best serve the aims of the school, the needs of pupils and teachers and the demands of the curriculum. These suggestions will involve the support of teachers and managers, affecting timetabling and other human and material resources. The role, competencies and qualifications of TAs cannot be taken for granted as they also change with experience and training.

However good the TAs are, their potential can be realised only if their use and management facilitate its realisation. Also, classrooms are not islands where teachers close the door and do their own thing, respected for a professionalism learnt at college in no need of updating, as was the case in the early 1980s. School teams and policies are in place to ensure the pupils receive a coherent and continuous education with consistent messages from all the staff. The importance of the whole school ethos and climate is also emphasised. TAs do not work in isolation. They work with pupils and teachers and can work with other adults with whom they come in contact, as part of a team and under guidance. Chapter 4 describes what good practice in school management can achieve.

Chapter 5 gives some of the procedures, structures and systems that are needed to support the TA team.

Chapter 6 considers the various procedures that can be put in place to support the appointment and management of TAs from recruitment through to review. These procedures need resourcing and reveal further

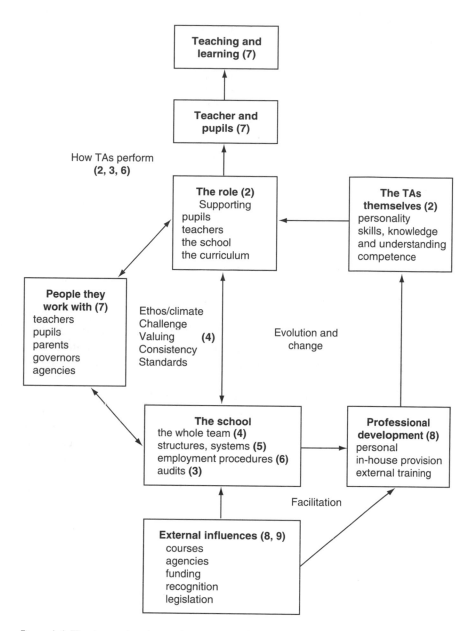

Figure 1.4 The interrelated constituents providing the support mechanisms for learners
(the pupils) through the work of TAs (relevant chapters are in parentheses)

activities which can be undertaken by the school or the TA to enhance effectiveness, raising standards for the school as well as providing fulfilment for the TA.

Chapter 7 explores these classroom relationships and ways in which they can be enhanced. TAs cannot be hired and placed with an individual pupil or teacher and suddenly the improvement in learning takes place. Chapter 7 describes how TAs not only can support teaching and learning, but also need to understand what this entails. While working under the direction of teachers, TAs teach and can support teaching, given the right opportunities to form appropriate partnerships with the teachers in non-pupil contact time. Teachers as well as managers need to understand the potential of TAs, and to manage them as part of their responsibility for the learning of their pupils. This challenges the traditional role of the teacher of the twentieth century, as the one skilled and knowledgeable adult in the classroom.

TAs' potential does not stay still. All those working in school are entitled to personal and professional development but those working directly with pupils can potentially have the most significant direct effect upon the learning outcomes. TAs are mostly very keen to undertake further study, but need the support and guidance of the school in undertaking it. Chapter 8 discusses the training and development of TAs, their career progression and their development as a profession in their own right. While external training is beneficial, there is continuing need for in-house training and communication. Increasing skills and understanding among the TA team must be utilised by the school or it is lost.

Schools need a vision and strength of their own; effective schools are learning communities. Chapter 9 explores some of these broad ideas in relation to the employment of a TA team. Some schools feel that they can do this better alone: 'I just want to get on with the job' is their cry. There are valid concerns about central bureaucracy and paper overload. The chapter sums up the ideas proposed in the book and proposes some more which could enable schools to move towards a more flexible way of considering the learning of all their stakeholders.

Chapter 2

What TAs can do

> As the numbers have grown, so too has interest in what the assistants actually do, what they might be encouraged to do and what they feel about what they are asked to do. The last decade has seen a number of important papers published, commissioned by Government bodies, local authorities, academic institutions and trade unions. Out of these, as will be seen, a remarkably uniform picture emerges.
>
> (Adamson 1999 p. 1)

This chapter examines the potential purposes of employing TAs, the role, the kind of people they are and the nature of performance and competence which can be expected from them. It indicates that there is a need for the examination of management practices. The range of educational and life experiences of TAs and the variety of a school's expectations have to be matched. Then the school will be able to make the best use of people, to create the maximum opportunities for increased standards in learning and teaching.

The role

Ancillaries: the welfare only role

Teachers and schools have always had their assistants, whether it is the 'disciples' of the Greek philosophers, the lay helpers to priests or the pupil-teachers of the nineteenth century. After the development of nursery education early in the twentieth century, the National Nursery Examination Board (NNEB) came into existence in 1945, and established the profession of nursery nurses with a two-year course, examinations and certificates for training young women of 16 to 18 years and over 'in the development, care and education of the young child from birth to five years of age, at the same time continuing with their own education in general subjects' (Parry and Archer 1974 p. 67).

In 1967 the Plowden report was published. It was a time, as now, of impending teacher shortage. Other areas of the report have received more attention, such as the importance of nursery education and the need to increase parent participation, but the report was uncompromising regarding assistants. Plowden saw one of the ways forward in mainstream schools as expansion in ancillaries, the then current developments not going far enough in their judgement – 'not everywhere and not comprehensive enough' (Plowden 1967 p. 318).

Only 22 per cent of schools had welfare assistants to 'relieve teachers in caring for the needs of young children' (Plowden 1967 p. 318). There was 'little logical pattern' in the employment of assistants; for some, class size was the rationale, some the experience (or lack of it) of the class teacher, and for some a definition of function. The help given by assistants at that time was seen as generally of a welfare-care nature.

> There is no reason why they should not prepare materials for art and craft, look after plants and animals, help with displays and exhibitions, and record school broadcasts. The combination of role with the school secretary is seen as helpful, although the 'all rounders' are unlikely to be able to also help with musical or mechanical equipment.
>
> (Plowden 1967 p. 329)

This view of TAs as merely 'paintpot washers' persisted right up until the end of the 1990s, and their talents as supporters of pupils' learning and teachers' aides, able to take a role in supporting curriculum targets, remained hidden from mainstream initiatives. Haigh's (1996) article caught the mood of change with its title 'To boldly go beyond washing paintpots'. TAs can do much more.

It is hard to separate the work of TAs into individual strands: their role is complex and varied. A TA supporting pupils in a literacy lesson is helping the aims of the teacher and supporting the policies of the school, but the four strands of support for the school, pupils, teachers and the curriculum form convenient categories for discussion of TA work. Observing TAs at work or interviewing them will reveal some of the attributes described next.

Supporting the school: care and welfare

Just as diet and housing environment can affect physical growth, the learning environment can affect brain function and learning. Schools with high standards are visibly welcoming and organised places to be. The learning environment includes the physical surroundings or the social, emotional, linguistic and cultural contexts of the learners. Smith (1996) promotes the use of a multisensory environment, with bright displays, plants, well-organised and accessible resources. The TAs' role in helping the school achieve this is an important one, and not to be dismissed just as 'washing paintpots'. Teachers and TAs can take joint pride in this kind of mainten-ance. Cleaning the paintpots has to be done, and TAs can supervise pupils to do it for themselves even from the foundation stage. TAs encourage pupils to clear up, to work tidily and to manage their resources appropriately. TAs can help with displays and may sometimes have more talent in this direction than the teacher.

Managing behaviour is about having a climate in which teaching and learning can take place; it permeates everything that happens. It is about attitudes and strategies which are consistent throughout the school and classrooms for all pupils, not just those who have problems conforming to whatever is the norm in the school. The new proposals have suggested that dealing with problems of behaviour may be done by people other than TAs, such as learning mentors, who would be specially trained in the role of a 'behaviour and guidance manager', to co-ordinate or manage a behaviour and guidance team, or co-ordinate the behaviour policy in a school. Whether people undertake such a specialist role or not, it is imperative that all staff understand the school's behaviour policy and put it into practice.

Supporting pupils

The Warnock report (DES 1978) described an investigation into the special educational needs of children. In 1981, this resulted in a major Education Act which has radically changed the educational possibilities for children with SEN. The support of SEN children, with help paid for by the LEA, was the beginning of the national recognition of the role of assistants in the classroom to support pupils.

As the numbers increased, there were concerns about the quality of people being employed in the newer, more wide-ranging roles. They were older women, generally untrained, with few relevant qualifications and little experience of SEN. LEAs had few considered policies about recruitment, variable appointment procedures and rarely provided training. The conditions of service and pay prospects were generally poor. While TAs were generally welcomed, they could be mismatched to the role in their knowledge and skills required to complete the tasks with the children, due to variations in their personal experience and training, a point taken up later in this chapter. There was and still is a diversity of role from school to school and classroom to classroom due to their management by the class teachers or SEN co-ordinators (SENCOs), and/or their deployment in the school. In auditing their school's needs, allocation of staff and management practices, managers may find just such anomalies.

The role of a TA which differentiates them from other kinds of assistants (such as administrative or lunchtime assistants) is their direct involvement in the teaching and learning processes of the classroom. TAs usually describe their own role as supporting pupils.

Case study evidence

TAs talked of supporting children, of changing things to make them suitable for the children they are linked with. They talked of carrying out the individual education plans (IEPs), developing fine motor skills, or life skills, as they have planned with the SENCO or the visiting SEN support teacher. They used technical terminology – autism, complex learning difficulties, Down's syndrome, poor language skills, motor skills or social awareness.

They enabled the children to make choices and decisions. They mentioned keeping children on task, getting them organised, of keeping their attention, encouraging, actually holding their hands (in handwriting), supporting practice, but most particularly, knowing the children's strengths and weaknesses.

One TA spoke of working with children who needed no obvious help. 'They love having a bit of individual attention, someone to sit there and say "that's really good" or "could you have done that a bit better if you move it round?".' Teachers spoke of 'a little bit extra will make the grade', 'extra cuddle, extra time, extra explanation', 'everything, getting children to meet their targets' not necessarily IEP targets, but the teacher's intentions for that day.

The children themselves saw their role in terms of getting more attention, saying, 'they have less children to cope with', 'she can tell you in a bit more detail from the whole class' and 'help some people catch up'. TAs gave more information, checked their work and helped them if they were stuck or not going fast enough. One child added, rather honestly, 'you wouldn't sit and do it if someone didn't make you'. A teacher spoke of 'hooking the kids into feeling wanted'.

The TAs showed great perception. One said about her charge,

> We try to use language because she can't think of words to express what she wants to say. It's like trying to get blood out of a stone getting her to talk about it. It seems stuck in there and she can't get it out, you see her do something with her hands. When there is something she is excited about and she's really enjoyed it, the words do come out and things like sequencing and remembering things, but she could stand up and sing the latest Spice Girls' songs and do the latest Spice Girls' dance because she enjoys doing it. She can do sequencing, and moving, because she's enjoying doing it'.

It is difficult to ascertain the influence of TAs in hard outcome data. Blatch-ford *et al.* (2002) tried in their KS1 study but the variability in quality of provision precluded them from making firm conclusions.

TAs supporting learning is observable more as process and in its outcomes. The Ofsted (2002a) report regarding TAs gives the following list of strategies that HMI observed where TAs help pupils to learn better:

In whole class teaching . . .

- minimising distractions to the whole class by dealing with individual welfare issues and behaviour problems
- keeping individual pupils on task by prompting their responses
- repeating or rephrasing questions asked by the teacher
- providing additional or alternative explanations for individual pupils
- providing specialist support, for example for hearing-impaired pupils
- observing and noting reactions and contributions of the pupils so that the more passive members of the class can later receive extra attention
- enabling less confident pupils, or those of lower ability or with SEN, to make contributions to the lesson.

During group or independent work, teaching assistants help pupils to learn better by:

- providing support for an individual or a group of pupils which enables them to tackle tasks that would otherwise be beyond them
- giving more individual explanations of a task than would be possible with the whole class
- giving feedback on the pupils' learning to the teacher so that he or she can adjust the challenge or pace of learning in later lessons
- giving pupils' immediate relevant feedback on their work.

(Ofsted 2002a p. 11)

O'Brien and Garner (2001) were convinced that the accounts of LSAs them-selves showed that they could enable 'children to think in a more focussed way about their learning . . . by: modelling positive behaviour, establishing and developing relationships, increasing learner confidence and self-belief, encouraging risk taking – in fact empowering the learner' (O'Brien and Garner 2001 p. 3).

While TAs often know little of learning theories, although on courses they can show a great deal of interest in them, they do understand about the individual differences between children. TAs understand that some chil can be well physically, properly cared for, and have every encoura learn, but they do not progress in the way the rest of the children can. They recognise something is different in the way a certain child's brain works when he or she is tackling activities. TAs' descriptions of pupils continually show an insightful sensitivity and understanding into the way the children's minds can work. They set small but appropriate challenges for the children they know well. This can all be seen when observing them at work.

They provide the scaffolding to learning too. The 'penny dropping' moments are not observable every day, but learning is going on internally. 'True learning is active learning, in the sense of direct and active involvement in the substance of one's learning . . . this kind of developmental learning is empowering' (Gipps and MacGilchrist 1999 p. 47). TAs report with pride when they describe the progress their charges make, and do see these jumps of understanding.

Supporting pupils with a physical impairment can mean their participation in mainstream schools, or keeping up with their more physically able peers. Attitudes to learning, self-esteem and motivation powerfully affect the learning process. TAs use many positive verbal and non-verbal signals to encourage and give pupils regular attention and praise, boost self-confidence and self-esteem, increase motivation and reinforce success. They recognise the emotional difficulties of some children that hinder their progress. Farrell *et al.* (1999) suggested that the key to creating independent learning for pupils is for TAs to have flexibility in the way they work, to be clear about when to intervene and when to become a general resource. Lacey (1999 p. 33) spoke of 'just the right amount and type of support for individual pupils'. This flexibility was observed in the case study TAs, in particular, their mobility and multitasking, and their 'thinking on their feet'.

Case study evidence
While they were working so closely with individuals and small groups of children, they saw the need to develop children's independence – getting the child to hang up his coat and deal with his lunch himself, giving children confidence to act on their own, for example to answer the teacher, reinforcing that they should think for themselves. One said: 'I want these children to learn on their own, I'm there to help them learn independently, on their own . . . I have one little boy who said, "I'm special needs" So what!' A perceptive TA comment was: 'The target is to do myself out of a job'.

Good TAs recognise the need to introduce the children to a collaborative way of working. They make sure pupils are part of the whole class by stopping their activity or speech whenever the teacher speaks to the whole class. They largely work with small groups of children, and need to be clear within these when the tasks are for individuals to complete and when the task itself is co-operative, for example in practical science work or a discussion.

Good TAs question and challenge. Galton and Simon (1980 p. 199) described the higher level and higher order of teacher interaction as 'important determinants of pupils' progress'. They provide role models as learners for the children, keen to make the children think about what they are doing and extending their ideas. TAs themselves are learners, often very conscious of their own apparent lack of paper qualifications to prove they could do the job of a TA. The empathy for the role of the learner, and in cases of school-based course work, presentation of themselves as a role model of lifelong learning, may influence both the way they work and the perceptions that the pupils have of them. They can be examples of the fact that learning is not just about school or about being a child.

Supporting the teacher

Despite some dissenting voices, Farrell *et al.* (1999) indicated that TAs can contribute to the teacher's understanding of pupils' needs from their observations. TAs can both transmit information and make sense of it for the groups of children with whom they work. They can support individuals and small groups by being the personal interpreter of the subject matter for the children. If the class teacher relies on class teaching, the TA may be the only opportunity the pupil has to explore meanings. The case study material illustrates the teaching capacity of TAs.

Case study evidence
One teacher, trying to explain the difference between a teacher and a TA, said:

> They are teaching and guiding. I think they have a different relationship with the children. I think the role has changed though over the years and I think the children do see them far more. It's very hard to describe the relationship. It's hard to put your finger on it. It isn't Mum, it isn't friend, it's beyond that, it's different. It's not that. It shouldn't be that because it's a working situation that perhaps they do see them as there for them more, but that's wrong too. Hopefully, they see as teacher, you're there for them too. But, the responsibility is different. The teaching assistant, to the children, appears to have more time because they're working with a smaller group, therefore for them.

And then later, when discussing the possible dependency that such a relationship might engender, she added,

> I think that's where you manage as a class teacher and beyond that as well. Having said that, I think the teaching assistants are taking that on more as they are becoming more skilled and learn more about the process. The role of a teaching assistant has changed a lot too, over the years from being a helper to being involved in the children's education. I think, in the past, they were helping and not taking on responsibility for the children's development as they are now.

The following skills of teaching can be observed when watching a TA at work:

- planning and preparation
- performance
- exposition – giving instructions, directions, explaining, using the correct language (naming things)
- questioning facts, ideas or worth
- challenging, pacing, motivating – increasing amount which could be done; extending ideas, encouraging thinking or imagination, using appropriate praise (verbal or smiles)
- intervention and non-intervention – promoting active learning
- working with groups or individuals or a whole class
- supporting practical work
- resource management – organising and suggesting methods in and out of lessons
- multitasking
- supporting practical work
- assessment activities – observing, feedback and reporting.

These skills can be recognised and developed by the school and are so important that Chapter 7 includes a more detailed description of developing and managing this aspect of the role. Good TAs come out well when compared with the criteria from texts on teaching skills. Some Ofsted inspectors have done observations of the quality of teaching of TAs and found it similar, if not better than that of some teachers on occasions. It is the role that has been recognised by government as capable of being used to support teachers' workload in a new high level role (DfES 2002a, 2002b). The crucial adjunct to all this observed teaching activity is that it is always done under the supervision of a teacher (DfES 2002c). It is also the area which some teachers find threatening. One of the objections which the unions had early on was the possible usurpation of the teacher's role by unqualified staff. Managers may have to deal with such concerns as they recognise the potential of their TAs.

The TAs' close and frequent contact with small groups of children, allied often with their being able to follow these children from class to class as they get older, gives them a perception as to their competence and a knowledge of what they had already done. TAs assist the children to develop skills using demonstration and verbal instruction. Where TAs themselves have skills, for instance in a craft area, they understand the expertise which would be required in the future and are able to present appropriate steps to the pupils. Ofsted found that 'teachers value highly the support provided by teaching assistants and the benefits of having another skilled adult in the classroom' (Ofsted 2002a p. 4). They also quoted Ofsted Section 10 reports where it had been found that the quality of teaching in lessons with TAs is better than without them.

The National Advisory Committee on Creative and Cultural Education report called *All our Futures* (NACCCE 2000) discusses the characteristics of teachers who can develop creativity. TAs, using active listening strategies, certainly encourage

- autonomy on both sides; a feeling of ownership and control over the ideas that were being offered
- authenticity in initiatives and responses, deciding for oneself on the basis of one's own judgement
- openness to new and unusual ideas, and to a variety of methods and approaches
- respect for each other and the feelings that emerge
- fulfilment: from each a feeling of anticipation, satisfaction, involvement and enjoyment of the creative relationship.

(NACCCE, 2000, p. 91)

Children need to learn to think, become independent learners and understand their own learning styles. 'The job of the school is to motivate the learner; to encourage her or him to want to learn; to help the learner understand how to learn; and to believe that it is possible to do so . . . This will also be dependent on the way she is being taught' (MacGilchrist *et al.* 1997 p. 36).

Supporting the curriculum

The DfE report (Mortimore *et al.* 1992) examined the different roles of various categories of staff and the boundaries between them, by looking at twenty-five case studies of innovative practice, and aimed to identify the benefits of making more use of support staff. They were still seen as non-people (the 'non-teaching staff' part of the title of the report) although one

of the recommendations of the report was the need for more positive nomenclature, suggesting associate staff. The report found it relatively easy to identify the purposes of jobs and benefits, but not so easy to collect information
on cost-effectiveness. The analysis in terms of educational value was much
less clear cut. When writing a book based on the report, the authors said:

> These assessments of the benefits of the innovation would appear to pass
> a curriculum 'test', in the sense that the change is having an impact upon
> the activity in the classroom. As with so many decisions in schools, the
> assessment of its benefit for learning involves informed judgements and
> cannot be reduced to an objective calculation.
>
> (Mortimore *et al.* 1994 p. 24)

The study raised questions about the impact that TAs have on learning and
curriculum as well as child support. The report suggested:

> Their enhanced role could actually be more challenging, with greater
> professional and pedagogical (rather than administrative) commitments.
> It may not be to everybody's liking – but it may lead to more effective
> schooling and more efficient use of resources.
>
> (Mortimore *et al.* 1992 p. 178)

In the late 1990s, the introduction of the National Literacy and Numeracy
Strategies (NLNS) had a further profound effect upon the use of TAs in
primary schools. They had supported teachers and pupils, but now with
the insistence of the strategies on group work they became an essential component of classroom organisation to support the curriculum. A survey I
undertook in the summer of 1998 showed up the increasing use of TAs to
support the curriculum (Watkinson 1999a).

Survey evidence
The 635 responding TAs gave very rich descriptions of the work they
did. The emphasis was clearly away from the care aspects of TA work
and domestic support or resource management to curriculum support –
particularly in literacy and numeracy. It was clear that literacy and
numeracy were predominant and although the NLNS had not actually
started at that time, schools were beginning their training.

I visited many schools during 1998 and 1999. Most schools rearranged their
TA provision to cover literacy and numeracy lessons. TAs were much more
included in in-house training and government funded initiatives such as the
Additional Literacy Support (ALS), which resulted in mass training sessions

by LEAs for TAs accompanied by a teacher. The partnership of the two was being seen at last as an essential component of the provision for children.

Learning also has a social context; no one is totally isolated from another human being. Much of what has been described as schooling's hidden curriculum, for instance, consists of what children learn by their social relationships, rather than as a result of what they are formally taught. TAs are often seen in schools contributing in informal times. As well as the social aspect, they can support the English curriculum when talking with children in cloakrooms or the playground, mathematics when assisting changing – matching, pairing, counting, science in the school grounds, the humanities on school trips, or more generally they can contribute to the pupil's self-esteem through their behaviour management strategies. Ofsted indicated that TAs 'make a significant contribution to the quality and breadth of the curriculum' in the successful primary schools they investigated (Ofsted 2002b p. 26).

Survey evidence
A rather long quote from one TA sums up the picture:

> Educational Support staff are an intrinsic part of a school. They are an effective way of giving extra support to both teachers and children. A teaching assistant can ensure that all children, not just those with special needs, get help and encouragement. Teaching assistants learn continually from their work, and I feel that many schools do not use their TAs to their full advantage. Just because they may not have a recognised qualification does not mean that they are unable to aid children in all areas of the curriculum. Many schools call their support staff non-teaching assistants; however from my experience we are a vital part of the child's learning. In my school, the TAs take a spelling and mental maths group from the year the same as the teachers; this makes the groups smaller and therefore more effective. We take small groups who need extra help for a given task as well as working within the classroom to aid all children, which gives the teacher more time to spend with each child. We take our share of playground duties and enforcing the school's policies, as well as taking after school clubs and many other areas of the school's life. A TA needs to be made to feel as important a part of the teaching staff as the teachers are.

The person of the TA

TAs cannot just be defined by the job they are employed for or the one they end up doing. Their presence as people, not just a resource, must be recognised. There are certain characteristics of TAs which managers must take into account when considering their function.

Personality

In early reports, the TA had been described rather as another piece of equipment in the school. The TA as a person with desires, experiences, capacities or competencies which could be tapped or developed was largely ignored. Certain things stand out time and time again when good TAs are watched at work, such as:

- Intrapersonal traits and attributes
    - sensitivity and timing
    - concentration/commitment to task, perseverance
    - professionalism balanced with respect for teaching profession
    - confidence in action balanced with a lack of self-esteem about competence
    - humour, enthusiasm, interest and love of job (Figure 2.1)
    - enjoyment of company of pupils
    - high standards/expectations of self and others
    - using initiative/responsibility within the structure of the class
- Interpersonal skills
    - relationships with the children and adults
    - showing knowledge and understanding of children's needs,
    - sharing and co-operating with other adults
    - empathy and sympathy with pupils and adults
    - friendliness, bonding, ability to listen
    - respect for other adults and children
    - supporting self-confidence and self-esteem in pupils
    - being constructively critical of self and others
    - communication with the teacher, including checking and marking work
    - role-modelling learning strategies
- Physical activity
    - constant mobility and multitasking
    - physical contact – just being alongside the children and appropriate comforting and closeness to children in need of security
    - control or behaviour management through non-verbal gestures.

Figure 2.1 Outward-going TA personalities

Comments made in TA course evaluations reflected the enthusiasm that the TAs develop. 'I hadn't been told working with children is addictive . . . seeing the children develop and flourish . . . you can see the excitement in them when they achieve . . . it is something great to witness'. 'It is the best of both worlds: work with children without ultimate responsibility'. 'Most of the preparation work I had to do for this child was done outside school in my spare time. I found there was never enough hours in the day for me to be able to do this at work'. Colleague advisers often used to comment on the joys of taking courses for TAs: 'the light is still on in their eyes'. Reading the *Untold Stories* of TAs (O'Brien and Garner 2001) can give a fuller flavour.

Case study evidence
The TAs I interviewed were modest and tend to dismiss their capabilities, yet they told of initiatives with pride. One described making a book of photos to show an autistic boy his new classroom before the end of the summer term, for him to refer to during the summer break; another to doing things for a specific child, making sure where she was; a third to a child's toileting needs. They knew when to sit with a child apart and when to integrate them with a group and how to deal with

tantrums, because they recognised frustration. A typical comment was: 'I do the best for him on that score'. They shared ideas, they talked to each other, and spent time looking through resources. They made resources. They were aware of being a role model for children, even to how they used their own body language. They mentioned the use of gestures for control, and developing them, using simple language, for example, reducing the number of words in a sentence, and using signs, such as having a red line on the playground for control. They had a great sense of personal achievement with individual children, and loved the work. One mentioned wanting to give something back as her own children had had problems.

They referred to deciding 'off the top of my head' or 'whatever off my own back'. One started her interview with the comment about her job: 'A lot of it is really thinking on my feet' and another summed it up at the end of her interview with 'using my own common [sense] if you like'. One TA, who had had a lot of experience, and high level training, recognised that some of what she did was instinctive. The discussion, with one of the teachers present, had been about challenging and questioning children. The TA said: 'I know it sounds big-headed, but I'm just myself and that's what I do normally. It's not something I've learnt to do'.

Farrell *et al.* (1999) saw personal qualities as a better criterion for employment than qualifications, a point that you may consider when interviewing for TA posts. Also, these outward-going characteristics must be considered by teachers. One teacher can appreciate a TA's initiative, but another can feel threatened or resentful. Boundaries need to be established both by the school and individual teachers – an issue discussed in Chapter 7.

Skills

Observing TAs will reveal that they have clearly developed certain skills of behaviour management, task completion or actual teaching skills, but as can be seen in the previous case study evidence, they are often very reticent about them.

Case study evidence
In interviews, TAs mentioned things like the development of handwriting by actually guiding the children and one talked about the way she had developed skills with her teacher to 'pre-empt the subjects'. 'She lets me

know [what they are doing so that I can] pre-empt a subject that after-noon or the next week so that they know what they are talking about and have the confidence to know about things and put their hands up'. The use of observation skills was greatly appreciated by the teachers, and one TA had developed the use of sheets to assist in this. Planning and using tools such as a trundle wheel were skills mentioned by teachers.

Talking to the TAs themselves of the teaching skills I had seen actu-ally caused a problem. One TA, who reckoned she was quite confident, when I spoke of her good 'teaching', got quite disturbed. She thought I was saying that she was presuming to take the role of the class teacher. It took several minutes to reassure her that teaching skills and being a qualified teacher were different things. She insisted that she was 'very aware of my role in the class', meaning she knew her place.

These skills and personality are not a reflection of the rationale for employing TAs. The case study schools observed closely to provide much of the evidence for this book, employed TAs ostensibly for different reasons, one to support SEN pupils and the other to support the NLNS. The ways the TAs worked and their characteristics were strikingly similar, a point borne out by other writers. Weddell describes the two forms of help that he saw – 'firstly, designed to enable children to take part in the normal curricular activity in the classroom ... to bypass their particular learning difficulties as far as possible [and] secondly, help is aimed at supporting children to overcome particular difficulties. Clearly there is no hard and fast separation between these two forms of support' (Weddell 2001 p. 90).

Knowledge and understanding

The TAs I studied knew the children that they worked with well, their capabil-ities, whether the children had 'switched off', and how far they could go for instance in managing behaviour. They talked of the children's progress very professionally, particularly in spelling and handwriting and where they had been closely involved in developing targets and reviewing IEPs. Their under-standing of curriculum matters had grown, which was enabling them to undertake the differentiation and 'pre-empting'. Their comments confirm their understanding.

Case study evidence

In literacy, letter formation, sequencing, the language itself were all mentioned and in mathematics, patterns and number bonds. TAs said things like: 'He can read quite well, he's past that stage and he's into written instructions'. 'I know what he needs to work on. I go back and look – he may need to work on vowels – he doesn't know what a vowel is – but I think he needs to work on a "g".'

'Knowing what we are doing and where it affects her group' was the important thing to the teachers; 'she'll fine tune it', one said. The teacher summed up her interview by saying: 'I tease her sometimes, I say "I'm not coming in tomorrow – you can do it" and she would. She knows exactly how everything works.' This summed up their understanding of the need for integration of the curriculum and the needs of the children.

The National Numeracy Strategy (NNS) indicated strategies which imply a level of understanding and skill of TAs often previously ignored, while clearly indicating the continuing responsibility of the teacher. It said

Ask the assistant to:

- ensure that children interpret instructions correctly, concentrate and behave responsibly;
- remind children of teaching points made earlier in the lesson;
- question children and encourage their participation (you will need to suggest the questions and prompts that would be appropriate, and any particular children whom they should focus on);
- look for and note any common difficulties that children have, or mistakes that they make, so that you can address these in plenary and future lessons;
- use and make available to children a number line and/or 100 square, visual or practical aids or a computer with suitable software, especially when they are helping children with difficulties or misunderstandings;
- include assistants and adult helpers in whole-school training days.

(DfEE 1999a p 25)

Competence

In trying to unravel the complexity of the TA role observed, and the personality and effectiveness of the person doing the job, the concept of competence is useful. The concept of competence in employment assessment terminology is relatively new and has come in with the formal introduction of National Vocational Qualifications (NVQs). The idea is that people can show in the workplace that of which they are capable, be assessed there, certificated, and recognised for it in terms of career structure and pay. National Occupational Standards (NOS) are drawn up by the national training organisation (NTO) with expertise and interest in the particular occupation under scrutiny. The NOS are then used by the Qualifications and Curriculum Authority (QCA) to regulate any awards in the occupational area including NVQs, and can be used in personnel discussions with employers and unions. For TAs, the NTO was the Local Government NTO (LGNTO), whose website www.lgnto.gov.uk lists the NOS for TAs.

NOS, and subsequently any approved NVQs, are organised in levels to correspond with traditional levels of qualifications. The NOS are based on the recognition of qualification levels proposed by the old National Council for Vocational Qualifications now subsumed into QCA. Level 1 covers qualifications for those doing repetitive tasks (rarely found in education), level 2 is considered to be General Certificate of Secondary Education (GCSE) or the old Ordinary (O) level, level 3 Advanced (A) level, level 4 indicates undergraduate levels of study, and level 5 is postgraduate. There is more about the NVQ developments for TAs in Chapter 8.

It is not possible to use a tick sheet of competencies, even in a tabular form, for observation purposes as TAs do not show everything they are capable of in half-an-hour. The NOS for TAs cover only levels 2 and 3 and use 42 and 111 pages respectively to describe them. As level 2 shows a comprehensive coverage of what a competent TA can do, it is obvious that beginner TAs will not have achieved this level. Also, although there is as yet no level 4 NOS, TAs are also operating at a managerial level in many schools and the government have recently brought in the idea of a higher level TA category (DfES 2002a, 2002b). Table 2.1 shows a possible summary of competencies, including qualified teacher status (QTS) as a level beyond that of a level 4 TA. People operating with less than the indicated 'beginner' range should not be employed to work with pupils.

National recognition

In the mid-1990s, the first public recognition of the role came with John Patten, the then Education Secretary, announcing the provision of government money to train specialist teacher assistants (STAs) in supporting teachers with basic skills teaching at KS1. It caused an outcry as some thought that it could be a way of getting teachers on the cheap, and the phrase 'mums' army' was coined. HMI reported on the first years of the STA training. In their pamphlet *Training Specialist Teacher Assistants* (Ofsted 1997) which has guidance on recruitment, mentoring deployment and assessment to competence, they conclude: 'The support for teaching and learning given by trained STAs is helping teachers to give the children in school improved learning experiences and to raise standards' (p. 10).

Table 2.1 Possible levels of expectations and competencies for TAs (from Watkinson 2003)

Level	Competencies expected (supporting the teacher(s) and personal development)	Experiences typical in school (supporting the school)	Knowledge and understanding (supporting the pupil and the curriculum, teaching and learning)	Possible title	Pay scale
1	Carry out instructions; show common sense; follow school policies; relate appropriately to pupils and adults	Domestic chores; basic child care; in class: follow and repeat instructions of teacher	Understand how the school community works and how to be part of a team; take responsibility for own actions; use equipment safely	Welfare or care assistant	Entry levels on single status scale
2	Able to work under the direction of teacher with selected children; assist in classroom task set by teacher; take charge of their own professional development	Facilitate curriculum delivery; carry out practical tasks; work and interact with groups, in sight of teacher; aware of resource provision; see individuals are different; facilitate independence	Has a framework of understanding of learning theory and child development; needs intended learning objectives with activities; support pupils with SEN and facilitate their learning; attend IEP reviews; carry out NLNS responsibilities after training	Competent teaching assistant	?
3	Able to use initiative appropriately in tasks, especially in private nursery situations, but not take responsibility for children's learning in school; evaluate routines, provide welfare, guidance and support to children	Under direction of teacher: devise resources and activities to support learning; take groups outside classroom; participate in planning and assessment; provide reports and records; perform teaching activities; understand education system and code of practice	To have an awareness of parts of the NC e.g. literacy and numeracy, or early learning goals; know about physical, emotional, intellectual, spiritual, cultural development; support children with particular needs and develop expertise; contribute to IEP reviews; relate to parents	Advanced or specialist teaching assistant	?
4	Work in partnership with teachers; share in planning and assessment; contribute to decision making; training and management responsibilities; teaching skills of: exposition, questioning, challenge and behaviour management; working with parents and carers	Can take responsibility, under direction of teacher, for a particular aspect of curriculum development, resource management, or equipment maintenance; able to lead a team of other TAs/adults; take a class using planning directed by teacher and reporting back to teacher; specialist skills e.g. languages, music, ICT or science technology, phase specialism or SEN area	Able to undertake study with reflection and assignments; understand some of the requirements of the NC; know about learning objectives and aspects of NC; have some understanding of teaching and learning theory; understanding of principles of pedagogy, child development and behaviour management; able to contribute to the formulation of IEPs	Lead or principal teaching assistant	?
QTS	Undertake responsibility for teaching and learning of pupils; manage additional adults etc.		Teacher requirements	Qualified teacher	Teachers' pay scales

Source: Watkinson 2003 pp. 136–137

Her Majesty's Chief Inspector (HMCI) reported on the work of TAs seen on inspection:

> The use of non-teaching support staff is increasing in both primary and secondary schools . . . In addition to providing practical help with the organisation of teaching materials and equipment, assistants can, when trained and working under the supervision of teachers, make a direct contribution to developing pupils' knowledge, understanding and skills.
>
> (HMCI 1996 p. 51)

After the general election of 1997, a Green Paper (DfEE 1998a) proposed that teachers should have some support in order to cope with the increasing demands on their expertise, and to provide additional entry routes to a profession with a recruitment crisis. This resulted in a fivefold set of initiatives underwritten by £330 million over 1999–2002 and promised funding continued until 2004. Overall £750 million is to be spent on TAs between 1999 and 2004. It has meant:

- money through the Standards Fund for recruitment
- the Standards Fund allocations to include an element for induction training, materials for which were written centrally and delivered by LEAs
- the publication of guidance for management of TAs
- a career progression ladder to be underpinned by NOS
- pathways to teaching to be eased by increased emphasis on workplace-based routes. All of these are now in place and will be referred to in relevant places in this book.

The induction training was, and in some cases still is, being delivered by LEAs in England. This does not carry an award, unless one is given locally, but its content has been matched against the new national standards. Any work done by TAs for this course can be used in assessment processes for any TA NVQ being organised in a locality. It covers some of the aspects needed for a level 2 qualification. The mapping can be found on www.teachernet.gov.uk/teachingassistants, as can copies of all the induction training materials for both primary and secondary levels.

The recent proposals indicating a further development of standards and training for the higher level TA roles also promise funding for such a programme, continuation of career progression frameworks and the development of routes to teaching (DfES 2002a).

Qualifications

The demand for training following the success of the STA award led to the development of over 200 other qualifications, some local and some under-

pinned by the national awarding bodies. This has made it difficult to understand what a TA is capable of from their qualification background. In a
national survey in 2000, only 50.8 per cent of staff were found to have five or
more GCSE/O levels and only 14.0 per cent had two or more A levels.
However, there was also a wide range of vocational qualifications and over
twice as many were interested in studying for a qualification (LGNTO *et al.*
2000 p. 12).

As well as the general educational qualifications, many local authorities,
colleges and universities have instituted their own courses, certificates and
awards. As these are so diverse, in order to take them into account, it is
necessary to enquire what TAs actually did and learnt on the course and what
use they have put it to. Even where the course had a recognised NVQ equivalent level, the lack of quality control and assurance on a national scale
through external verification was haphazard and meant a considerable variation in standard. Most courses had some kind of end-product in paper
terms, and TAs may well have retained their assignments or portfolio, which
could be looked at. The picture should now be much clearer, as from
September 2002 the new awards all had to be approved by QCA and matched
against the NOS. More information can be gained from the Employers'
Organisation (EO 2002) document *Qualifications for Teaching Assistants*
which lists most of the major accredited and non-accredited qualifications
up to September 2002. This is also available on the DfES website
www.teachernet.gov.uk/teachingassistants.

Experience

Because of the haphazard state regarding qualifications, managers do need to
consider other relevant experience.

Survey evidence
Essex survey respondents in 1998 described the following experiences.
Some respondents mentioned more than one category, so these figures
are not mutually exclusive.

- 94 per cent had experience as parents with 27 per cent currently still
  having children at school
- 86 per cent had voluntary work experience often with children or
  young people
- 19 per cent had had paid child care experience
- 4 per cent had worked in a medical field
- 12 per cent had had other paid work before becoming a TA.

(Watkinson 1999a)

Given that only 1 per cent of the total number of respondents in Essex and nationally (LGNTO *et al.* 2000) were male and the age distribution showed a high proportion of mature women, experience can be a significant indicator of ability to do the job.

The role of management

The flexibility of local management of schools

A major influence on the development of TAs was a result of the Education Reform Act 1988. This brought about not only inspection and the NC but also local management of schools (LMS). This gave schools the opportunity to be creative with their staffing through having greater financial independence, and a growing emphasis on cost-effectiveness raised the profile of support staff.

The importance of the involvement of the school management has become clearer since the early 1990s. HMCI stated:

> In most cases non-teaching staff are effectively deployed and have a positive impact on the work, especially in classes with younger children. Where Specialist Teacher Assistants have been properly trained and suitably deployed they contribute significantly to raising standards in numeracy and literacy.
>
> (HMCI 1998 p. 28)

> In such circumstances, assistants save teachers' time and enable more flexible use to be made of trained staff within the classroom.
>
> (HMCI 1998 p. 64)

> They [LSAs] make a valuable contribution in all subjects by supporting individual pupils and by working with groups. They are successful when they are involved with planning pupils' work, and the most successful LSAs contribute to assessment and recording.
>
> (HMCI 1998 p. 50)

Moyles and Suschitzky (1998 p. 53) suggested that teachers 'require training in how to manage teams of support staff'. Lorenz (1998) and Balshaw (1991, 1999) emphasised the role of the school as well as the teacher in the support of the TA, providing materials to help schools. Lorenz pointed out that not only do newly qualified teachers need help in managing additional adults as a core skill but also 'it is vital that a similar programme of training be put in place for experienced staff, if schools are to be progressively more inclusive' (Lorenz 1998 p. 93). Blatchford and colleagues commented that 'Some staff and adults were effectively used by teachers and some were not' (Blatchford *et al.* 2002 p. 6).

The need for appropriate employment procedures in a school was there, even prior to LMS. Extra staff meant basic recruitment, induction and contractual obligations. Allocating a TA to a teacher is a management decision, as well as the placing of a child with SEN in a class where an assistant is allocated. The single status agreements being drawn up between LEAs and the support staff unions have meant that schools have had to look increasingly at the budget implications of defining the jobs that their TAs do more closely. Some schools are now considering performance related pay for TAs in line with the teaching staff. Governors have become increasingly interested with the work of TAs as their profile is raised nationally. The proposals (DfES 2002c) define what is specified teaching work and the way in which TAs will have to be supervised. These are likely to become effective from late 2003.

The picture is one of an increasing number of TAs with increasing visibility. But they still have these diverse, complex and ill-defined roles allied to a trend for them to be much less involved in care and domestic tasks and much more involved with pupils and the teaching and learning processes, across all key stages. The issues are still there for schools, of professional boundaries, supervision and management, with the need for more explicit expectations and rationale for employment. Effective resources for teaching and learning include all human resources as well as material ones. Cost-effectiveness and differential responsibilities become higher profile and thus the importance of having whole school structures and systems as well as the need for national recognition, training and policies.

It is essential for each school not only to investigate their own TA team, its characteristics and capacity, but also to match these to the needs of the school. However, there may also be a need to look at the school's management strategies, for TAs can only be as effective as their management allows. Chapter 3 looks at ways of auditing the provision of TAs and ensuring that both the TAs and their support maximises their potential for effectiveness in fulfilling the school's aims.

The local circumstances

Auditing the existing situation in a school

> One of the most striking features of the work of classroom assistants is how little attention has been paid to it by researchers, practitioners and policy makers ... Even the label 'classroom assistant' is by no means universal ... This is due in part to their historical invisibility.
>
> (Swann and Loxley 1997 p. 2)

This chapter offers various strategies for auditing and observing TA practice in the school. It includes the importance of involving TAs themselves in any process to examine their work and the kinds of protocols involved. The possibilities of looking at hard and soft outcomes from their work are described. While poor practice is generally rare, its presence is recognised.

Looking at your own situation

The national picture is so diffuse and complicated that it means that no one can take for granted that employing TAs is a good thing, effective, value for money and that there is consistent good practice throughout the school. As there must be very few schools, if any, who are not already employing TAs, the place to start is with what is already happening in your school. Managers should know:

(a) how many TAs there are, how long they work for, and where
(b) what they were employed for in the first place
(c) what they are called and why
(d) what they are being used for currently
(e) what hours and weeks they work
(f) what they are paid and why
(g) what kind of contracts they have

But managers should also find out:

(h) what they are being valued for
(i)   what qualifications, experience and skills they have
(j)   whether they are the best people for the job to be done
(k) how things could be improved.

Because of the confusion over the way in which they have been employed historically, (b) and (d) are likely to be different. A TA first employed to support a named pupil may well have become the information and communication technology (ICT) expert or excellent at mounting displays, while the one employed as a technician may be proving to have good rapport with pupils in the laboratory. While it is tempting to try to resort to numerical data outcomes to evaluate the work of TAs, the reality will be much harder to evaluate. TAs are believed to make a difference to pupils' test outcomes but they are also valued for the soft outcomes of their work, their ability to provide the extra pair of hands, the personal contribution they make to life in school, the raising of pupils' self-esteem and confidence. A collection of these possibilities within the audit procedure will help the subsequent monitoring process. This means attempting some kind of review or audit.

Audits

Simple audits

Audit materials can be found in various locations. The Funding Agency for Schools (FAS 1999) produced a booklet on making effective use of support staff which also contained some simple audit materials as well as strategies for planning change, maintaining good communications and managing support staff from recruitment, training and development to evaluation. One page merely provided a register of the kind of information outlined above. It had names, salaries, number of weeks worked per term, number of hours worked per week, location and job responsibility or task. In practice, each TA may have several contracts and is very likely to work in several different places in a day. This basic information in itself is often revealing about the mixed patterns which exist in the school, and immediately prompts questions about effective deployment.

The second page consists of a sheet to be completed by each TA:

> **Name; Job title; Location**
> Detail tasks in brief.
> Does the job description cover the tasks undertaken?
> Who is the main line manager and how regularly is there contact?
> Do other staff regularly share functions with or do work for the postholder, if so which posts?

Do you consider any tasks which are currently undertaken are no longer necessary?
Qualifications held by postholder and any training undertaken.
Skills of postholder which are not currently being used.
Are there any training needs for the current job?
Location of current job, is access to equipment, co-workers and line manager adequate?
Any suggestions for improvements to current work?

(FAS 1999 p. 52)

These can be augmented this with other questions:

How much does your school rely on the goodwill of the TAs to enable the communication to take place between them and the teachers? Is this right?
Do all the teachers know what the TAs do in other classrooms than their own?
Do the TAs meet together? With each other? With teachers with special responsibilities in whose area they might be working? With senior staff?
Do your TAs have a job description?
Have you a shared ethos?
Are all staff consulted when formulating the school's development plan? Are all views valued even if the decisions are opposing?
Do all staff know all the relevant policies? Is there a staff handbook for all staff?
Does your staff development strategy include support staff?
Who attends which meetings? Why?
Do you utilise the training budget in your school for the best development of all the adults in your school?
Have you thought of a mentoring system for all your staff?
How do you know what the adults in your school feel about themselves in relation to your school?
Is your whole school a learning environment?
Do you know the professional development needs of all the staff?
Does the school employment and pay policy reflect the needs of the school and the qualities of all the staff?
What determines the number and hours worked by the TAs in the school?
Do you know what training opportunities, resources and accreditation routes are available in your area?
Do you know what other schools in your area are doing?
Do you know what funding may be available for adult learners?

(Watkinson 1998a p. 3; 1998b p. 4)

TAs as part of whole school reviews

These questions are not so simply answered and move managers into less definable but important areas such as communication, consultation and climate. These areas will be dealt with more fully in later chapters; most need to be considered in relation to whole school development and policies.

One way of considering TA provision is to look at their needs alongside all the other priorities of the school. Booth *et al.* (2000) have produced audit materials for looking at inclusive practice within the school through the school development plan (SDP), which includes some sheets for looking at support staff. Readers may consider that this is a helpful way to tackle the deeper questions relating to TAs.

Another whole school route to consider is that of Investors in People (IiP). Rose, a former HMI still closely in contact with Ofsted, also responsible for leading the team developing materials for the DfEE and DfES with regard to TAs, says 'there is a strong association emerging between schools with IiP status doing better in managing TAs than those without IiP (Ofsted data) – obvious but interesting' (personal communication 22 June 2002). IiP helps a school to become more effective by establishing and linking key organisational features in this way:

> 'Everyone working with a clear sense of purpose
> managed through
> school development plans focussed on raising pupil performance
> guiding
> regular staff development planning for individuals and teams
> leading to
> targeted and supported staff training and development activities
> informed by
> evaluation of the benefits for staff and pupils feeding back into school
> development planning.
>
> (DfEE 1997b p. 5)

This document then considers areas like vision, commitment, communication and school development plans relating them to a development process for *all* staff.

The whole school route available to all schools is using the school development plan review. Strategies for using this opportunity to tackle TA issues is further detailed in Chapter 4.

Mounting a TA investigation

For the TA project leaders, the most comprehensive and trialled materials can be found in part 3 of the *Good Practice Guide* (DfEE 2000a). This booklet is available free to all schools, and all managers should send for a copy of this. The audits it contains should help managers to query their existing practice, in order to identify the next moves. The very asking of the questions may well alert staff as to their needs and possible directions for development.

Whatever kind of investigation is instigated in the school it is vital that that its purpose should be clear and the processes transparent. All relevant people who might be observed, contacted or affected should be told and preferably involved in the style, timing and conduct of the operation. Unless this is handled carefully, support staff will immediately consider that their jobs are at risk, and teachers will think either that they are going to lose their help or that their own practice is being criticised.

There are eight lists of questions covering six indicators of good practice in the guide. Each page is set out with a four-point scale for each question asked. There is space on the page for comments. These pages can be photocopied and used as a questionnaire, retrieved and collated. The audit contents are as follows:

1: Schools should have clear policies outlining the roles and responsibilities of TAs.

2.1: Managers' and teachers' management strategies provide clear guidance as to how TAs should work in their classrooms.

2.2: The expertise, skills and knowledge of TAs is used flexibly to foster the learning of pupils.

3.1: TAs work co-operatively with teachers to support the learning and participation of pupils.

3.2: Teachers and TAs learn together to improve the quality of their work.

4: TAs develop effective working partnerships with people involved in education.

5: TAs meet with others for the purposes of planning problem solving and staff development.

6: TAs are supported in relation to their induction, mentoring and development needs.

I suggest that managers choose only a limited number of indicators in the first instance, rather than trying to look at the whole field of TA practice. Managers need first to decide:

• Which member of staff should lead this audit review?
• Which staff members could constitute a task group to take it forward (ensuring that TAs themselves and at least one senior manager is part of the group)?
• When should the governors be informed and could/should one be involved in the process?

- Is there anyone else who should be informed of our intentions: pupils, other staff, parents, advisers?
- What budget can we commit to the review?
- What time in the year would it be best to proceed?
- Is this to be part of a larger review of school practice?
- Does this fit in with any other project coming up in the next year?
- What kind of audit would fit our perception of the current circumstances?
- What are the priorities of the school? Where should the school focus?
- What will happen to any report or recommended action produced by the task group?

The task group then needs to:

- Prepare a costed action plan and submit it to any relevant school authority for approval
- Inform all staff of the existence of such a plan.

Then consider:

- Who needs to be involved?
- Which bits of which audit framework are to be used, in what order?
- What paperwork needs to be prepared?
- What meetings need to be convened? Where will they be and what records should be kept?
- What will be done with any data obtained? Who can have access to it?
- What data can be trawled from existing data banks?
- Will interviews or observations be undertaken?
- What protocols will need to be set up?
- How will any report be made?
- How will any action be taken as a result of any conclusions reached?
- Who is to do what by when?
- Are there any required outcomes which must be addressed as a priority?

It is then up to the individuals named to prepare materials, inform, collect data, collate information and report back as agreed.

Balshaw and Farrell (2002) highlight some key issues:

For the assistants:

- effective examination of role through a focus on job descriptions, flexible deployment and management practices in respect to these;
- staff development opportunities and induction processes.

The key issues for management were:

- senior teaching staff and school leaders developing awareness of the issues identified within the indicators of effective practice;
- an appreciation of the need to change management practices;
- resulting developments in both policy and practice.

In addition important factors within the action research were:

- a senior member of staff strategically fulfilling a leadership and advocacy role;
- this role kept the 'voice' of the action researchers on agendas for staff meetings and in discussions with key groups of people such as senior managers or governors;
- self-advocacy generated by both the lead researcher assistants and the whole teams of assistants.

(Balshaw and Farrell 2002 p. 98)

The authors also describe the need to place TAs

firmly at the forefront of staff and practice development and school improvement. The lead that assistants took at the national dissemination conferences was impressive, their appreciative audiences applauding them and their presentations, their confidence and their work. Listeners were impressed with the accounts of the development of confidence and self-esteem that came from their involvement in action research. The assistants are rightly proud of these achievements.

(Balshaw and Farrell 2002 p. 98)

Clearly, while this could be seen as a time-consuming process in an already overloaded timetable for senior managers, the very act of delegating the TA review to the TAs themselves, with the manager taking the lead role, is itself a further step towards recognition of that role.

Looking at practice

While it is possible to audit school processes with questionnaires, the actuality of what is going on in the classroom can be different from what is reported; TAs also need to be observed at work. Managers may decide to leave this process until appraisal procedures for support staff are set up within the school. The improvement in learning outcomes seen in the way pupils are operating with TAs, rather than what can be achieved by pupils in the next test, should be an important indicator of the TAs' effectiveness.

Observation procedures

If TAs are to be observed, then a proper procedure should be followed. Any observation procedure needs protocols to ensure there are no misunderstandings as to purpose, that the methods are open and clear, the results are confidential between observer and observed and that there is proper feedback. The needs of the pupils should come first, to reduce intrusion. Extra adults observing are a common occurrence in schools, and are usually largely ignored, but they have to be considered. No one can be a fly on the wall in a busy classroom: behaviour changes as a result of the presence of a stranger or being watched. All staff need to feel they have a way of dealing with concern they might have over the observer's comments or behaviour. The observer must be prepared to leave the observation to another occasion if circumstances within the classroom are not settled – they are not Ofsted observations! Equally, there must be an understanding about what happens if the observer sees something that contravenes school policy. It is important to have written protocols such as the following.

> **Purpose**: to try to find out how specific TAs actually work with children
> **Intended outcome**: a synopsis of the variety of roles seen for general circulation among TAs and teachers
> Plus individual feedback session for each TA

Protocols to be observed could be:

- Either side should make comment at any time in the process if there is any discomfort or suggestion about what is taking place or being said.
- Openness, honesty and integrity will help, as sometimes what is left unsaid can indicate issues.
- The main audience of any summary written material will be the relevant TAs and teaching staff.
- It may be that this process might show up matters within the school which need wider dissemination (say to governors), then all participants should agree to the format to be circulated.
- Anything written for this purpose will be shared first with the staff involved so that comments could be made and points of accuracy checked.
- All names are to be changed in the final report to preserve confidentiality.
- Photocopies of all that is written down about any member of staff in observing or talking to them – scribbled notes or observation sheets shall be given to the member of staff concerned. The originals will be kept by the observer securely until the end of the process and then destroyed.
- Individual comments would be anonymised, or amalgamated with others to preserve confidentiality.

- The observation material will be fed back to individuals, who would not be able to change what was seen but could add comments.
- If others are involved, then they would be covered by the same sort of protocols.
- Permission of the parents of any children known to be closely involved will be sought by the school.
- The taking of video and photographs needs separate negotiation.

Observation schedules can be used with or without video recording. I found that recording changes or differences in behaviour, to ascertain the range of what was taking place, was more productive than working to a strict time observation schedule, although some people may find it preferable to do this. I found that the TAs worked so idiosyncratically, responding to the needs of the particular children, I needed to catch the interactions as they occurred. The observation sheets in Figures 3.1 and 3.2 can be used for observing. They are also reproduced in the TA file of the induction materials (DfEE 2000b; DfES 2001a). The intention is to watch the TAs in action for half-an-hour to an hour while doing their normal activities, particularly when working with children.

Narrative:

Date and time:

Context

Teacher's name

TA's name

Room

In classroom or not

Lesson focus

What went on before

Introduction of me to class

Other adults

Children's activities and learning objectives if known

Figure 3.1 Cover sheet used for an observation schedule

Time	TA's activity	Children	Teacher	Comment

Figure 3.2 Observation schedule for watching TAs in the classroom

Interview procedures

In order to really find out what is going on during the time that the TAs are observed, the observer will need to talk to the TAs, the teachers and if possible the pupils. Similar protocols need to be established with them to ensure the purpose and outcomes of the process, which can be part of the feedback established for the observations. By doing such in-depth work it is possible to see how the school context is affecting the way the classroom dynamics operate as well as getting a greater understanding of the issues for the participants. Half-an-hour would give both an opportunity to say what was needed. A quiet place to talk is obviously preferable. The date and names of the interview participants need to be noted, security and confidentiality of any notes ensured and checks made with those interviewed about what was said. The use of any kind of recorder to help remember what is said must be negotiated. The checking is important. I had one transcript of a tape recording which read that a certain pupil involved was a 'demon'. The TA on checking this told me the word was actually 'diamond', which puts a quite different connotation on the discussion.

Ask the TA to talk through what he or she thought was going on in the session. Prompt questions could be:

- Was this different because I was coming in?
- What was the objective for the session for you?

> For the teacher?
> For the child/ren?

- How do you know what to do?
- Did you plan together?
- What assessment and/or recording do you do?
- Are you involved with parents at all?
- What involvement in IEPs do you have?
- What difference do you think they make?

> To your job?
> To you?
> To the children's learning?

- Can you describe your relationship with the teacher?
- What helps this relationship? What hinders?
- What is your relationship to the child/ren?
- What changes would you like to make?
- Can you remember any particularly good sessions? or any disasters?
- What qualifications do you have?
- What training has the school given you?
- What involvement in meetings do you have?

- What would you like to do in the future?
- Anything else?

The questions would be similar for the teachers except they should be able say more about the learning objectives and outcomes. Getting two perspectives on the same question can be illuminating.

Pupils can say what they thought the TAs were doing, supposed to be doing and what the TA was there for. Prompt questions could be:

- Have they always been there?
- Are they there all the time?
- Do they make any difference? If so, what?
- Will you still have a TA helping you as you get older?

Using questionnaires or meetings

The above questions can be made into paper questionnaires to save time, although they are less conducive to frank and informative answers. Also, body language can tell one a lot about whether the answer given is a true reflection on the situation.

Holding meetings of TAs is another way schools use to ask questions about how the job is perceived. Where TAs feel intimidated by the thought of observations or individual interviews, they may well feel more secure when surrounded by their colleagues. Schools sometimes try this way of introducing appraisal; the meeting becomes a sort of joint appraisal or review before introducing the individual approach. Senior managers need to sense the background feelings in the school to ensure the best outcomes. It may be that the first meeting has to be informal, with no notes taken.

At the end of such procedures managers should be able to amplify the basic employment data collected at the beginning of the chapter with information based on the categories of the preceding chapter.

A sheet based on the categories described in Chapter 2 could be used:

Name
Date of audit
Methods used
Role being undertaken, supporting

  the school: care and welfare
      behaviour management
  learning
  teaching and teachers
  the curriculum

Personality

personal skills shown
knowledge and understanding shown

Competence shown
Qualifications
Relevant prior experiences
Issues raised during audit

Looking at outcomes

Collating test results

While TAs do seem to be most valued for their work in the affective domain, the collection of 'hard' data, particularly over a period of time for in-house evaluative purposes or to produce for inspection or even research would be a helpful adjunct to the school's information. Arguments using such data do have a weight at the current time. Deciding about what 'hard' data to collect can be a problem because of the diversity of roles undertaken by the TA – which bit of help that they give do we count? But this problem is also compounded by the variation in quality of the TAs, the variety of pupils and teachers and their needs with whom they come into contact, the changes in curricular emphasis from time to time and the moving of the test and examination goal posts.

Blatchford *et al.* (2002) had to resort to sophisticated statistical techniques and use data collected over several years with a team of researchers and a variety of supportive research methods to reinforce the hard data. If you are interested in statistical methods then you will need to start to tease out and collect what might be relevant additional data. For example, the names of pupils who regularly get certain kinds of support and the times and dates of such support might be collected. Where TAs have been involved in such initiatives as Catch-up or ALS their time could be quantified. One school I worked in identified target groups of pupils who were not on the SEN register, but needed 'a bit extra'. This would be an ideal group of pupils to track over several years.

Blatchford *et al.* (2002) looked at school entry booklets and submitted termly questionnaires. From that, they calculated measures of class size, pupil:teacher ratios, pupil:staff ratios, pupil:adult ratios both registered and experienced.

SEN data

Another area of data collection available to schools is in SEN. IEPs provide a rich source of data about progress of pupils who may show little progress on more conventional tests. Some schools used the 'P' levels of assessment, designed for use before the NC attainment target levels are achieved. The rate and number of pupils who come off the SEN register would be an indication of the success of the school's provision. Too often, once a pupil is 'labelled' and the school's funding is earmarked to their support, the support is not reviewed with a view to decreasing it. The following is an example of the kind of analysis one school did to evaluate their TA support.

Case study evidence

One of the schools I worked in evaluated their SEN support for certain identified pupils over the years following my research there. All the following pupils would probably have been in a special school fifteen years previously. The data were as follows:

Andrew was 6 when observed; his statement referred to complex learning difficulties, his behaviour having many characteristics well along the autistic spectrum. Two TAs and a midday assistant (MDA) covered his needs. He had been statemented soon after coming to school. As a rising five, he had been difficult to control and communicate with. I had seen him working on his own in the classroom full of other children, rarely communicating with them and occasionally sitting with them in whole class lessons, the TA being physically nearby. A year later he was able to work in groups in a Year 3 class and needed close supervision only in the freer activity times, such as physical education (PE). His standard assessment tasko22;s (SATs) scores at the end of Year 2 indicated him as working towards everything except spelling and maths where he was level 1, the target for a Year 2 child being level 2. At the end of Year 3, he was still having problems with conceptual understanding and creative subjects, he was unable to make up anything from imagination, but his reading age was 7.0 when his chronological age was 8.0. He was able to participate in class performances and sports day.

Barbara had Down's syndrome and was also 6 when observed. On completing her Year 2, she had progressed to a Year 1/2 class. While her English results indicated her as working towards level 1, she had scored a level 1 in mathematics. Her learning had plateaued in the two years following my visits. She had had a period of saying 'can't do', but was then enjoying school again although still achieving little academically.

Cathy was a statemented girl, with global learning delay. The speech therapist was involved in her support. She had poor motor skills, and sequencing and memory problems. Two years later she was in a class below her chronological age, and might still need to go to a special school at 11 rather than the local secondary school. Her reading age had stayed at 7.3 for two years, and her chronological age was 9.6. The TA support had enabled her to be in a mainstream school for her primary years, with a curriculum differentiated for her and with one-to-one support. Her maturity and confidence had developed noticeably, however, she was gaining life skills, including being able to talk to her peers in class. The TA was helping with specific life skills training, doing such things as teaching her how to cross the road safely. These life skills were not being taught as such at the local secondary school, and her scores would put her in 'the bottom group'. These skills were taught at the two nearest special schools.

David had come to the school in Reception, but he could not speak at all, or communicate other than with a grunt or by grabbing; he had to go to a specialist unit in a nearby town for two years. At the school with the unit, he was gradually reintegrated into the mainstream and had rejoined his catchment area school, statemented, prior to my observations. He took a long while to settle down into a normal routine when he came back to the school from the Speech and Language unit. There, he had been in a class of ten with five adults, and missed all the curriculum except literacy and numeracy. After two years he was a Year 6, completely settled, and he was leaving and going on to the local comprehensive. He probably need not even have been labelled as being on Stage 3 Code of Practice level, but the school was leaving him there, because of the transition to secondary school.

Eric was statemented for global learning delay. After two years, now a Year 4, he had scored level 2s in all his Year 3 SATs, and a 3 in his Year 4 Mathematics SATs. His writing and spelling had let him down in the Year 4 English SATs. His general language understanding and application was very poor, and he was not very sociable. He was getting only five hours' support, and did not understand class instructions. A decision had been made to keep him at the school and not send him to a Speech and Language unit. His speech was sufficiently competent, and it had been considered he would benefit more from staying in a mainstream school.

Francis was a statemented child with Attention Deficit Disorder, who had been excluded from his catchment area school and came about

> five miles by car to this school. During the second set of visits, it
> became known to him that he would be leaving at the end of term to
> go to a residential special school. This upset not only him, but also
> his TA, whose job hours partly depended on the allocation of money
> for his support.

'Soft' outcomes

It is clear that for data collection on TAs to be meaningful it has to include non-numerical or 'soft' data. Some of these data can be converted to numbers as there are increasingly available rating scales for things like behaviour, self-esteem and teacher stress. Some of these need personnel who are trained in observation or recording techniques and readers interested in this are recommended to find specialist literature on the subjects which interest them or take advice.

Ofsted confine themselves to quantifying the grades on their inspection reports, which limits the data to their definitions. Not all readers will agree with their criteria or be willing to use their style of recording. Their reports on individual schools, however, do show the positive impact a TA team can have on teaching and learning, and Ofsted's (2002) evaluation describes some other areas valued by schools:

- Teachers value the support
- The quality of teaching in lessons with TAs is better
- Training has improved TAs' knowledge of subjects
- The DfES training helped TAs' competence, confidence and management
- Career progression for TAs is increasing
- TAs contribute to the wider life of schools.

(Ofsted 2002)

Ofsted also note the need for management to recognise competing demands on TAs' time, and for them to enter into monitoring and evaluation procedures. Teachers, while valuing the support that TAs can give, also found that this took time to organise.

One outcome that is rarely measured is that of the effect of valuing and developing the TAs themselves. Their personal growth as people and educators is an indicator of their usefulness; such a measure is likely to be very rewarding for them, and impressive for their colleagues and the teaching staff.

A word of warning

Poor practice and possible negative outcomes

I have found it rare to record poor practice in TAs, but it does happen, as seen in this diary extract.

Diary evidence

A group of TAs in one school had an attitude problem when observed in the playground, and when I met with them in the staffroom later, they seemed not to like children. In another school with serious weaknesses, I saw a TA sitting with the children during a class session totally unresponsive to the lesson (which was at a low level for the age of children), then merely keeping the children on task during the group work, and quietening their fidgets. At the end of the lesson, she left quickly without communicating to the children or the teacher. Possibly, she had personal problems, but it was uncharacteristic.

Another example was noted where ostensibly the structures were in place for supporting the TA. She was observed 'creating a dependency culture' while supporting a child with SEN using a computer. 'She did not allow the child to access the computer for himself . . . she used letter names not sounds . . . she used an upper case keyboard with a child with learning problems . . . his seat was inappropriate . . . she sent him back to class before printing out the names typed in'.

Another TA in the same school drew pictures for a child.

It is easy to see that pupils supported by adults who really do not like dealing with them, who do things for them, or who operate at a mechanical prompting level are not going to enhance teaching and learning and could even be detrimental to both. The role models offered in these cases clearly are not helpful.

Blatchford and colleagues suggest that 'more support does not necessarily mean more effective support, even when the staff involved are individually effective' (Blatchford *et al.* 2002 p. 47). Their case study evidence picked up a class where individual observation of TAs' skills were described as excellent but there were so many adults supporting (this included volunteer help) that the teacher could not brief them all properly and planning was difficult. Lack of TA preparation, missed opportunities for learning, complexity of arrangements and the possibility of 'dead' time were also described. They list some of the features that seemed to apply when helpers were not effective as follows:

inflexible and didactic
see role as dealing with correctness of work and behaviour
limited warmth and praise
little probing or questioning or efforts to help children understand why
they might be mistaken
little knowledge of the task undertaken by the children
little effort to ensure equal opportunities for all.

(Blatchford *et al.* 2002 p. 43)

Blatchford *et al.* also pointed out that TAs may model themselves on the class
teacher and weak TAs will need more support from a teacher and therefore
add to the teacher's workload, not provide assistance.

I found in schools with poor practice:

• it is difficult to disassociate the TA from the class teacher, as the directions given by the teacher delineate the task for the TA
• schools with serious weaknesses, which included weaknesses in the quality of teaching, also had poor TAs
• some schools had given no directions to the TA
• relationships were sometimes strained
• communication was lacking
• TAs were underused.

Diary evidence
In one school I observed, in a difficult social area, the TAs were being
used to contain unruly children in order to support the weak teachers,
but with little worthwhile tasks to give them to do. Another school in a
favourable catchment area visited had sent TAs on the Open University
Specialist Teacher Assistant Certificate (OU STAC) course and supported them well. As co-ordinator of this course for the LEA and the
adviser of the school, I visited regularly. All went well until a couple of
severely disruptive children arrived. The teachers were unused to the
problem and dealt with it by excluding the children from the classroom
with the TAs to an isolated area of the school. The TAs did not know
how to cope either; the school had never needed a positive behaviour
management policy, and eventually the children were permanently
excluded from the school.

Again, following up some OU STAC students from other schools
where the headteacher was concerned about the poor performance of a
TA, in one the problem appeared to be a lack of communication with the
teacher, and in another a clash of personalities. One TA reported on a

local course that a teacher would greet her with 'Oh you are here again' in the tone of voice which indicated a nuisance rather than help. Another TA at the same session reported her mentor as 'aggressive' towards the SENCO who had organised the TAs' participation in the course.

Clearly, poor practice concerning TAs can be with the TAs themselves or the teachers or the management.

Schools must also consider whether it is appropriate that their least well trained and lowest paid staff should be working with their most challenging pupils. Blatchford *et al.* (2002) indicate that just increasing the number of adults does not affect children's progress in literacy at Reception level, but a smaller class size (i.e. pupil:teacher ratio) does.

Dealing with poor practice

If during the audit process poor practice is uncovered, which could be detrimental to the learning and teaching of the school, it must be dealt with, and not just considered as an item to add to the list of improvements to be made. In the same way that poor practice of any kind is dealt with in the school, the people involved should be told of the problem away from the classroom and other people, suggestions made as to dealing with it and support offered to improve the situation. It is to be hoped that this situation will be rare.

Realising potential

By auditing the TAs within the school they will become more visible, and by default if not on purpose, the value of their work will be revealed. It is still possible for them to have diverse, complex and ill-defined roles allied to a trend for them to be less involved in care and domestic tasks and more involved with pupils and the teaching and learning processes, across all key stages. The issues then are there for schools to develop more explicit expectations and rationale for employment as effective resources for teaching and learning include all human resources as well as material ones.

So far this book has described the work of TAs in school, their potential and investigated the reality of this for their school. The next step is to identify what areas of school work the TAs should undertake to increase the overall effectiveness of a school's most valuable and costly resource – the staff. Any changes that managers make cannot be solely based on their judgements of the TA situation; they need to have a view of the need of:

* pupils with SEN or for whom English is an additional language
* the needs of the NLNS and other curriculum areas

- the stress and workload levels of the teachers
- any areas of skill or curriculum weakness
- the range of jobs that have to be done to maintain a quality school environment.

Given that any audit process will unearth a multiplicity of provision, concerns and joys, the next step is to make some sort of sense of it and to consider what the various possibilities are for the school. Managers are in a position to match the talents and potential of their staff to the needs of the school. By comparing the potential of their existing TAs with that described in Chapter 2, and holding this alongside their priorities for school development and improvement, managers can make a start on considering what the school management and class teachers can do to ensure the best use of a valuable, resourceful group of people.

Chapter 4

Maximising the potential of TAs

> The substantial increase in the number of teaching assistants in schools and the corresponding increase in our expectations of what they do, not surprisingly has made the management of teaching assistants more complex.
>
> (Ofsted 2002 p. 18)

This chapter looks at the whole school issues which should be considered alongside the employment of TAs. Climate and ethos can radically affect their effectiveness and development as well as the consistency of experience for pupils. They interact with many different groups of people in the school community. Their role as team players is essential, and some ideas for team building are included. Good communication, collaboration and celebration of good practice within the school all contribute to the effective use of TAs and their personal effectiveness.

Chapter 2 pointed out that however well qualified or trained the TAs are, they can only be as effective as their use, deployment, management and support will allow them to be. Or to put it another way: given a particular group of TAs, effective support can allow and encourage them to develop professionally, effective deployment will ensure their skills can be put to best use and effective management can enable them to grow as people, and promote their best use by teachers and teams. Kerry (2001) talks of the school leadership trusting the support staff to work effectively, in effect abandoning control because they are so good at using their own initiative. But it needs more than that: TAs need the positive support and encouragement of their class teachers and senior managers to develop their full potential.

Consistency and climate

Environment

Consistency, communication and a positive climate with the need for whole school policies and plans were three of the key factors identified as contributing to what makes effective schools (Mortimore *et al.* 1988; Sammons *et al.* 1995). Consistency of practice enables pupils to feel secure and provides a learning environment which facilitates curriculum progression. TAs operating the same policies regarding health, safety and security matters, behaviour management strategies and carrying out teachers' instructions in the way that the school has determined ensures the minimum of confusion.

While schools complain about red tape imposed from outside, the existence of internal policies as distinct from assumptions of accepted practice does mean that newcomers to a school world will understand what has to be done when, how and why. The suggestions as to what these policies might be regarding TA employment are described in Chapter 5. The same is true about communication. So much of TA practice in the past has been based on implicit assumptions; development of good practice was a question of sensitive TAs picking up what was expected of them and teachers assuming that TAs somehow innately knew what to do. Instructions, boundaries of responsibility and levels of action do need to be spelt out explicitly; TAs as well as teachers need to know of organisational or policy changes that are proposed. This will mean attention to meetings and paperwork, sometimes inviting TAs to participate in or receive material originally designed only for teachers and sometimes designing occasions or documents specifically for TAs.

> School climate is the heart and soul of schools. It is about the essence of a school that leads a child, an administrator, a staff member to look forward to being there each day. School climate is about that quality of a school that helps each individual feel personal worth, dignity and importance, while simultaneously helping to create a sense of belonging to something beyond ourselves.
>
> (Freiberg and Stein 1999 p. 11)

Hall and George (1999) correlated classroom climate to a school's climate, and both to the impact of the principal.

The headteacher promotes the ethos and climate, has an overview of consistency, and is responsible for setting up systems of communications. The climate and conditions depend upon the ethos and history of the school, and all school staff following the aims and policies of the school. Ethos is not built up overnight and is dependent on the leadership of the headteacher with a committed team. The atmosphere of a school is tangible and does not depend on architecture or age of the building. Many parents feel this when trying to select a school for their children. Indeed, any visitor to a school experiences this. It is salutary to stand back and consider what your school might appear like to a visitor.

What does a visitor see in your school?
Was it easy to find the car park and reception?
Is the entry foyer welcoming?
Are the plants watered?
Are notices up-to-date?
Is there somewhere for a visitor to sit while waiting?
Would you like to sit there if it was the doctors' waiting room or a hotel reception area?
Is available documentation reader friendly?
Is there a display showing pupils' work?
Are rooms labelled, and fire exits clear?

How do people behave?
What is the attitude of the receptionist to telephone calls?
Do receptionists make eye contact with visitors even if they are busy on the telephone?
Do receptionists make sure whether visitors need a drink or the lavatory?
How do receptionists hand over to a member of staff?
Is the visitors' book and fire register properly maintained?
Who shows visitors round the school?
How do adults speak to each other in the corridor?
How do pupils talk to visitors?
Who smiles?
What are the noise levels?

Role models have been shown to be powerful guides to the TAs on how they should conduct themselves. Where staff have high expectations of themselves, each other and the pupils in both academic and behavioural areas, pupils respond. Externally accredited courses for TAs are highly dependent on work experience. These courses can be effective in raising standards of TAs only if the work experience gives the TAs the appropriate expectations of their role. The issue of mentoring is discussed in Chapter 6. Where TAs have developed their teaching skills, it is usually by watching the examples they see in the classes they work in. Where they have been employed to work in several classes they compare effectiveness, having opportunities for observation that teachers themselves do not have of their colleagues. This extends to expectations of dress, manners, standards of work presentation in adults and pupils as well as behaviour.

Case study evidence

Teachers, senior management and TAs referred to the 'St. So-and-so's way' or of 'one big family' when describing the behaviour of the adults. The senior management looked forwards as well as recognising the changes taking place at the time. TAs and teachers talked of future training, of how to manage the fluctuating budget with its various pockets to the best advantage of the people in the team as well as the children, how they would like a male TA to serve as a role model, particularly for some of the more disturbed boys with dysfunctional family backgrounds. All the staff treated each other and the pupils with politeness and expected to be treated in the same way by the pupils: doors were held open for someone, adult or child carrying a load or hurrying; school work, notices and messages were expected to be legible; drawers or shelves were to be left tidy whoever they belonged to. Pupils or staff with emotional problems were treated with understanding. Understanding of staff's personal background featured high in conversations and humour infiltrated many conversations. This meant that the TAs could challenge and provide companionship and humour for those carrying greater responsibility. They were sources of local understanding and contacts, and in this school provided a parental point of view to a teaching staff team with few teachers who were parents. 'The equation has become unbalanced . . . but we'll work it out'. TAs were part of any social event organised by or for the teaching staff.

MacBeath *et al.* (1996) gave the five key features of school climate as:

- The school is a happy place to be
- There are places for pupils to go and constructive things to do outside class time
- Pupils and staff behave in a relaxed and orderly way
- Pupils, staff and parents feel that their contribution to the school is valued
- The school is welcoming to visitors and newcomers.

(MacBeath *et al.* 1996 p. 34)

This state of affairs does not came about by accident although often visiting such schools, it looks easy.

Teaching and learning cultures have to be built and developed through induction, professional development, joint planning, coaching and mentoring, sharing good practice and researching the evidence. The bedrock of this culture are the norms, values and beliefs that bond a community of like minded people into the common commitment of continually improving practice and raising standards of achievement for pupils.

(Brighouse and Woods 1999 p. 105)

Sometimes the problem is that the school staff are not a community of 'like-minded people', and there is a need to put something in place to develop consistency of practice if not of belief.

Case study evidence
The access to the senior management team was informal and effective in both study schools. 'Anything we are unsure about we go . . . and have a chat about what we are all confused about . . . and we'll have a meeting about it'. TAs told of meetings to share ideas, and involvement in IEPs. They talked about suggesting painting for the afternoon, for example, and were allowed to have a go with their ideas. However, one said:

> We're not included in maths so I still say borrow and they say exchange. It makes me look a right 'nana' in front of them. We are not included in learning the new phonic system, so when I go in and I say 'le' and they all go 'lll' I look a right Wally. We want to be included. How are we supposed to support these children in the way that the school wants us to if we are not included? And this school's a really good school, you know, really good; some schools, well I wouldn't work for them but we still need to be included and kept up-to-date with everything.

Another said about their teachers and the course they were on at the time 'They don't actually know what I am learning'.

One answer lies in inclusion, the point made in the first case study in this chapter: TAs were part of the social event arranged for the staff. This kind of move may not happen overnight. The midday assistants in one school declined to come to a summer barbecue arranged by the governors as they said they would feel out of place. The secretaries and TAs went, and many of the teaching staff. The governors repeated the barbecue the following year, and hoped that all staff would then join in. In another school, the retirement of a popular deputy encouraged all the staff and partners to attend the leaving party. It broke the ice for future occasions.

On an everyday level, it is the simple things which are meaningful, such as where TAs hang their coats or take coffee, or the way in which people are named. It is still the habit in some schools for the male teachers to be called 'Sir', the females are 'Miss' and the support staff are called either 'Miss' or in some cases their forename, dating possibly from when pupils and staff so named worked together in pre-school groups. Some schools even address pupils using such terms as 'You, boy' or 'Come here, girl'. Schools which care about individuals' feelings of worth have staff who bother to learn the pupils' names and expect to be addressed by their names and titles. Some have resorted to name badges, both to help pupils know their names and to identify visiting adults in this security conscious age.

There are still reports of staffrooms where TAs are not welcome, and while there may be genuine problems with support staff using car parks, small staffrooms and even toilet facilities as total staff sizes grow, other schools find ways to overcome the problems. In a DfES (2002a) consultation, it has been recognised that growth in support staff may well mean an increase in certain basic building provision and funding has been promised for capital expenditure in this area (DfES 2002a). Ben-Peretz *et al*. have described how staffrooms (which they refer to as teachers' lounges) in schools are influential in improving the learning environment in schools.

> It is highly probable that lounges, as sites for teachers' interactions, provide the necessary conditions for the development of strong teacher networks and the generation of communal knowledge about teaching. This knowledge might lead to more effective teaching modes.
>
> (Ben-Peretz *et al*. 1999 p. 150)

Diary evidence

At our first courses for TAs in 1994, we had many tales of a 'them and us' culture. Our first OU STAC course with its quality assurance visits to students' schools also found us having to make tactful approaches to headteachers to ensure the TAs were being treated appropriately, that the course was not just something they could send a TA on because it was free, and forget about the consequences. So, we worked hard at communication with schools prior to them recruiting course members, and by the end of 1998, a note made after the study skills session prior to the OU course reads:

> of the 29 potential students who came today only two do not go to staff meetings on occasions, all take part in literacy hour and have been part of some form of literacy training within their schools. No one mentioned any problems with access to the staffroom, and the

whole climate of the way in which the students are approaching the course is different from four years ago. They already come with a certain confidence and understanding of what is going on in the classroom, with a sense of partnership and self-value.

It is worth checking the following:
How do your TAs come to school?
Where do they park their car, bicycle or motorbike?
Is the local public transport school-day friendly?
Where do they hang their coat and keep their personal belongings during the day?
Is there room in the staff toilet area for them?
Where do they have their refreshment breaks?
Are they welcome in the staffroom before and after school?
Do they have sufficient break for lunch?
What do they do for lunch?
What names are your staff known by?
Are they treated with respect by pupils, as well as treating pupils with respect?

What are you doing about any ill feeling about any of the above from teaching staff?

Ethos and culture

The TA problems I have found were all from schools with a marked negative ethos, although these were not necessarily failing or potentially failing schools. This group was characterised by variety of headship problems: lack of competence, illness, stubbornness, bereavement, arrogance, or even lack of a headteacher at all. Similar relationship problems could also begin to show after major changes in senior management. The staffroom relationships in such schools would appear friendly, but conversations were rarely about learning or children, more often television soap serials or holidays. It was difficult to get at the tangled webs of relationships within such schools, but working with them over a period of time, it was clear that they were really uncomfortable places in which to be, jealousies and suspicion allied with incompetence and inadequacy creating entrenched ways of working, and preventing change and communication. TAs became negative about their situation and with the children, poor role models, and were unable to see any other way of working. They would be surprised and defensive at suggestions, occasionally even aggressive, certainly disillusioned. Some of the TAs observed had qualifications, and were experienced in their schools, external training was not the problem. The underlying problems of the schools went beyond simple changes in routines.

In *Schools Speak for Themselves* MacBeath *et al.* (1996) give twelve 12 indicators of ethos which were developed by the Scottish Office Education Department:

- pupil morale
- teacher morale
- teachers' job satisfaction
- the physical environment
- the learning context
- pupil–teacher relationships
- discipline
- equality and justice
- extracurricular activities
- school leadership
- information to parents
- parent–teacher consultation.

(Macbeath *et al.* 1996 p. 97)

The suggestion is that members of the school community can rate them from 1 to 4, 1 being excellent, and then group together to share their results and reach a compromise to obtain a final score.

The school ethos and culture should be inclusive at all levels, tinkering with mechanistic strategies and systems to determine practice without attention to the underlying philosophy will do little to make long-term improvements. Valuing staff empowers them to contribute. The strategies described in the next two chapters need to be underpinned by a way of working for the whole school community – all staff, governors, pupils and parents.

Leadership

The role of headteachers and senior managers is crucial to the setting of ethos and culture and so to the work of TAs. This can be seen most readily when it occasionally breaks down.

Diary evidence

One school visited had communication problems. In it, the TAs, having their coffee separately, were using the time as a planning session. They said: 'We are putting the learning objectives to the list of activities that the teachers have given us . . . cannot even pass the time of day with us, doesn't enquire whether we are well or unwell . . . bad vibes within the school . . . lack of moral and spiritual backbone within the school'. These TAs were well qualified and this diary note concluded: 'I am appalled by the waste of talent that sort of situation creates within the school and at the reduction in learning opportunities for the children. The negative role models [of senior staff] must surely affect the whole atmosphere within the school'.

On another occasion, after an afternoon with a group of TAs from a consortium, their first time out of school, they raised all kinds of issues. The subsequent meeting of the headteachers was described in the diary:

> My presence was tolerated . . . They did not want their TAs to meet in case they came back opening up cans of worms with which they could not deal . . . That was what had happened when their administrative assistants met . . . are the heads threatened by these people in that it might mean that they have to do more?

In the series of cameos of good practice I collected in 1990s for the DfEE, management strategies as well as TA characteristics were similar. My adviser colleagues gave me the names of schools where they had seen good practice. On telephoning them, I found in all of them the senior management or the headteachers

- had a clear understanding of what was happening in their schools
- spoke of their TA teams
- saw external and internal training as important
- had regular meetings of TAs
- allocated non-pupil contact time to meetings or planning or teacher liaison time
- valued their TAs highly
- enabled the TAs to participate in policy formation
- usually had job descriptions frequently allied with appraisal processes
- encouraged TAs to help with after school activities
- enabled TAs to participate in the formulation of IEPs
- and in some of the schools, recognised higher responsibilities with higher grades of salary.

One diary entry recorded a headteacher of a successful and happy school with nine TAs for five classes. She stated a belief in expenditure on people, as well as the environment and equipment. All the staff worked together, staffroom discussions were largely on professional matters, but there was a lot of care and empathy for the human side of each other. The headteacher said apart from their work in the classrooms, the TAs 'relieve stress of teachers and keep absenteeism down, and they contribute to humour and morale by their attitude and support'. Visit notes later commented 'clear support of TA by teacher, team /partnership, reiterated by headteacher (HT). The HT spoke of the team – of taking three years to find people who fitted. All but one teacher had their own TA – plan together – all staff went to Ofsted feedback. Standards were good, the teaching and the use of the TAs were good'. Several schools, as this one, had developed supply TAs, so that these would know how the school worked.

Mortimore *et al.* (1988) established that the purposeful leadership of the staff by the headteacher was one of the key factors in a successful school and 'all the research confirmed by HMI and more recently Ofsted, suggests that leadership in schools is the key factor in improvement and success' (Brighouse and Woods 1999 p. 45). These authors go on to say it is much more complex than just 'leave it to the headteacher', leadership of all who work in the school is important. However, it is impossible to disassociate ethos and culture from the influence of the headteachers, and a paper handed to me by a group of TAs in a school exemplifies this. They do not mention the headteacher, but the leadership and management strategies are clear, the relationships are positive and the TAs part of a learning community, which depends for its effectiveness on the headteacher.

Diary evidence
Why it works so well in our school
Teaching assistants are given planning time to get resources and ideas for the right approach ready for lessons to come that week.
We are treated as part of the [school] team and we all support each other.
We know each other (the whole school) socially.
The teaching assistants are encouraged to go on courses and use training schemes.
We are included on the progression of IEPs and forward our comments and ideas.
The teaching assistants which have achieved their STAC course would love to go further.
We work with outside agencies i.e. speech therapists on behalf of the child's teacher and report back to the teacher with progress and ideas.

Relationships within and between the school teams

If you use some of the audit materials suggested in Chapter 3, they will have revealed aspects of the culture and ethos of the schools that are relevant to TAs. The *Good Practice Guide* (DfEE 2000a) Indicator 3.1 talks about teachers and TAs working co-operatively and gives specific instances of activities that show co-operation. As most of the instances need time outside contact time with the pupils in the classroom, it is clear that management decisions to pay for and timetable such opportunities will encourage co-operative working. Indicator 3.2 talks about learning together, which requires meeting together, joint commitment and partnership. Indicator 4 looks at TAs attendance at functions, the involvement of governors, parents and visiting advisers in liaising and linking with TAs and liaison within the schools of relevant senior staff and TAs. Indicator 5 also talks of meetings, liaisons and communication. All of these require commitment and funding from senior management, neither being easy to obtain in schools' current circumstances. Tennant (2001 p. 187) when suggesting 'In consultation with the SENCo, the senior management would need to arrange a thorough audit of the special educational needs provision for the children in the school', unfortunately concluded 'despite major research projects such as Farrell *et al.* (1999), necessary changes are not realised quickly' (Tennant 2001 p. 188). The *Good Practice Guide* was based on this research (DfEE 2000a).

TAs and teachers alike need to feel confident that time spent on such joint activities is worthwhile, not just to themselves but to the way the school operates as a whole; they certainly like to feel trusted. Some schools talk about this kind of thing explicitly. Rose (2001) describes working in a 'failing' school, where some teams had excellent communication but not all.

> You cannot work as a team if some people will not let others have responsibilities or ideas on how to help . . . A strong headteacher and senior teachers were needed to show a direction for the school . . . people who are willing to listen to others and accept their views but also have a clear view of where the school is going and a good knowledge of the children.
>
> (Rose 2001 pp. 77–78)

The school later got a strong leader with 'a new approach to communication between staff so that everyone was involved. There was a new sense of trust – this is really important for support assistants as it shows them respect' (Rose 2001 p. 78).

Case study evidence
In one school I visited, the teachers expressed their feelings about their TA team. They felt they were very lucky in the quality of their TAs. One said:

> [It's] having a very enthusiastic group of TAs that keeps me on my toes, because I'm never sure what they are going to ask me when two of them march in together and they are smiling and you think what are they going to say? It works in two ways – rather than me go and find them all the time, they are so enthusiastic!

The teachers liked the 'more bubbling in a managed way' that the TAs brought to the school.

MacBeath *et al.* (1996) give the five key features of good relationships as:

*   There is a shared sense of teamwork among all staff
*   Older pupils help younger ones
*   Bullying is not tolerated
*   Parents and governors feel welcomed and valued in the school
*   People address one another in ways which confirm their value as individuals.

(MacBeath *et al.* 1996 p. 36)

Working together, helping each other, intolerance of bullying with adults and pupils, the welcome and the means of address all express value of the members of the school community for themselves.

The whole school team

The team approach

The effectiveness of the TAs is not just due to individual interpersonal relationships at classroom level, but to being part of a whole school team, and forming their own TA team.

> *Teamwork* leads to better decisions and speedier completion of work through the pooling of expertise and the sharing of tasks . . . Teams are working well when:
>
> *   members are clear what needs to be done, the time-scale involved and who is to do what;

- members feel they have a unique contribution to make to the work of the team;
- mutual respect prevails among members;
- a climate of trust encourages the free expression of ideas, suggestions, doubts, reservations and fears;
- individual talents and skills are used effectively;
- members are able to discuss alternative approaches and solutions before taking decisions;
- there are established ways of working together which are supportive and efficient in the use of time;
- progress is checked regularly and members are clear about who they report to and when.

(Hargreaves and Hopkins 1991 p. 137)

Case study evidence
The children in the study schools commented that the TAs 'were all the same', it did not matter which one helped you. TAs spoke of how they talked together, came upon things together, devised things together. Some of the understanding was unspoken, but they knew what was expected of them. The headteacher said: '[It's] creating a synergy really ... Their [the TAs'] opinions are as valid as the teachers' on some issues ... It's having well-defined bits contributing to a much stronger whole, it's having a variety of backgrounds ... But also, [it's] in what they contribute to the whole community'. He also told me of watching the TAs as volunteers in the school, before he went through the formal interview process. It helped him see whether people would fit the team.

One teacher summed it up: 'There is no "them and us" in this school, they are part of a team, they are welcome anywhere and everywhere. I don't know if we can do anything to improve, or if they have said differently, but I don't think we can make our situation any better apart from what finances and time would give us'. The headteacher was confident that any individual who had a comment would come and talk to her. She referred to 'the community atmosphere' and 'the supportive school'. The changes she had implemented had not caused resentment; on the contrary the staff had risen to the challenges.

One TA said: 'We can always go to her anyway if there wasn't anything you were quite sure about how to approach, she'd come into the classroom and show you how to do it. If we want more meetings we just say we want a meeting. Everybody's happy with that'. One TA summed it up: 'I think there is a lot of team spirit, but not just the TAs, but the teachers, we all work together as a team. I get a lot of support from everybody really at the school. It's a nice school'.

TAs and parents and carers

The relationship of parents and carers with TAs varies with the school and the needs of the pupils. Where the pupil has distinct physical needs, it makes sense that the TA liaises directly with the parent or carer to report on any changes in their needs. In some cases of supporting SEN, it becomes more useful and appropriate for the TA to deal directly with the parents.

Case study evidence
Andrew's TA had a very close relationship with his mother saying, 'She's quite good if I tell her what we've been doing – she'll pick it up' referring to the way that Andrew, with autistic characteristics, was currently being encouraged to be self-reliant. The TA made a photo-graph collection album for Andrew of his new classroom and teacher at the end of the summer term, for him to take home over the holidays to help familiarise himself with where he was going in the September. So good was this TA–mother relationship that the mother suggested that the TA should accompany the child to the visit of the school doctor, rather than herself. The TA said, 'She agrees that I could get more from him than she does'. The TA was aware that Andrew knew his letters, so she was able to inform the doctor, who was then able to perform a full eye test, and discovered that Andrew's eyesight was extremely poor. The TA talked about training methods with Andrew's mother, and to me about their friendship. Another TA in that school talked of having informal chats, where the mother wanted mainstream school and not full support, and others told of mothers whose expectations of a TA were difficult, yet were able to discuss suitable clothing for school.

In other schools, there is little or no contact between the TAs and parents directly. In some schools, communication can be by note, such as with pupils in a unit for the hearing impaired, who were bussed to school. Notes would accompany the hearing aids if there were problems. In a secondary school visited, where the TAs were part of the SEN support team, it was the defined role of the TAs to liaise with parents regarding day-to-day needs, and they always sat in on any visit of the parent to the school where logistically possible. In one school the TA did home visits with the teacher, and attended the induction meeting. TAs are sometimes only shown IEPs, and in others are fully involved in review meetings and helping plan targets. The Code of Practice (DfES 2001d) suggests that TAs be included in IEP reviews, and the training of TAs for secondary schools promotes this kind of involvement.

TAs have not voiced problems over themselves being parents of children at the school. One of the comment from the teachers was: 'They are parents most of them, so you are getting a very healthy interface between the teaching staff and the parents, and some of the teaching staff that are not parents themselves need to be told occasionally by a parent what it is like'. The headteachers saw the TAs' parenting experience and local knowledge as a positive factor. The TAs in both study schools knew a lot about the families and the social background of the children with whom they worked. One problem which then faces TAs, coming as they largely do from the locality of the school, and often parents themselves, is how to deal with the enquiries from anxious parents who see the TA as a source of information on what goes on in the school. This reinforces the importance of early discussion of confidentiality.

Managers must decide what contact the TAs are to have with parents and carers, how and when. This means deciding on consultation and reporting procedures, visits to school and homes and all the concomitant communication systems. Managers must ensure that parents and carers are aware of the roles and boundaries of TA responsibilities.

TAs and governors

Governors are increasingly aware of the role and needs of TAs. I had good attendance at recent workshops run for governors on the issues raised by the employment of TAs, showing an increased recognition of their need to understand the developments. Since 1998, support staff have been able to elect a representative to the governing body in the same way as the teaching staff do. Many support staff themselves still seem unaware of this. Sallis (1999) suggested that 'it is not easy to translate into daily good practice', recognising 'It is a tough assignment to represent staff whose jobs may include little communication with each other, few common concerns and different working hours'. She added, 'Establishing the equality of all governors is not going to be easy' (Sallis 1999 p. 10). Governors are also part of the whole school team, and responsible, through their delegation to the headteacher, for the employment of all staff and the standards achieved in the school. Governors should see TAs at work when they make their classroom visits, and TAs' successes can be mentioned in governors' minutes and annual reports, as well as any policies relating to them.

TAs and other agencies

TAs increasingly work directly with advisers and specialists visiting the school, again under the guidance of teachers. They can be trained by physiotherapists and occupational therapists in the exercises needed daily to maintain flexibility or assist pupils with conditions like cystic fibrosis. Schools which employ special needs support teachers may use them to liaise with TAs or even to train them. Educational psychologists (EPs) or speech therapists find it useful to consult TAs because they have a more intimate knowledge of the pupils.

Case study evidence
One speech therapist took the idea of motivators from the TA, rewards for good behaviour, such as being able to play with toy cars. The TA commented that sometimes the therapists suggested boring things that meant sitting at tables with pencil and paper, even drawing pictures. She felt her pupil needed active, doing things. She felt that she could say these things, as she had to implement the programmes and knew the pupils. She seemed to have done it in a sharing, professional way which had not upset the specialist. Another TA sent for information from the Down's Syndrome Society, another had followed the ideas of the speech therapist, and developed them.

The *Good Practice Guide* (DfEE 2000a) has a section about creating partnerships with other people involved in education with paragraphs covering:

• Working with outside agencies
• Regular meetings with SENCOs
• A channel of communication with parents
• A channel of communication with ethnic minority communities
• Inviting TAs to participate in school functions.

Team building

Some schools have tried the team-building techniques, rather favoured in some industries and businesses. On the whole, these tend to be considered a bit false by school staff, although some aspects as part of a whole school in-service education and training (INSET) day may create some light relief and fun. In one school all the staff went on the local abseiling wall, but others opted for more practical school-based activities such as joint attendance at training sessions.

The whole school INSET day can be a powerful way of indicating that policies and practice within the school are for everybody, that there is only one philosophy for all. If all sectors of the staff are consulted on the agenda beforehand, an even better message is given, that all views are valued. Clearly the larger the school the more difficult such an exercise becomes. If the teaching staff is 100 strong it is likely that the support staff is even larger, and the INSET day becomes a fully fledged conference – and why not, if only once a year or even once in three years? Consortia of primary schools sometimes set up conference days with national speakers for all attendees, followed by specific workshops for teachers, TAs, midday assistants and administrative and caretaking staff.

Some schools regularly begin the academic year with such a day or half day, beginning the year as they mean to go on. One example of successful practice is to hold a whole school day or conference off site every three years as part of a triennial review of the school aims and objectives, and a major revamp to the SDP. If the SDP is merely a tool, documenting change, sometimes seemingly for change's sake, it becomes yet another piece of paper, however worthy or useful.

The school needs to revisit its own aims and purposes every so often. The day is preceded by questionnaires to all sectors of the school including pupils and parents so that their views on the ways forward for the school can be included. The TA audit could be part of the pre-INSET day agenda. All staff and governors attend. A short talk or presentation could sum up the findings. An external facilitator can help. Once various aspects of the direction of the school have been re-examined, a SWOT (strengths, weaknesses, opportunities and threats) analysis with all sectors represented can be really helpful. Consideration of government and local initiatives and their impact on the working lives of all concerned with the school helps a sense of collegiality. Support staff coming from the local community often have suggestions and views that can be revealing to senior teaching staff who may live considerable distances away. Priorities, strategic policies and procedures can be discussed openly. Task groups can be formed with representatives of all sections who can spend time actually putting action plans with dates together.

In this way, the deployment and management of TAs can be put alongside the school priorities in a transparent and open way; all sectors of the school community can contribute.

Governors, heads and staff have all reported how development planning encourages collaboration, and how this makes implementing the plan both more enjoyable and more effective. The school's partners often want to help but do not know how to do so: development planning provides genuine opportunities for harnessing this goodwill and support.

Collaboration:

- creates a commitment to a common purpose among governors, head and staff and the school's partners;
- improves communication and reduces misunderstanding;
- fosters creativity in finding solutions when problems are discussed;
- enhances motivation;
- prevents individuals from becoming isolated;
- generates a sense of collective achievement;
- supports teamwork.

(Hargreaves and Hopkins 1991 p. 137)

Kerry (2001) gives the characteristics of what he refers to as 'superteams' which promote 'creative dissatisfaction' as teams who:

- constantly revisit what they are trying to achieve;
- are persistent;
- set high expectations and standards;
- are highly committed to each other and to the task;
- communicate effectively with others;
- are proactive;
- bring in others to help the work of the team;
- prioritise and hit their targets;
- are never fully satisfied.

(Kerry 2001 pp. 60–61)

The fundamental ethos and philosophy on which the school is based is vital in order that TAs can be supported and used appropriately. Provided this is secure, the practical strategies for operating a smooth running team are described in the following chapters. Systems and structures based on a collaborative culture will provide the mechanism to enable discussion, facilitate working together, and provide accountability. Such schools are places where adults and pupils enjoy spending their time as well as providing enhanced opportunities for learning.

Chapter 5

Management systems and structures relating to TAs

> The recruitment and initial training of teaching assistants will only add value if assistants are deployed effectively by teachers and managers inside schools.
>
> (Morris in DfEE 2000a Foreword)

In this chapter, the systems and structures which can be in place to support TAs are outlined, beginning with the place of TA development in the overall scheme of school development and improvement. The importance of allowing time for development within a clear vision of what is needed by the school and the people who work in it is explored. The need for clear line management, explicit policies and practice for TAs, including an appropriate pay structure is described.

Systems

Evolution

It is difficult to separate structure from systems, but I do it deliberately here to try to distinguish between them. 'Structures' is the term I use to indicate finite frameworks for action rather than more fluid operational 'systems', but the two interact. 'Systems' are likely to be still evolving and 'structures' more set, thus worth considering separately.

Case study evidence
The picture in both study schools was one of constant evolution, of gradual change, as informalities became accepted ways of working, then incorporated into the systems and then the structures of the schools. The structures of the two schools were apparently different in their way of using TAs, the one for individual children and the other for teachers to support the curriculum, yet the way in which the schools operated showed a great similarity. The senior management constantly

referred to developing or evolving systems in both study schools, which may later become structures. Both were:

- developing regular meetings for their TAs
- developing planning and feedback systems
- considering policies, job descriptions and appraisal strategies
- committing sizeable portions of the general school budget to TA salaries
- keeping governors informed
- incorporating the TAs in school-based INSET
- committing time to the professional development of TAs
- giving line management to the deputy head
- appointing new TAs was seen as important a procedure as appointing teachers
- using advertisements and interview processes
- setting criteria for appointment.

TA policies were in their infancy. The recording systems and appraisal were in their pilot stage. The meetings had provided a venue and opportunity for the TAs to discuss their ideas more openly in a group. Individual appraisals developed later. The TAs were observed frequently by the senior managers in an informal way, and by their teachers, who also talked with the senior management. The headteachers indicated that, as confidence grew, these observations may well become more formal. Already, reflection on the TA role was part of the SDP review, and governors were showing an increasing interest in the work of the TAs. TAs spoke of going to the INSET days and of their use of the SENCO's room to keep their resources. They had ready access to this and changed things as they needed to. Access to and understanding of the school schemes was evident, TAs spoke of using the Nelson handwriting scheme and the Early Reading Research approach to reading (an Essex and University of Warwick research programme) as well as the National Strategies. The headteacher met with the TA team formally at least once a term not only to talk about specific issues like child protection, but also to give them an opportunity to feel the pulse of the developments, and allow the TAs opportunity to voice their opinions – which they apparently did increasingly forcefully as their confidence increased.

In the school employing its TAs to support children with SEN, two or more TAs were always allocated to a particular child with exceptional needs. This affected the way in which the adults worked, the necessary communication systems, and the outcome for the child. It added a dimension to the provision for that child as more than one adult was providing ideas for dealing with the problems. The regular meeting set up with the visiting SEN support teacher, the development of meetings with the SENCO, the growing development of professional development meetings, the introduction of job descriptions, and the production of a TA policy all showed the gradual embedding of the less formal ways of working into the regular formal fabric of the school. The headteacher spoke of 'reaching a threshold' where although the TAs had always been part of the school, they were now able to challenge the senior management, even talking in terms of having similar status to teachers to do so.

In the other school, using their TAs to support the NLNS, the senior management spoke of how they had 're-jigged the whole timetable basically so that we try to get the TAs to support the school'. This referred to the decision to change the literacy and mathematics to being all morning focused. Each teacher knew how much time they had been allocated, but used it to suit their own purposes. The Wednesday morning TA meetings had been set up initially as a 'focus point, so that they all met each other' – but 'they know each other and work very well together anyway'. The management team however 'needed everybody together if you're trying to get messages across'. It supported the new initiative of the target groups, but also recognised that different teachers had different recording systems. From this came the TA initiative of devising a more common format: 'Everybody brainstormed'. The timetable of TAs was set up so that teachers could plan knowing what hours they had got, but 'they are not set in tablets of stone, because they can negotiate with each other'. The TAs said they liked the Wednesday morning meetings. The teachers also referred to the attendance of the TAs at their training sessions, for example the booster class training. The Wednesday mornings were also seen as a place where TAs could pick up the ways of the school – such as how particular sums were done in the school. TAs had general job descriptions, but not specific, individualised ones. It was recognised these needed updating. The deputy head had been appointed to be the TAs' line manager, a role which was seen as part of her professional development as well as helpful to the headteacher's workload and the TA team.

While managers can impose structures, the above examples show that they can grow and evolve and need not be implemented all at once. This development did not come from a TA policy, but a need by the school to tackle particular issues – in their cases SEN and NLNS. The specific policies were then coming from the practice.

The role of the SDP

The SDP is pivotal to managing a school's direction although its effectiveness depends on the type of plan in use. It should be reviewed annually. Many authorities have materials for reviewing SDPs or other quality assurance materials. Essex has what is called a Quality Framework, which defines good practice. It was drawn up by advisers in consultation with many different stakeholders in the authority, and has accompanying materials which include questionnaires for managers to use when reviewing particular aspects of their practice. Some people use the Ofsted framework, but it is worth considering whether this framework covers the issues that the school thinks are important as well as those inspectors consider important. The Strathclyde school self-evaluation framework for school evaluation looks at their priorities against indicators of good practice, and comes up with a practical way forward to address their findings. In his book evaluating the use of the framework, MacBeath (1999) describes the stages as follows:

1 Create the climate
2 Agree a process
3 Agree the criteria
4 Develop the toolkit
5 Focus on teaching and learning

A major review looking at the school's fundamental aims, culminating as was suggested in Chapter 4 in a whole school INSET day, would be a triennial event, unless significant changes have taken place influencing the school's direction. A change of headteacher, a major new initiative in a curriculum area, school amalgamation, an Ofsted inspection, even the TA review or audit itself could raise the need for a rethink of the school's priorities.

Some schools are adopting a two-pronged approach to the regular annual review of the SDP – one part having the new developments for the following year, sometimes called a School Improvement Plan, and one part containing all those things which still need planning and costing but happen every year, sometimes called the School Maintenance Plan. In schools where the ethos and culture is good, where there is consultation and communication at all levels of staff hierarchy, TAs are already involved at all levels of the plan. They contribute to it, appear in it and help evaluate it. 'School development processes should seek to nurture the conditions that facilitate the tasks of teachers and LSAs working together effectively in classrooms' (Farrell *et al*. 1999 p. 55).

Figure 5.1 gives some examples of SDPs relating to the work of TAs. Figure 5.1a is part of an SDP where TAs are the focus of changes and Figure 5.1b is an example of a page from an SDP where TAs form part of the section on human resources management.

Typical headings in the school development plan that include provision for TAs are:

- any strategic changes proposed
- professional development strategies for all staff

    in-house meetings
    off site training

- policy reviews particularly

    SEN and inclusion
    teaching and learning
    assessment, recording and reporting
    pupil support and welfare
    behaviour management

- community links

    with parents
    liaison strategies

- management issues

    people
    resources

All items can have success indicators, responsible names attached, cost implications and ways in which any changes are going to be monitored and evaluated.

If the decisions are made at a whole school INSET day to make changes in the TA provision, it is an ideal opportunity to set up a task group to look into the practical ways of implementing the suggestions. However, it is more likely that the changes will be made gradually, as time and opportunity present themselves. It is still important that someone in the senior management team has overall responsibility for the team of TAs, their work and development. Chapters 6 to 8 are devoted to the practical strategies that can be used.

Monitoring and evaluation

It must also be remembered that TA development does not stop after an initial audit. The audit materials mentioned in Chapter 3 give many tools for monitoring and evaluating the work of TAs. Probably the most difficult

Global target – to improve and develop the skills of classroom support staff	2001/2002		
Objective	**Interim steps**	**Resources**	**Time scale**
1 To provide LSA staff ideas for playtime games/activities	2 half-hour sessions looking at games and playground markings		September 2001
2 LSA staff to be confident in using RM desktop	2 sessions + 2 follow-up sessions using RM desktop	All school laptops Instruction pack	Sept–July 2002
3 LSA staff to develop an understanding of Accelerated Learning	2 half-hour sessions on Accelerated Learning. Whole school INSET	Funding for INSET	Jan 2002
4 LSA staff to feel confident in the use of guided reading and book banding	2 half-hour sessions	Book banding book Guided reading video	Sept 2001
5 LSA staff to have an understanding of the principles of Early Writing	1 half-hour session	Early Writing video	Nov 2001
6 LSA staff to be aware of positive and protective handling strategies	Whole day INSET	Funding for whole school INSET	Jan 2002
7 For LSA staff to become trained in ELS project	3 LSAs to participate in LEA training alongside teaching staff	ELS trolleys 3 whole day sessions at PDC time for feedback and preparation sessions	Jan–July 2002

8 For LSAs to continue/begin EAZ funded Trac/LEA training	Attendance at courses as appropriate	Release time for attendance at courses	Sept–July 2002
9 For LSA staff to be confident when dealing with first aid	All new staff to attend first aid course	Afternoon release time Funding for trainer	March 2002
10 For designated LSA staff to feel confident in dealing with issues surrounding hearing impairment	Newly recruited LSA to work alongside Teacher for the Hearing Impaired	Release time	Jan 2002 ongoing
11 For LSA staff to be aware of and confident in using the school Health and Safety Policy	1 × session on policy	Time	Feb 2002
12 For LSA staff to be aware of child protection procedures	1 × session with designated member of staff for Child Protection	Time with JS and VP	March 2002
13 For LSA staff to be aware of new developments in Numeracy	1 × session with Numeracy coordinator	Cover for Numeracy coordinator's class	May 2002
14 For LSA staff to be aware of Special Educational Needs within the school	1 × session with SENCO	Release time for SENCO	June 2002
15 For LSA staff to be aware of own professional development needs	All LSA staff to be involved in preliminary meetings for appraisal cycle	Release time for Professional Development team and LSA staff	May–July 2002 (provision and review to begin in Sept 2002)

Figure 5.1a Example of a school development plan
Source: From Our Lady of Peace Junior School's SDP

Dimension 8 People Management
With regard to this dimension, we wish to maintain our Investors in People status and build upon this achievement. We also wish to look closely at how the team structure might be developed in order for it to contribute effectively to the standards raising agenda.

Objectives/ targets	Success criteria – expected standards to be reached	Action to be taken	Time scale/ completion date	Person responsible – lead, monitor, report	Costs – time, training, financing and resources	Monitoring of target (data to be used) Outcomes of proposed development on pupils learning	Evaluation process – method of assessing impact – progress check
To review the team structure in terms of its contribution to raising standards throughout the school	An effective team structure is in place with a clear brief to contribute to the raising and maintaining of standards throughout the school	Senior management team to consider the current team system and the contribution it makes to school improvement. Recommendations to be drawn up and submitted to governors	By April 2002	HT and senior management team	Time for discussion and decision making	Do minutes of team meetings indicate agenda of standards raising? Is there evidence that teams are making a difference to the education provided in the school?	HT and personnel committee to monitor
To review our staff development procedures with a view to maintaining our IiP status	Staff development enhanced and IiP status retained	Use new IiP standards to review current practice and make changes accordingly	By summer 2002	HT, staff development manager	Time and eventual costs of IiP review	Staff development meets IiP standards	HT, senior management team and personnel committee
To ensure that the performance management procedures are operating effectively	Performance management policy fully implemented for this round and in the future	HT and senior management team to manage this process in line with policy	Ongoing	Senior management team	Time and release costs – £2000 per year	Performance management helping to focus minds on school improvement	HT and senior managers to consult staff re effectiveness of this process
To continue to develop the development portfolios for support staff	Support staff have opportunities for development and professional dialogue	DHT to take leading role in organising the development portfolio meetings	Ongoing	DHT	Time – release costs for DHT	Do LSAs feel supported and valued?	HT to monitor

Figure 5.1b Example of a school development plan
Source: From Maldon Primary School development plan

question to answer is whether the TAs are directly affecting teaching and learning in a measurable way. It also gives strategies for watching TAs at work. It seems likely that the value of TAs is in the facilitation of school systems, their contribution to the team of staff, and their support of the learning process in class rather than in measurable learning outcomes at the end of the year. Only the school can decide where they wish to attribute value. If the school has determined its rationale for the employment of TAs, then evaluation must be against that rationale.

TAs can:	*Possible action*
Support inclusive policies enabling pupils otherwise excluded from mainstream school to attend the school	These pupils can be identified
Enable more time for pupils with SEN to spend with their peers	This can be counted in hours. Examples would be the presence of a TA enabling pupils to be in a science or PE lesson they would otherwise miss, or to take part in a class plenary session
Enable teachers to function in a less stressful way	Ask them. Count the teacher absences. Monitor time spent by teachers and TAs on various tasks
Enhance the systems of the school	List the tasks the TAs are actually performing
Raise the self-esteem of learners	Watch the pupils in class and at informal times. Look at truancy rates, staying-on rates, and participation of pupils in school functions
Provide counselling sessions	Monitor pupil stress
Provide liaison with parents or outside agencies	Monitor time spent by teachers and TAs on various tasks
Manage resources	Monitor time spent by teachers and TAs on various tasks
Assist learners to understand about their own learning	Monitor pupils' activities when they have left – how many go on to further education immediately or later?
Bring additional skills and dimensions of challenge and support to the school	Audit them

One measure which will probably not be an aim when employing TAs is to 'grow' people, or enable and encourage them to grow professionally and personally. It is significant, however, that effective schools often are known for their rate of staff turnover, not through stress or difficult pupils, but because teachers go on to 'greater' things and get promotion. Effective schools enable their TAs to undertake accredited courses, mentor them, and in the words of some headteachers, 'grow their own teaching staff'. The TAs either want to become a 'really good TA', or move forwards to getting a degree and qualified teacher status. It is worth recording such progress over the years and recognising the value that can be added to the lives of adults as well as pupils.

The next most difficult question is whether such support is cost-effective. When looking at case studies of innovation, Mortimore *et al.* (1994) suggested four principles of cost-effective analysis. The list could be used to determine what it is managers are hoping to improve by employing the TA.

• Fitness for purpose: challenging existing working arrangements

Comparing the school needs with the skills of existing staff
Appointing staff with particular skills for a particular purpose
None of these require any change in cost of the postholder, but will result in greater efficiency.

• The staff audit: identifies gaps in expertise

Reviews the needs of the school
Can identify areas of overload in highly paid postholders where some tasks could be undertaken by a lower level member of staff

• Costing innovations: does not need to be a detailed breakdown of costs

List methodically the resource implications of any proposal such as salary costs with on-costs, accommodation and equipment needs
Supervision costs – TAs cannot operate without being responsible to a qualified teacher
Joint planning time, mentoring time, time given to induction and appraisal etc.
What will happen if the innovation does not take place?

• An assessment of anticipated benefits – defining success criteria before the innovation.

Mortimore *et al.* (1994) also emphasised that the 'final justification, in each cases, is that there are sufficient *educational* reasons for a proposed change' (p. 206). The chapter discussing issues associated with employing support staff ends by saying that doing so may well result in the

reduction in the absolute numbers of teaching posts in a school [but which] would be likely to lead to an enhancement of the teachers' role. This enhanced role will be more challenging and have greater professional and pedagogical (rather than administrative) commitments. It may not be to everybody's liking, but it may lead to more effective schooling and more efficient use of resources.

(Mortimore *et al.* 1994 p. 206)

The school support

While the DfEE has not laid down how TAs should be employed, the *Good Practice Guide* (DfEE 2000a) makes clear that TAs can perform to their potential to support children only where they themselves are supported:

> These four strands of support are only one part of the story . . . At the same time the school has a responsibility to support the TA in fulfilling the expectations of the role . . . This obligation calls for consideration both of the way TAs are managed and of their professional development needs: management support should enable them to perform the job to the best of their abilities, and they should be encouraged to develop their skills and their potential. Clearly this view of two-way support requires the close co-operation of class teachers with whom TAs work as well as of headteachers and other managers.
>
> (DfEE 2000a pp. 8–9)

Lacey (1999) suggested that while the duties of LSAs in managing inclusion in different schools were similar, the greatest differences 'between the schools lay in the area of planning and preparation' (p. 20). She considered the vital ingredients at school level to be

- a positive planned, whole school approach to inclusion
- active management support for those who carry out the inclusion
- clear and shared aims for included pupils
- enthusiastic and knowledgeable teachers
- well trained and valued LSAs
- sound communication between different sites and units

(Lacey 1999 p. 33)

An audit should have revealed the area which the school management need to concentrate on first, provided the climate and relationships are ready for them.

Communication

One of the essential ingredients is a clear line of delegation, and this is not necessarily hierarchical. Governors can delegate to the headteacher yet they retain the overall responsibility, for instance for the delivery of the curriculum. Headteachers can utilise a flat form of management, often choosing to have a teaching timetable, even if modest, while another member of staff holds the 'front of house' position. SENCOs can organise the SEN provision or provide it themselves – it depends on their expertise and their philosophy for SEN. However the delegation is arranged, all members of staff need to know who to go to for what. TAs particularly need to know who to go to for anything from first aid and stock to advice on child protection, from where the materials for a task are kept and who to approach if they run out, to advice on a complex curriculum question raised by a pupil. Information on changes in school systems like timetables or behaviour management, dates, absences, new appointments, good news and bad is not just needed by the teachers, and managers should make this information readily available to TAs.

> Check the following:
> The staff notice board – do all see it?
> The staff day book/diary system – does it reach those it needs to?
> The parents' newsletters – do all staff get a copy?
> The annual report to parents – do all staff get a copy?
> Are all staff invited to social events?
> Can support staff access the policy documentation easily?
> Are support staff adequately represented on the governing body?
> Do all staff see the governing body minutes?
> Are the deliberations of the senior staff meetings minuted? Are the minutes available for perusal by staff?
> Are departmental communications as effective as the whole school ones?
> Who knows about changes in staff responsibilities, changes in staff circumstance which affect their role, changes in the community?
> Do all staff reply to consultations and if not why not?

Communication has a varied pathway, it is not all about the managers or the teachers telling the TAs things. TAs as a source of local information and dissemination are worth listening to and using as such. Managers need to tell not only the school staff about TAs, their purpose and methods, but also pupils, governors and parents. Too often TAs appear to the surprise of the class teacher, and then they have to introduce themselves to the pupils and the parents. Governors may even find out by default.

Structures

Developing policies

The NOS values and principles state:

Working within statutory and organisational frameworks

Teaching/classroom assistants are an integral part of the school staff team and as such have a responsibility for working to agreed school policies and procedures. In turn, the day-to-day work of the school takes place within a wider legislative framework affecting the content and delivery of the curriculum, health and safety, child protection and other aspects of school life. Teaching/classroom assistants need to be aware of these school and statutory frameworks, particularly those that directly impact on their own work with pupils.

(LGNTO 2001 p. 5)

Schools are required already to have formulated certain policies for delivery of the curriculum, appraisal (for teachers), SEN and inclusion, etc., and are recommended to have policies for equal opportunities, salaries, school development and teaching and learning.

The NOS refer to several of these areas:

Supporting inclusion
The principles underpinning inclusive education are those of setting suitable learning challenges, responding to pupils' diverse learning needs, and overcoming potential barriers to learning. Many teaching/classroom assistants are employed with specific responsibilities to work with individual pupils, others are given more general classroom responsibilities. Both roles are key to supporting inclusion by facilitating participation and learning, helping to build confidence, self-esteem and independence so that all pupils are enabled to reach their full potential alongside their peers.

Equality of opportunity
Teaching/classroom assistants have an important role in ensuring pupils' equal access to opportunities to learn and develop. Some pupils need additional or different support in order to have equality of opportunity and teaching/classroom assistants are often employed to provide this for individuals or small groups of pupils. Sometimes, working under the direction of the teacher, teaching/classroom assistants will work with the whole class in order to free up the teacher to work with individual pupils who need special attention.

Anti-discrimination
Teaching/classroom assistants must not discriminate against any individual or group on the grounds of gender, racial origins, religion, cultural or social background, disability or sexual orientation. They must comply with legislation and school policies relating to discrimination and should practice and promote anti-discriminatory practices in all interactions with pupils and colleagues.

Celebrating diversity
Teaching/classroom assistants should demonstrate their valuing of pupils' racial and other personal characteristics in order to help them develop self-esteem and a sense of identity, as well as promoting an

understanding and appreciation of different belief systems and cultures in all pupils.

(LGNTO 2001 pp. 5–6)

The way school policies are worded and practised will influence the way in which TAs are employed. If the SEN policy, for instance, indicates that all pupils will be included in classroom activities and withdrawn only in exceptional circumstances, the TAs will have to work with pupils in the classroom, not at a table outside or a room down the corridor. If a teaching policy requires all lessons to have a formal whole class instructional element, then this will have implications for the occupation of the TAs during a time when all eyes and ears should be on the class teacher. If appraisal is in place for teachers, equal opportunities should require similar arrangements for all support staff. The SDP, the way in which it is drawn up, consulted upon and reviewed can have considerable implications for the involvement (or not) of staff other than managers. The way in which parents are received or involved is going to affect the involvement of TAs in IEP reviews or their own contact with parents.

The awareness and the involvement in the formulation of the policies of the school by the governing body will make a difference to the type of TA policy that will be necessary or produced. Where policies are written with reference to existing policies, not only can the wording be less, but also the underlying aims, philosophy and forward strategy of the management run clearly through all that the school is trying to achieve.

Once the managers feel ready to formulate their TA policy in writing, somebody should be delegated to draw up a draft. Attempting to write such things from scratch with a group is hard. The following list of questions may help in getting started:

Strategy 5.9 Formulating school policy with respect to classroom assistants
Formulating policy is a good way to clarify one's own thinking, as well as a way of informing relevant others (such as school governors). A policy about the employment and deployment of classroom assistants might answer the following questions:

> How many assistants are employed in the school?
> What are their backgrounds (e.g. who are qualified, who are trainees etc.)?
> How are they used?
> With what classes/groups of pupils?
> To serve what purpose?
> Specifically, what learning gains are expected from the employment?
> How are assistants to be involved in planning for learning? Is time allowed for this?

What wider involvement do they have in the life of the school (e.g. are they expected to assist at school events such as the Christmas play)?
What mechanisms are available for assistants to express their views and observation?
How do assistants relate to teachers on the one hand and other school employees on the other?
What behaviour is expected of pupils in relation to assistants?
Are they involved in continuing professional development (external courses etc.)? When? In what ways?
Are they included in staff meetings, training days and school-based training?
Are salary levels appropriate? Are there opportunities for career progression?

(Kerry 2001 p. 85)

Many of the things listed below will be dealt with in Chapter 6 in some detail.

The policy could contain:

- The rationale for employing TAs in the first place
- Arrangements for appointment, job descriptions, induction, professional development review or appraisal
- Relationship to existing school policies such as teaching and learning, SEN, behaviour management, pay, grievance and discipline, health and safety
- Communication systems relevant to the TAs, including consultation, sources of information, line management and help
- Any specific things determined by the school such as expectations of attendance at meetings or other out of class provision, personal standards of behaviour
- Specific boundaries of responsibility particularly between qualified teachers and TAs
- Participation of the TAs in the school processes of long-term, medium- and short-term planning, IEP formulation and delivery, and assessment procedures
- Systems for monitoring and evaluation of provision.

The draft copy can then be circulated to all who might need to see it for their comment: the TAs themselves, the teachers who use TAs, governors, heads of department and other senior managers, especially the SENCO. Meetings can be held, questionnaires used – whatever the current school methods are. The final version may bear little resemblance to the first draft, but that was the point of the consultation.

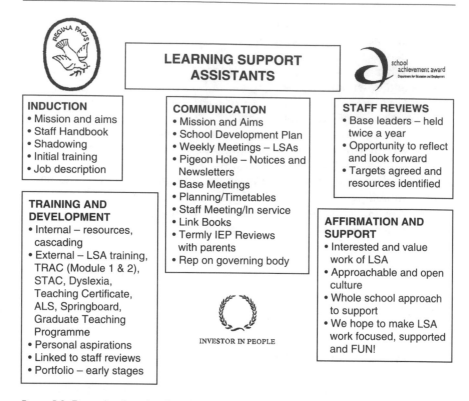

LEARNING SUPPORT ASSISTANTS

INDUCTION
• Mission and aims
• Staff Handbook
• Shadowing
• Initial training
• Job description

TRAINING AND DEVELOPMENT
• Internal – resources, cascading
• External – LSA training, TRAC (Module 1 & 2), STAC, Dyslexia, Teaching Certificate, ALS, Springboard, Graduate Teaching Programme
• Personal aspirations
• Linked to staff reviews
• Portfolio – early stages

COMMUNICATION
• Mission and Aims
• School Development Plan
• Weekly Meetings – LSAs
• Pigeon Hole – Notices and Newsletters
• Base Meetings
• Planning/Timetables
• Staff Meeting/In service
• Link Books
• Termly IEP Reviews with parents
• Rep on governing body

INVESTOR IN PEOPLE

STAFF REVIEWS
• Base leaders – held twice a year
• Opportunity to reflect and look forward
• Targets agreed and resources identified

AFFIRMATION AND SUPPORT
• Interested and value work of LSA
• Approachable and open culture
• Whole school approach to support
• We hope to make LSA work focused, supported and FUN!

Figure 5.2 Example of a school's policy summary sheet
Source: From Our Lady of Peace Junior School, Slough

Figure 5.2 is a list of headings which one school has drawn up to indicate its policy towards TAs.

Line management and deployment

There are various models of line management for TAs existing in schools and each has something to recommend it. One is the SEN/SENCO model where the TAs are employed ostensibly to support SEN and therefore the SENCO is in charge of their deployment and professional development; one is curric-ulum based where the co-ordinator or head of department manages a group of TAs for their subject from among a larger TA team; one is teacher/year group based where the head of year is the line manager, a model which is more often found in secondary schools, but could be part of a foundation stage/KS1/KS2 management model; and the last one is where the TAs are managed by a senior TA or another member of the support staff such as the bursar or school secretary. These models can apply to primary or secondary schools. In any of these, a senior manager must still have overall responsibility, delegating certain aspects of it to any other members of staff. This is particularly important in the last scenario, in order that the overall priorities for teaching and learning are retained.

Because of the history of TA development, the SEN based model is the one found in most schools. In secondary schools, typically the line manager for TAs has been the SENCO, and as this is usually a post of senior management with its own budget, the budget management, induction, appraisal and professional development responsibilities have lain with that SEN department. In primary, the SENCO was often the headteacher, until the job became so great that it had to be delegated, or the headteacher saw professional development possibilities for another member of staff, who then became the SENCO. In my study schools, the SENCO, in one case the headteacher and in the other a separate person, both got involved in the professional development and training of the TAs, but line management was given to the deputy headteachers. Because the schools were relatively small and the systems and structures were evolving, the actual meaning of the various roles became blurred. Following the needs of specialisms within curriculum in secondary, especially in areas such as science or languages, and the emphasis on the NLNS in primary, more assistants are being managed by heads of department or subject co-ordinators.

Whatever is agreed, the proposed new regulations will have to be taken into account regarding the supervision of the work of TAs. 'Qualified teachers must have the overall responsibility for teaching and learning' and

> determining what should be delegated, the nature and the extent of supervision should primarily be a matter for the professional judgement of headteachers and qualified teachers than for rigid national determination; the kind of supervision, regulated by law, could be quite distinct from any arrangement the school will decide to make for the line management of the relevant member of the support staff; the purpose of this kind of supervision is to ensure high standards of teaching and learning.
>
> (DfES 2002a p. 17)

This proposal will be statutory and the draft regulations are already published (DfES 2002c). These draft regulations include guidance and specimen job descriptions.

The guidance on establishing a system of supervision covers all categories of people called teachers who do not have QTS as well as TAs, and so recommends a differential system depending on the qualifications and experience of staff as well as the job they are required to carry out. As managers will have audited this information about their team of TAs, this aspect of their role should be simple to carry out. The regulations also remind managers about all the standard checks that need to be carried out before anybody works in a school, including obtaining information from the Criminal

Records Bureau. The system of supervision decided upon should be included in the job description of the TA. The supervisor can be the line manager, with the day-to-day oversight being maintained by the class teacher, providing the line manager is a qualified teacher. These supervision arrangements must spell out whether the TA can work unsupervised with a group of children, or can undertake whole class responsibilities. Clearly, as TAs progress in qualifications or change jobs, the arrangements for supervision will need to be reviewed.

One of the problems voiced by TAs is that of following the 'hour here and an hour there' deployment method. Managers tend to see it as providing an equitable distribution of a rare resource or a way of getting the best value for money by following curriculum areas that have the greatest need – an assistant trained in ALS can go and do it in several classes, but TAs find such a practice unrewarding and only exacerbating the problems of planning and feedback with teachers. They find, as managers do who visit several classes to observe practice, that all teachers, however well they are adapting to the expected ways of their schools, will put their own 'stamp' on the classroom routines and teaching methods. The TAs then have to pick up these nuances, which they usually do well, to fit in with the particular classroom climate in which they are deployed. This is also true in secondary schools, where the model until recently was always to employ assistants to support a particular pupil, thus the TA went, and in many cases still goes, with the pupil to anything up to eight different lessons in a day. Unless there are carefully briefed teachers, and excellent communication systems, the participation of the TA in the full support of the teacher might be curtailed.

Another consideration is the need to fit the skills of the TAs to the needs of the school. Unless there is a careful matching of such skills, there is likely to be an underuse of the qualities of those employed in the school, and maybe some opportunities for pupils missed. Managers' audits of skills, qualifications and experiences will prove invaluable here, when set alongside the consideration of the needs of the pupils and teachers.

The meaning of management can be indistinct in all these cases and needs to be defined. Managers must decide who has responsibility for the following areas:

Supervision as defined in the new regulations
Timetables
Individual pupils' needs
Curriculum outcomes raising test results
Induction
Appraisal
Ensuring welfare and communication systems are working
Mentoring for course development
Professional development taking place in-house

These can all be the responsibility of one person, or shared, but the TA must not fall into gaps, where one person thinks another person is doing part of the job. Kerry (2001) outlines the strengths and weakness in managers as voiced by special needs teaching assistants (SNTAs) in his survey:

Strengths
He/she:

- provides plenty of suitable work for the SNTA;
- delegates responsibility;
- recognises a job well done;
- is supportive;
- is available for consultation;
- holds regular planning meetings;
- is a good and frequent communicator;
- produces a relaxed and friendly atmosphere in the unit;
- understands the value of praise for employees.

Weaknesses
He/she:

- is too busy;
- does not get to grips with problems;
- doesn't organise paperwork;
- takes advantage of employees' goodwill;
- doesn't maintain continuity in the employee's role;
- doesn't plan ahead sufficiently or brief the SNTA.

(Kerry 2001 p. 101)

Pay and conditions of service: budget implications

Farrell *et al.* (1999) raised the issues of contracts, career structure and pay, as well as management. They commented on the lack of relevant job descriptions and on conflicting ideas about appropriate employers – LEAs or schools. The onus, in the view of the DfEE, is quite clearly on the employer:

> The Government takes the view that pay and conditions for teaching assistants are best determined at local level . . . Work on the new national occupational standards and a qualifications framework . . . should [make it] then be possible for employers of TAs (local authorities or schools) to compare their local arrangements with what is implied by the framework, satisfying themselves that those arrangements properly recognise different levels of responsibility and encourage development through training and the acquisition of relevant qualifications.

(DfEE 2000a p. 4)

The 2002 proposals for higher level TAs do not alter this. The government proposed to 'liaise with the National Joint Council for Local Government Services as it develops guidance for schools and LEAs on the framework for grading support staff, with the aim of ensuring that schools and LEAs include the proposed higher-level roles within their future thinking on grading levels' (DfES 2002a). The local level can be school, LEA, supply agency or an Education Action Zone. This means that TAs could be employed on any pay scale commensurate with their responsibilities. The qualifications they have should determine the kinds of responsibilities for which they are employed. Qualified teachers can be employed as TAs, but will not be paid as such if the job is not to take responsibility for the teaching and learning of pupils.

Since the arrival of single status agreements, at least many schools are undertaking a job evaluation exercise which is making it clearer that the responsibilities of each TA must be determined. However, in practice the pay scales used by schools still put the evaluated job below that of administrative assistants and bursars, let alone instructors or teachers. Increased membership of unions may well result in pressure on schools and LEAs to reconsider this. While historical views on pay for TAs persist, and whole school budgets do not allow for expansion in the TAs workforce, increases are unlikely. One of the problems is that most TAs are part time, and so even quotations of annual pay at a low level are misleading. So often, they are still employed through specific funding allocated to the school for supporting pupils with SEN, and this funding is allocated for a certain number of hours at a particular rate. This makes no allowance for the need for inclusion of TAs in the processes of the school, the meetings, planning, preparation and feedback so necessary to do the job adequately let alone effectively.

There was an expectation among some, early on in the STA qualification history, that getting the award should entitle holders to a pay rise. Some schools did implement this, but the rise did not necessarily indicate any change in duties. Responsibility could also increase with no commensurate pay rise. Traditionally, the argument has been that not only was the school funded for only a particular set of hours at a particular scale, but also any increase on this made by the school would inevitably result in less of the 'cake' to go round, therefore fewer TAs would be employed or everyone's hours would be cut. Teams of TAs, ever loyal to their colleagues, would voice the opinion that they would rather be low paid and keep everyone on the team than any pay rise be awarded. TAs like their job, they may do it well and being conscientious just go on giving their own time through goodwill. The pay may be 'less than a shelf stacker in a supermarket' but there is greater job satisfaction.

While TAs often do feel valued by their school, despite their pay, the school strategy must be fair. While the pay is so low, few men and young people will be attracted to the profession, and women needing to support their families will continue to resort to the tax credit system. If the school budgets really cannot support the appropriate pay for the job required, then the school management and governors must lobby for an increased total school budget. TAs are relatively powerless to do this on their own behalf.

Basic rate of pay is not the only thing that needs to be set. Managers must also consider the associated conditions of service, such as:

- all the issues of culture and ethos
- the domestic arrangements
- ensuring grievance and discipline policies are for all staff
- knowing who the union representatives and the health and safety representatives are
- where to enquire about employment problems
- contracts which reflect their jobs
- hours and weeks of work
- appropriate names – never non-anything
- what kind of job security is available
- whether mentor support will be available for course attendance
- all the policies concerning pay whether:

    paid planning time and meeting time is included
    there is entitlement to superannuation or holiday retainer pay
    contracts and pay rates cover the INSET days or not
    performance pay is for all staff or just teachers
    any cost of courses will be met

Nicholas (2001), as a TA, makes the comment:

    the instability of the hours can be worrying and the fact that even if you have a job things become uncertain for you when a child with a statement moves to another school. This means that, on the whole, the job does not attract younger people or men. It is more of a second career, taken up by women like myself who became involved after having children.

Job or salary reviews

The TA review may have revealed the need for comprehensive job or salary reviews, in which case a full-blown readvertisement and reappointment procedure will have to be instituted, with the possible results of creating redundancies. If this is the case, the school management would be well advised to take expert advice from personnel advisers, in order that the procedure is sensitively and properly carried out. It is not the intention of any development to cause pain to people, but it can happen in this process. If the level of support for pupils, learning and teaching needed by the school was found to be of a higher order than that possible with some of the existing staff, whose personal intellectual capability precluded them from training to the required level, or it was discovered that highly qualified people drawing inappropriate remuneration were fulfilling less demanding roles, there may be some personnel problems to face.

Diary evidence

A school had been employing a nursery nurse on a higher pay scale than the TAs were on, to support their early years class. The nursery nurse contract was a permanent one, with a full-time (32.5 hours a week 48 weeks a year) element. As numbers going to the school were forecast to be low over the next three or four years, the budget forecast for the school was a decreasing one. The early years (EY) class took the summer-born 4 year olds only part time in January, and full time for the summer term, with the spring-born 4 year olds part time in the September. This meant that the nursery nurse was in the habit of supporting the summer-born 4 year olds part time in January, and full time for the summer term, with the spring-born 4 year olds part time in September. The nursery nurse was therefore supporting the Year 1 and Year 2 class considerably more during those light pupil number terms. As a highly trained and competent person, she was greatly appreciated. Nevertheless, her salary was a considerable drain on the budget. TAs were also employed on a part-time hourly paid basis, on the lowest scale with temporary contracts throughout the school, from Year 1 to Year 6, largely to support some challenging pupils, but they had also been trained to support the NLNS. One of these TAs had an STA level 3 qualification, one a level 4 OU STAC qualification (one-sixth of a degree) and two had attended SEN courses for specific disabilities. Considerable LEA funding supported the SEN aspect of the school's work. The governors on examining the situation took advice, and after explaining the situation had to institute a redundancy situation for all the TAs and the NNEB. The NNEB, having been on a permanent contract, was entitled to redundancy pay, and took voluntary redundancy. The school managers then redefined the jobs they felt still needed doing and advertised within the school. It was not the easiest of times for the school, but the openness, consultation and sensitivity implemented the change effectively with the least trauma for the staff concerned.

Given the school has systems and structures which enable TAs as a group to be managed appropriately, their individual management actually starts before they are appointed, when they are 'but a twinkle in the manager's eyes', that is when first considering the appointment of an addition to the team. Chapter 6 looks at the tactics which can be used for each TA to enable the strategies suggested in Chapters 4 and 5 to take place for the TA team.

Employing TAs

From recruitment to review

> To perform well you need to know what it is you are supposed to be doing
> . . . Because the role of the TA has been evolving, and as it varies according
> to the school and the experience and qualifications of the TA, the task may
> well require more thought than it does for other members of staff whose
> role is better established. It may require more monitoring and follow-up.
>
> (DfEE 2000a p. 15)

This chapter looks at the school processes and procedures which should
ensue when TAs are recruited, inducted, mentored and reviewed appropriately. It covers matters of job descriptions and person specifications,
the construction of personal professional portfolios and the sort of
documents TAs need to carry out their job effectively within the ethos of
the school.

Following a review

During the audit and review procedures suggested in the previous chapters,
there will have been a consideration of what jobs need doing in the school,
as well as looking at what the existing TAs do, or could do. Also, it is likely
that the current list of jobs to be done has accumulated historically, from
SEN reviews, curriculum initiatives, in-school projects or even emergency
stop-gap procedures as a result of a shortage of qualified teachers. Another,
much more likely and positive situation is where the review has shown an
increased demand for teaching and learning assistance of one kind or
another. This will leave the school with several options. It is possible that
the budget situation is such that there is no flexibility for either increasing hours or changing pay scales for the TAs to adapt their current contracts
to the new circumstances. However, it is also clear from research, that
where schools are prepared to use their budgets creatively and flexibly both
are possible.

Case study evidence

My two study schools at the time of the research, not a time of either specific standards funding for TA recruitment or generous funding from government or LEA, both employed a team of five or six TAs. They were one-form and one-and-half-form entry primary schools, that is they had six and nine classes respectively. Both had taken the opportunity to train two of the TAs under the OU STAC scheme, and undertook considerable in-house training and support. Both funded their teams from a combination of individual pupil earmarked SEN funding, the school budget allocation of earmarked funding and a contribution from the general budget. One decided not to employ a specialist SEN teacher even for a few hours but to depend on their in-house SENCO expertise, the other employed a specialist teacher, but included liaison and training of the TA team in the job description. All TAs in both teams were part time. At that time, equivalent schools were often employing only half the same number of hours' worth of support. Both the schools paid for non-pupil joint teacher planning time, meeting time and INSET attendance and fully funded any expenses incurred by training. At the same time TAs in other schools were being sent on courses in their own time at their own expense. Budget allocations to schools in the authority were similar for similar numbers and circumstances.

The schools that wanted to employ a quality team were doing it, with no apparent loss to equipment resource allocations, buildings' maintenance, or teacher recruitment. Not being party to the details of their school budgeting it is not possible to state where savings were made in those schools. Where I was aware of such details in other schools, the indications were that the class sizes were slightly larger, possibly only by two or three pupils per year group, or the salaries of the head or posts of responsibility were set marginally lower than in other schools. £5000 could, at that time, fund a TA on the lowest scale for 20 hours a week in term time, or be added to one senior teacher's salary, or be provided from admitting two extra pupils a year. It does mean a review of the school priorities; many teachers are willing to trade a slightly larger class for the prospect of the extra adult for a portion of the week. Only the school can make these decisions.

With the changes in funding, some directly forthcoming for TA recruitment, and some just an increase in general schools' budget following government increases or LEA changed priorities, many schools have been in the enviable position of not only being able to increase the pay levels and hours of existing staff, but also recruit new people. The practical issues to do with retraining and developing TAs come later in the chapter. Ensuring that new and existing staff have the appropriate support from the school, including paid meeting time, is as good a place to start as any.

Recruitment

The process

'The recruitment of staff is one of the most important management activities and it is therefore worth investing more care and time to select the best' (Brighouse and Woods 1999 p. 116). The appointment of support staff is no less important than that of teaching staff, although in the past has followed a rather informal, ad-hoc route. Certainly, when I was a headteacher, I used to observe volunteer parents helping in school and with the collusion of teaching staff, inviting the likely potential member of staff to accept a short, say five hours per week, contract to support a child with SEN whose statements and funding had just been approved. With the encouragement and support of an interested governor, we started a formal advertisement and interview process for new posts. While this was time consuming, it immediately revealed that among the community were highly trained, interested and interesting people welcoming the new job opportunity. Colleagues in urban areas were finding that for one teacher applicant to an advertised post, they were getting over a hundered applicants for a TA post. Clearly, there was a need for properly instituted procedures to make things open, equitable, fair and provide the best possible staff for the education of the children. Whatever recruitment procedures the school has in place for teachers should apply to all staff.

> *Some things which you can check*
> You may want to involve your LEA Personnel Department or local adviser.
> Decide what it is you want from this recruit and where this appointment sits in the school development plan.
> Consult with senior staff and the teacher who will be working with the potential candidate.
> Consult with the Personnel Committee or people-related committee or members of the governing body delegated to deal with staffing matters.
> You could discuss the role with relevant people outside the school – an SEN adviser, early years adviser, literacy or numeracy adviser, or the general school adviser if needed.
> Decide what will be the line management of this recruit.
> Consider what the future opportunities will be for this person within the school.

Think about the implications for other staff in the school, your training programme and domestic facilities.

Then, decide on a job description and a person specification, including qualifications, experience, type of contact and pay scale to be offered.
Advertise appropriately – consider parents' magazines or newsletters, community newsletters or local papers, the local LEA staffing circular.
Decide on the wording of the advert to reflect your needs and the ethos of the school.
Decide the time, place and nature of the selection process.
Will it just be a simple interview? What questions do you need to ask?
Prepare a simple pack for the administrative staff to send to applicants, with some details of the school, the job description and person specification.
Shortlist with a senior member of staff or a relevant teacher, and an appropriate governor. The support staff governor should not be involved in case the appointment would affect their status. Send for references, considering them at an agreed point within the process.
Meet them informally beforehand if possible to answer their questions and enable them to be shown round the school if they have not been before.
Interview as for any other member of staff, remembering all the equal opportunities issues, and answering their questions.

Discuss and agree successful candidate with panel. Notify successful and unsuccessful candidates.
Prepare an induction programme.

The person specification

With personality and competence so important in the work of TAs the appointment process for them is crucial. The heads in the study schools freely admitted that while they were using open advertisements in their employment processes, the volunteers, whom they had seen in operation in a positive light, had an advantage at selection time. Of course, in secondary schools the opportunity for seeing volunteers at work is much less likely than in primary schools: parents, who are keen to volunteer when their children are small, and the school is near home, tend to go to get other paid employment once their children start at secondary school.

Qualifications, mentioned in Chapter 2 and dealt with in greater detail in Chapter 8, have also become much more available and with the NOS, a much clearer recognition of what the job of TA is should emerge. Managers will know what kind of personality will fit into their existing teams, both whole school and TA teams, and can define the qualifications and experience,

possible including that of having been a volunteer in a school, in the advertisements. The person specification is a set of criteria against which each
candidate can be matched, and if desired, scored. Each characteristic can be
marked E or D – essential or desirable – and can cover the experience, knowledge, skills, qualifications and personal qualities which would ideally fit the
needs of the school.

If teachers can be asked to teach a class on interview, consider asking TAs
to work with a group. For new TAs, a probationary period of up to six
months would be acceptable. Personnel advisers would be able to give
recommendations about such periods. These would be the same arrangements that can be made for all support staff now the Single Status Agreement
is coming into play. In this way managers can see how the TAs perform, give
appropriate feedback, and can give people previously unknown to the school
as fair an opportunity as the in-house volunteer who is better known.

Entry level

As induction levels are not defined in the NOS, there is no national guidance
about the basic levels expected of a person who can be employed in a school.
All potential employees are subject to checks of identity, academic qualifications, references, employment history, criminal record and a health check.
Information on carrying out pre-appointment checks can be found in DfES
guidance issued in May 2002 (Reference DfES/0278/2002). It is recommended that an enhanced disclosure is obtained for TAs, the same as for
teachers, from the Criminal Records Bureau. These checks will show up only
standard items and more than these checks are required when appointing a
TA. A possible list, which could be adapted for individual schools, is supplied
below. It was part of the proposal put forward for an orientation programme
during the consultation for the Qualification framework for those working in
the early years sector (QCA 1999). Some of its qualities are incorporated in
the level 1 of the competency Table 2.1 in Chapter 2.

Essential criteria for suitable personal characteristics of candidates
• ability to relate to children; warmth
• potential to change attitudes and question own values; respect for differences amongst people
• willingness to learn and evaluate own practice
• commitment to complete training and assessment and to sustain work/
  training programme including assignments and other set course work
• personal maturity appropriate to the age of the applicant; not seeking to
  work with children in order to meet own emotional needs
• ability to assess situations and know own limitations; willingness to seek
  advice/support
• ability to remain calm under pressure or in crisis/emergency

- understands the physical requirements of working with young children (or pupils of age of institution)
- enthusiasm
- good timekeeping
- potential to develop the ability to prioritise and judge relative significance of conflicting demands
- anti-discriminatory attitudes, awareness of prejudice.

(From Annexe 3 of the QCA Consultation Paper November 1998)

Schools must also decide whether any particular qualifications are required. These could be in the SEN area for instance – a qualification in signing, or dealing with a particular disability.

The job description

It is not easy to give an exemplar job description given the diversity of role of the TA, and each member of staff may need a different one. Personnel departments will again be able to help, particularly in the light of the NOS and the Single Status Agreements, or managers can use the NOS themselves. It is usual for TAs' job descriptions to follow the practice of having general and generic sections and specific ones. For the latter it is helpful to consider each of the four strands (discussed in Chapter 3) when formulating job descriptions.

Some useful subheadings with examples of areas to be defined could be:

Main purpose of the job
Duties and responsibilities
- *Support for pupils*

    Develop an understanding of the range of learning support needs for 'a named pupil'
    To meet the child's physical needs as required
    To reinforce the pupil's self-esteem
    To implement a 'named programme'

- *Support for teachers*

    To provide practical support to 'named class teachers'
    To participate in specified planning time
    To provide feedback about the pupils to the teacher(s)
    To contribute to the maintenance of pupils progress records
    To liaise with 'named agencies'

- *Support for the school*

    To attend relevant in-service training
    To understand and adhere to relevant school policies and procedures
    To be included in the staff development programme

- *Support for the curriculum*

    To understand school policies in relation to 'named subjects'
    To observe pupils learning in 'named subjects'
    The take responsibility for the maintenance of 'named resources'

- *Support to be provided by the school:*

    Annual review of job description through an appraisal process
    Opportunities for career development
    Access to all relevant documentation
    Provision of mentor and line manager support.

- *Supervision arrangements*

    Observation by 'a named teacher' at defined intervals
    Performance review by a 'a named teacher'
    Meeting arrangements
    Class teacher planning and feedback times.

The items in quotation marks (e.g. 'a named pupil') would need to be replaced by names. Clearly this list does not cover specific tasks, and is likely to change with time – hence the need for constant review. These specific tasks could include anything from making the tea/coffee, carrying out photocopying, maintaining the video recordings library, to particular support for a particular pupil which might entail specific training. Whether or not the TA is to undertake whole class supervision, act as supply cover, or undertake other specific tasks traditionally carried out by teachers must be specifically spelt out and the supervision arrangements to match indicated. All job descriptions should be drawn up with the agreement of the person who is going to carry out the job or they can be meaningless, and in the case of TAs it would make excellent sense for the teachers or agencies named to be consulted as well. All of those named should have copies so that everyone knows what the TA is supposed to do.

After making the decisions regarding a potential new employee, the procedures are identical to those of any other member of staff:

    Advertising, probably locally in a shop or local paper
    Shortlisting using the job description and person specification
    Providing information and opportunities for visits
    Setting up any task completion or observation opportunity as well as the interview time and place
    Interviewing often with a relevant member of the teaching staff, and possibly with a governor, remembering all the usual equal opportunities issues
    Considering references and checks to be undertaken

Informing the successful candidate subject to checking procedures being satisfactory, and debriefing the unsuccessful candidates

Informing the school community of outcomes

Carry out checks

Prepare documentation and induction procedures, including agreeing specific job description.

It should be remembered that in interviewing, appointing successful people for the job, or debriefing unsuccessful candidates for a TA's post, that the TA may never have been through the procedure before, and may be unaware of the use of criteria for selection purposes or how the school proceeds from that point. Some explanations might be appreciated. Figure 6.1 is an example of a document for TAs to use to prepare themselves for an interview.

Induction programme

It is easy to forget the induction of a member of staff who may be working for only a few hours a week, but given the closeness with which most TAs work with pupils, it is essential. Because TAs have often come to the post via the volunteer route there is sometimes the assumption that they know all they need to know about the school processes. In addition, being people who are being appointed for their initiative and sensitivity, they are also likely to be able to find out what they need to know. However, I have found the following list useful to check against; some of the items will be dealt with in greater detail in later chapters.

Before the TA starts

The TA needs

- a map of the school, with a detailed timetable for his/her first day – and beyond if it is available
- a copy of the job description
- the expectations of the school in terms of dress code, titles and names used
- car parking, time of arrival and where to go in the school when he/she arrives.

The school needs to

- be aware of a new arrival to be ready to welcome them – children and all other staff
- have a welcome pack of appropriate documentation, or a list of where it can be found

TEACHING ASSISTANTS
Discussion sheet for interview

What do you regard as your personal strengths and weaknesses?
Can you tell me a little about yourself as a person rather than a potential LSA?
What made you apply for this position in school?
How well do you think you can work as part of a team? Examples?
There will be areas where you/we feel you need training – how do you view this?
How do you see your development within the school? Have you any aspirations or ambitions?
How would you deal with a difficult child in a group situation?
As part of the whole school team, which areas do you feel help the quality of education we offer?
As part of the whole school team, which areas do you feel help communication both inside and outside of school?
Do you have any questions you would like to ask?
The way LSAs are worked here is by need be it for individual children or class. Equally the funding is never straightforward. Therefore, hours are never straightforward either and are constantly changing. Do you have a problem with that?

Figure 6.1 Example of a discussion sheet for TA interviews
Source: Beehive Lane Community Primary School

- appoint a mentor for the first year, whether or not the TA is undertaking any outside course
- ensure somebody greets the TA and settles him/her in for the first day,

> introduces the TA to the teachers and pupils with whom he/she will be working closely
> briefs the TA on the contents of the documentation.

On the first day, if possible, the new TA should

- be shown round the school and introduced where appropriate including

> where to keep their personal belongings
> staff facilities for toilet, refreshment and rest/sickness

- be introduced to the mentor if that is a different person
- meet the people with whom he/she will be working closely
- shadow an experienced TA
- be given the document file/school support staff handbook and the contents briefly explained.

During the first week the following policies and procedures should be made clear to the new TA:

- health, safety and security strategies, particularly in dealing with emergencies
- confidentiality
- child protection.

Appointing a mentor

With the appointing of a mentor comes a commitment of resources of time of a teacher or the senior TA mentioned in Chapter 5, and possibly budget, on behalf of the TA. Anyone new to a post in the school should be allocated a mentor – a guide, a friend, not usually the line manager. It does not have to be a superior in the school hierarchy, but someone who has more experience of the ways of the school. While a senior TA can do the job of mentor to a TA, given sufficient knowledge and expertise, particularly regarding the more domestic support strategies, it is necessary that this senior TA have easy communication routes to a relevant and responsible teacher. It will depend on the nature of the mentoring tasks. If there is curriculum understanding and expertise to be explained, then a teacher will have the greater knowledge. If it is SEN expertise there must be direct routes to the SENCO. If the TA is appointed to support a particular area or classroom supervised by a teacher, it makes sense that the TA has easy access to the teacher concerned.

The teachers nominated may see such a mentor/support role as yet another job to do in an already overloaded schedule. This attitude can be overcome only by managers' recognition of the importance of such a role, and appropriate management strategies. This may include allocating temporary responsibility salary recognition to the teacher concerned, or providing extra pupil contact release time. Where this has been done, both school and teacher have quickly recognised the benefits of having well-informed, welcomed TAs and teachers who understand what the TA is capable of and that both are part of a whole school team. Dew-Hughes *et al.* (1998) collected comments from their course for LSAs in secondary schools, which emphasised the important role of mentors and whole school support in training TAs.

Diary evidence
In the early days of the OU STAC course 1995–96 in Essex, when doing mentor-training sessions with the teachers, there was resentment and even on one occasion anger. The whole teaching load for the course seemed to fall upon their shoulders, and questions such as 'Why are "these people" learning all this stuff?' were asked. While this response had largely gone by 2000, partly due to warning schools very clearly about the nature of the support required by the course, it was also due to the greater realisation by teachers of what TAs can do when they have the underpinning knowledge about the tasks they are asked to do. Teacher mentors were even known to declare themselves 'converts' to the TA working in their class after their mentor experience. Unfortunately, the part of the new induction courses of the DfEE requiring the attendance of a senior teacher/mentor at them for some sessions also brought out some feelings of resentment. Schools were invited to send their newly recruited TAs and mentors for training free of charge, paid for under the Standards Fund, and some schools, previously avoiding commitment to training or professional development of support staff, sent unprepared and even unwilling teachers with the TAs. In addition, where a senior TA was sent on the courses, they were sometimes unable, back at school, to influence the school managers sufficiently to properly support the TA on the course. Opportunities for observation and discussion had been available.

The mentoring may include an element of TA observation, allowing the teachers to share developmental needs with the TAs and the headteacher, but this is more akin to the appraisal process. The experiences of most induction courses, however, where the teacher was well briefed and their role understood by senior managers, were positive, as have been the responses of teachers who have attended ALS training with their TAs. An important issue for mentoring off-site courses is that all the teachers should be aware of the content of the course, not just the mentor, if the school is to be able to make full use of the TA once trained. TAs, encouraged by their mentors are quite able to take part of a staff meeting and explain briefly what they are studying and why. Some primary schools with a TA undertaking the OU STAC course used some of the OU materials, such as their videos, as staff meeting discussion material.

Mentoring

Mentoring has been found to be crucial to the success of in-house professional development, not only in teaching but also throughout business and industry. However, it is, perhaps, unrealistic to expect one person, a mentor, to be all things to another member of staff. A 'joint working' policy would help those teachers given a mentoring role. All the outside courses, from induction to higher education level, include some kind of in-house activity or observation, and all recommend mentor support, both to enable these processes to take place and for the mentor to interpret the course contents in the light of the in-house practice and policies. The very act of mentoring is recognised by some universities (such as the OU) as a legitimate subject for a master's study.

Mentoring is not just a requisite of courses. The concept can permeate a school philosophy; 'mentoring schools' have been recognised by colleagues. A useful model can be found in *Issues in Mentoring* (Kerry and Mayes 1995), where the authors describe progressive stages in mentoring.

In the first stage, the apprentice emulates the experienced practitioner, by practising under his or her guidance. This is particularly necessary for a new TA, who needs information and a role model in order to develop appropriate skills and understanding. The TA needs to be able to ask 'Why is the classroom set out in this way? Why is this particular piece of equipment in use now? What do you mean by this word? How do you want this piece of work presented? How do I use this tool?'

This can lead on to systematic training by the mentor of the TA where there is a realisation of the competencies needed and the underpinning knowledge required. The mentor can observe the TA and provide constructive feedback. The TA is allowed to experiment under the guidance of an agreeable teacher.

This in turn can lead to the teacher or mentor and TA focusing together on the needs of the pupils, looking at their learning, and talking about how best the partnership can develop. This needs openness of mind by both, it may confront the beliefs or values of either, and may necessitate changes in practice.

It is important for the management team to know how the TA feels about the mentor and the process and to review this as the process develops. The team needs to keep a watching brief, other staff should know in order to provide help, support and encouragement wherever possible. Telling pupils that adults are still learning and developing is an important part of the children's education. Pupils are also a useful source of information about the process and people if questioned sensitively. Governors need to know of the process and what it means for the school in terms of resource allocation and professional development of their staff. Parents of individual children might need to be informed if child studies are undertaken or regular observations are to be incorporated in essays. They are often interested and provide extra information about the child which adds further dimensions to any study being undertaken to the benefit of all particularly the child.

There are some points which need to be borne in mind. The professional relationship of a TA to a teacher is not that of a peer, certainly in career, pay and status. Prior experience and training can be very different and not necessarily one way. The TA may be a graduate, with specific understanding and skills in a subject area, and the teacher a certificated, very experienced teacher but without a degree. The assistants may have children of their own, and other life experiences which the teacher has not. TAs, keen to develop, can overtake their teacher in enthusiasm, and may become more informed as to current issues in education than the teacher. This was particularly true in the feedback for a few TAs undertaking the behaviour management modules in the induction training (DfEE 2000e; DfES, 2001c). TAs have more time for reflection with less paperwork. The mentor will be well voiced in the language of the classroom, explaining instinctual behaviour or their traditional activities, but may not be experienced in working closely with or developing another adult.

The context of each school, even in their different geographical layout, may influence the nature of the mentoring process; where the TAs cannot get into the staffroom because of its size, ongoing professional debate about individual children's problems is not so easy. The complexity of classroom dynamics can confuse. Support groups are very helpful, but need organisation and finance. External support is expensive.

The act of mentoring may also create an extra time commitment from the TA in school which should be considered and paid for. Senior managers must be alert for possible personality clashes or clashes of values, beliefs or educational philosophy, e.g. multiculturalism, attitudes to discipline. The TA may prove to provide a poor role model to pupils for cultural reasons, e.g. poor grammatical speech, which is however normal for their geographical origin. TAs often see more breadth of school practice than the classroom teacher and can be confused as to variations in practice seen. Literacy and numeracy levels of TAs may vary.

Professional development portfolios

The rationale of a portfolio

Many schools, before the start of the NC, began a process of accumulating Records of Achievement folders for pupils. The vocational qualifications developments depend on students accumulating evidence in portfolios, which is assessed as the student progresses; the student does not necessarily then have to undertake a final written examination. These developments have led to a general recognition that all of us could keep a personal portfolio of our achievements, which with evidence from work experience and accumulated qualifications becomes a professional portfolio. The concept is taken up in the government proposals for Progress Files (DfEE 2000f) and many colleges as a means of tracking learning achievements. Schools have sometimes developed their own for their teachers, and a few for all their staff, especially where they have been working for IiP status. The national TA induction training provides such a file and framework for TAs (DfEE 2000b; DfES 2001a) the contents of which can be downloaded from the website www.teachernet.gov.uk/teachingassistants.

Where portfolios are used as a management tool for professional development they have been found to be most helpful, but they are particularly helpful for the individual whose file it is. This is especially true for support staff who are likely to undertake an NVQ qualification. Evidence accumulated in a personal professional portfolio, in reality just a ringbinder with sections, can be photocopied where relevant for the assessment and verification process of the award. Completing the personal section at the beginning of a file just for them immediately gives the TA a feeling of self-worth and belonging to an establishment that cares about who they are and what they are going to do within that establishment. I have informally observed a SENCO introducing a professional portfolio to a new TA in a school, and watched the TA grow as she turned the pages, anticipating completing the personal pages, listing courses and undertaking a self-review. She recognised that how she progressed in her new job mattered to others as well as herself.

The portfolio construction

A portfolio is really just a loose-leaf collection of information and evidence about the person with sections and prompt sheets. Personal files can become quite bulky if too eclectic; a separate staff file for relevant school documentation and information and separate files for out-of-school courses may well be needed. Provide a sturdy ringbinder with the school name and logo on the outside along with the new owner's name. Provide a sprinkling of plastic pockets to take certificates, and section dividers, the wider ones which will overlap the plastic pockets for areas something like the list below. Each

Figure 6.2 Organising the paperwork in a portfolio

section can then have prompt sheets for the new member of staff to complete (Figure 6.2).

The first action of the mentor can be to explain the purpose of the file, suggest the completion of a few personal pages and set a meeting time to discuss the school pages. New TAs can insert their own job description, school map or other papers sent to them before their first day. The schools which have such a file for all their staff may have different contents for each category of staff. The contents are specific to TAs, and whatever system is used should be confidential and private for them. If the TAs are to compile a portfolio for accreditation, as in a vocational qualification, they will need to create a separate file and use photocopies of important documents in it if required. It will be the owner's decision whether any of the contents are shared with the manager or another member of staff. Observation sheets or appraisals or review material will be agreed on separate sheets, then kept by the owner in the file. It is a reference collection for the owner, a positive record of things he or she has done and can do. They should take it with them if they leave. The school/staff handbook is much more formal, containing relevant school documentation, which should be kept up to date by the school and returned to the manager when the member of staff leaves.

The personal professional portfolios of TAs should include a sheet in the personal section on life experiences. These can show how much the TAs brought to their jobs, in addition to their qualifications. To have brought up children, or cared for elderly people, been an officer in a club, playgroup or brownie pack, run a household budget, learnt to drive a car or use a computer, or explored foreign places, all give life skills and understanding of the world that sometimes young teachers do not have. It is a useful way for anyone to keep track of one's career and the file provides a place to keep those certificates and information that easily get put in an odd drawer.

Suggested sections and prompt sheets of a personal professional portfolio:

- Personal section

    name, address, telephone number etc.
    other important numbers – car, national insurance, hospital, telephone number of next of kin, etc.
    educational history (places and dates)
    examinations taken with results
    qualifications grades and dates (certificates and diplomas can be kept here)
    any other courses undertaken (dates)
    life experiences (clubs etc.)
    employment experiences (dates)
    records of anything produced (a booklet, a craft object, a child – photos?)
    major life events (travel, disasters coped with, celebrations)

- The job and place of work

    job description
    induction material
    school description
    school staff responsibilities
    some key policies or a list of policies contained in a separate school file
    useful contacts

- Progress and reflections on the job

    record of meetings attended
    record of courses attended
    jottings about personal progress
    self-review

- Appraisal or Professional Development Review process

    whatever the school policy and documentation is for appraisal or review

- Notes on courses (not course handouts – there will not be room) or evaluation sheets
- A section for personal jottings or diary

The TA File (DfEE 2000e; DfES 2001b) which can be downloaded from the website www.teachernet.gov.uk/teachingassistants could be used as an exemplar, although the file contains a lot of material about literacy, numeracy and behaviour management, which TAs use on the DfES induction course. An example from a school is reproduced in Figure 6.3.

School documentation

Copies of school documents

It is evident that TAs need copies of certain school documentation, including relevant curriculum policies, with behaviour management, health, safety and security and child protection policies being essential. It may be that the school has a special TA policy, SEN, English as an additional language (EAL), assessment (including marking), teaching and learning policies, and maybe others. It would not be helpful just to present these to the TA on his/ her first day without explanations; a list of their locations in the portfolio and timetable for their introduction would be better.

The school documentation relevant to TAs

>   Its aims, philosophy and ethos.
>   The staff structure with roles and responsibilities of the class teacher, roles of senior staff, duties of ancillary staff including the role of the governing body, and the support staff governor's name.
>   Basic school routines and procedures, e.g. registers, duties, marking, record keeping, reports, parents' evenings, sanctions, legal obligations (*in loco parentis*) and health, safety and security.
>   The school policy for child protection, including the identity of the named person; the policy for confidentiality, and behaviour management.
>   Copies of relevant documentation for literacy and numeracy, and any other curriculum areas.
>   The school's SEN policy and arrangements for working with IEPs, reviews and statemented children where appropriate.
>   Arrangements for staff meetings, working parties and consultations as related to the TA.
>   Arrangements for line management, the whereabouts of pay, discipline and grievance documentation, union membership if desired.
>   Resources available in the school and how the TA should access them: stock and curricular equipment including SEN resources; the school library and ICT facilities including audio visual aids, e.g. television, radio, tapes, films, video etc.; reprographic equipment.
>   Resources available locally: curriculum development/teachers' centres, libraries, museums, field study centres etc.

MALDON PRIMARY SCHOOL

DEVELOPMENT PORTFOLIO FOR SUPPORT STAFF

Introduction

The purposes of the Development Portfolio are:

1. To help you to make the most of your skills for the benefit of the children
2. To identify training and development needs
3. To help you keep a record of your contribution to school life in order that this can be appreciated and remembered
4. To be the focus of discussions with your line manager
5. To set targets for further development and achievement

Working and training background

- Please describe briefly details of your employment to date.
- Do you have any qualifications or have you undergone any training for any of your jobs?
- Which qualifications and training opportunities do you think are particularly relevant to working in a school?
- Do you have any other experience which has helped you with your work in the school?
- What are your interests?
- Please include any further information you feel might be relevant.

Personal and work related development

If you go on a course or receive training in school please complete one of these sheets. This includes, for example, a session with the I.T. Co-ordinator about working with computers or a session with the Literacy Co-ordinator, learning about Literacy Hour.

Training details and dates

How has this training helped me to be more effective in my job? (please add to this section as time progresses)

Self Review - before a development portfolio meeting, please reflect upon your achievements, training and career development needs. What contributions have you made to school improvement and school life in general (however modest)? Please consider your strengths and weaknesses. Is there any expertise and good practice you are able to pass on to other staff?

Work Related Observation

A development portfolio meeting will occasionally be preceded by a work related observation by a colleague. The focus of the observation will be agreed beforehand. The following proforma shou completed by the observer after an observation.

Observation of   by
Date:

Time:

Focus:

Brief description of session:

Issues arising from session:

(Points for action will be included on target sheet)

MALDON PRIMARY SCHOOL PERFORMANCE REVIEW STATEMENT

Name of LSA

Name of performance reviewer

Date of review meeting:
Progress against previously agreed objectives

New objectives

Monitoring
A short meeting to discuss progress against these objectives will be held on:

Lesson Observation

Training and Development (This section can be copied to the Staff Development Manager)

Statement agreed by...Date.................

MALDON PRIMARY SCHOOL

PERFORMANCE MANAGEMENT

MID CYCLE MEETING TO DISCUSS PROGRESS AGAINS PREVIOUSLY AGREED OBJECTIVES

Name of LSA ....

Name of Performance Reviewer..

Date of Meeting ....

Please refer to each objective in turn and outline progress made. Use an additional sheet if necessary.

Further training needs

Signed...................................(LSA)

Figure 6.3 Pages from a school's support staff development portfolio
Source: Maldon Primary School

Some suggestions for a school handbook relevant to TAs

While a handbook should be available for every member of staff, there will be differences depending on the category of staff for whom the handbook is intended. This should be a separate file to the personal portfolio, and (as explained above) the property of the school.

The TA handbook could contain:

General staff guidance: confidentiality, expectations of dress, punctuality, code of courtesy etc.

job descriptions, pay policy, discipline and grievance procedures, role of governing body
line management systems; staff structure; staff support systems
professional development procedures

Fire and first aid practices; health and safety procedures, security, and off-site responsibilities
Behaviour policy: expectations, roles of all staff, responsibilities and strategies
Child protection issues and procedures
Communication systems, including emergencies, bad weather etc., rotas and timings, dates including meetings and agenda/minutes, newsletters from school
Systems for recording incidents or assessments where appropriate
Siting of relevant school policies and support materials
Equipment and resources: roles and responsibilities, access
Wet playtime procedures.

Other useful information

There are some which must be explained at an early stage in the induction process, preferably during the first week.

TAs must understand what to do regarding
Health, safety and security:

- if a pupil or the TA has an accident or is taken ill
- if there is a fire or other alert
- particular needs of their pupil or the area in which they are working

Confidentiality

- that all matters regarding the school, written or verbal should be considered confidential to the people in the school unless otherwise stated

Child protection

* how to prevent themselves from being victims of false accusations
* what to do if a pupil shows signs of abuse or reveals incidents to them.

The following items of information could also be included in either the personal portfolio or the school handbook. The list includes items that TAs have found useful, particularly when they come to thinking about how their role in the school can be developed or they begin to seek accreditation for their work.

The community

* the school's prior admission/catchment area
* community liaison schemes e.g. church involvement, business partnerships
* neighbouring schools
* pre-school/infant/junior/first/middle/secondary liaison.

The local education authority and other agencies with which the TA may have contact:

* LEA role and administrative structure
* Advisory and Inspection Service
* educational psychologists, education welfare officers, education person-nel services, various therapists, Health and Social Services personnel associated with the school.

Further induction process

Giving it time

Induction is a lengthy process, and is not one sided. TA, mentor and school all need to participate, with any off-site course merely adding extra dimen-sions. The DfES induction course is designed to be a four-day course taken off site after about half a term working in a school, with induction probably taking a full year to complete. This should enable regular dialogue between the mentor and the TA to ensure further understanding. It means the TA will experience the range of activities the school undertakes, from performances to examinations, parents' evenings, social events and sports days. The devel-opment of relationships and partnerships essential to the work of TAs takes time. The whole school approach to TAs was described in Chapter 4; the more intimate and working partnerships with teachers will be dealt with in Chapter 7.

Figure 6.4 Feedback from a teacher to a TA after an observation

Review and appraisal

All staff should have some sort of formal review process at the end of a probationary period, after about six months and certainly before the end of the first year (Figure 6.4).

This kind of review should be repeated annually. The IiP principle on Commitment states in its Indicator 2 that people are to be encouraged to improve their own and other people's performance, and its Indicator 3 that people believe their contribution to the organisation is recognised. Appraisal or professional development review (PDR) is a formal process which ensures this happens. IiP also asks that people understand how they contribute to achieving the organisation's aims and objectives. Professional development for TAs, as with teachers, is not just a case of the person wanting to take a certain route or course, but of balancing personal need with that of the SDP. The new proposals for supervision of unqualified teachers working in classroom with pupils are specifically about providing safeguards over the teaching and learning process in the school rather than containing any sense of promoting the personal and professional development of the person without QTS, or fulfilling the longer term aims of the school. An appraisal should contain these elements.

Case study evidence
In one of my study schools, the TAs understood what appraisal was for. They said: 'I've had one of those – "Where's your job going?" and "What do you want to do in the future?".' It was appreciated. The SENCO, when commenting two years after my research visits, told me that the appraisal process had become embedded in the practice of the school. They had started by reviewing job descriptions as jobs changed and various training became available. The TAs so appreciated the opportunity, they hardly saw the reviews as appraisal. The line manager (the deputy) and the SENCO shared the process and both the TAs and the school gained from it.

Appraisal for TAs can sometimes be a sensitive issue for them. If they do not have experience of working in business or industry where appraisal is commonplace they may fear the unknown. On the other hand having had such experiences may mean they feel they are going to be graded, their pay be directly related to the outcome, and thus anticipate the process as being a rather traumatic one. There are various ways schools have got round this problem, usually taking one step at a time over several years.

Case study evidence
One study school started with a joint team discussion, with opportunities for individual personal discussion where required. They described a slow process of introducing the idea. They had found the TAs themselves nervous of such a review and so started with the whole group reviewing the role of TAs in the school with the headteacher. The original group of six became smaller groups the following year, and the intention was to have individual reviews as confidence built. TAs were consulted annually, along with all other staff, when the SDP review was done and so felt fully part of the aims and objectives of the establishment. This avoided there being any conflict between personal and institutional needs. Understanding was built in. Time given to such a process was not an issue to either school, people mattered.

Another school developed professional portfolios which are looked at by the line manager and headteacher and discussed with each TA at some point with targets for the future being set before introducing formal observation and appraisal interviews. Some schools have formal observations with feedback for the TAs by the line managers as a matter of course, but do not call it appraisal and do not necessarily link it with any formal changes – just reflect with the TAs on what and how they were doing. Some schools are taking the opportunities afforded by the single status review to observe and discuss the work of TAs with them, and establishing performance pay policies at the same time of all staff. While these processes may seem to be a time-consuming addition to an already overloaded timetable for senior management, the effect of such attention on the development is worthwhile, and has the additional dimension of giving a line manager, who may not be part of the senior management team, a professional development opportunity for themselves. A senior TA could be a line manager and appraiser.

In a full appraisal system the stages should comprise:

- a self-review
- an observation of the TA by a more senior colleague
- an appraisal meeting with feedback (sometimes called dialogue), review of job description and previous targets, and any training needs
- agreement about future targets and additional training
- regular repetition of the cycle.

Some photocopiable pages for self-review can be found in the DfEE primary TA file and the DfES secondary TA file of the induction materials. They contain the following items:

Areas to consider (for a self-review) include:
The job description – is it still appropriate? If not, what changes need making in relation to the following points?

- working with pupils
- relationships with other staff and adults you come into contact with at school
- knowledge of the curriculum
- behaviour management
- your knowledge about the skills needed for your job
- the resources available for the job
- the way you organise your job, e.g. time management and communication with others
- other?

What aspect of your job satisfies you the most and what the least?
What targets were set at the last appraisal/start of the job? What do you feel you have achieved?
Where you have not achieved the targets, what are the reasons?

Are there areas of your present work you would like to improve upon?
How successful was any training received?
What factors helped or hindered your professional development during the year?
Are there other areas you would like to extend your work into, that you cannot be involved in at present?
Consider your needs for career development; for example, where do you see yourself in five years' time?
What are your training needs for your current job and your future aspirations?
Would you like some formal observation of your work? If so, what focus would you like it to have?
  (DfEE 2000b, section 4, pp. 4.1 to 4.7; DfES 2001a, section 1.4, pp. 1.42 to 1.44)

The kind of outcomes from such a process is discussed in Chapter 8 where the professional development of TAs and the role of the school in such developments is considered. Clearly such a review of a job may well reveal budget issues for school managers to consider such as a pay review or the cost of any needed training. Meanwhile, Chapter 7 looks at the TAs actually assisting learning and pupils and supporting teaching and teachers.

TAs and teaching

Teachers as managers

Although no one should pretend that teaching assistants are teachers, when they are most successful they show many of the skills characteristic of good teachers: an understanding of children and their needs and behaviour; an ability to interact effectively with them to promote learning; and the ability to assess where pupils are in their learning and what they need to do to make further progress. Making the most of such abilities should certainly not threaten the professionalism of teachers; rather it should be encouraged and developed to the full.

(Ofsted 2002a p. 18)

It's the . . . love and affection I get from the children. I get respect from the parents and the teachers as well. I've got a very good relationship with the teachers.

(A TA, when asked what was the best thing about the job)

This chapter describes the way in which TAs do teach, yet always work under the direction of a qualified teacher, supporting the teaching processes of the classroom. The models, artistry and skills they display are explored, as well as the planning and feedback systems needed to facilitate their effectiveness. The need for establishing boundaries within each classroom is examined.

Empowering TAs to support the learning process

There is clear guidance in the recent proposals, that whatever happens in the classroom in terms of delegation of teaching strategies,

qualified teachers must always **oversee** [their emphasis] the teaching and learning process, using their training and expertise to identify learning activities and goals, and to define the pace and scope for individuals and groups [and] in doing this they may identify activities that will contribute to teaching and learning, and that in their professional judgement can be carried out entirely or partially by other suitably trained adults with an appropriate level of supervision.

(DfES 2002a p. 21)

Therefore, given this lead, TAs can assist, using all of the skills of teaching in its generic meaning, with mutual agreement about boundaries. TAs definitely do teach, but do not take the responsibility for the direction and organisation of the learning.

Chapter 2 looked at what TAs can do in terms of supporting the school, pupils, teacher and the curriculum. The NOS give an indication of the expectation of competence of TAs at level 2 and 3, and the new proposals indicate that the Teacher Training Agency will be commissioned to develop a set of standards for the higher level roles and a training programme to meet those standards. These could include elements from the level 3 standards and from the QTS framework. It is hoped that such a development will be in the public domain, with parts ready for use, during 2003 and completed in 2004.

Working with teachers in the classroom

Ofsted found that 'the shift towards teaching assistants spending more time on learning support, rather than the traditional mix of helping with welfare, preparation of materials, administration and learning' could adversely affect teachers' workloads 'at a time when strenuous effort are being made nationally to reduce them' (Ofsted 2002a p. 18). Teachers and managers therefore need to look carefully at not only the characteristics of their TAs and the whole school support of them but also how the best use can be made of TAs' and teachers' time.

TAs can provide personal support and companionship, the extra pair of eyes, ears and hands, which relieve the stress. Spending time on planning for and working with TAs can assist in all three of these areas. They can provide assistance in the short-term tasks, adding to the adult energy resource and enabling debate and reflection in even a short feedback time. Teachers frequently refer to the TAs' support of themselves, making comments like 'It's a terrific burden off my shoulders'. Teachers talk of emotional as well as practical help during inspections, and of being able to share the joys of a breakthrough in an area of learning for a particular pupil.

Teachers have not often in the past been trained to work with additional adults in the classroom, and sometimes find that planning work for them, managing them as well as the pupils, and taking account of their views merely adds yet another burden to the workload. Where a partnership develops between a teacher and the TAs who work with him or her, the strengths of the TAs can complement those of the teachers to raise standards and alleviate the workload and the stress. TAs assist in the teaching programme of the class under the guidance of a qualified teacher. The NOS values and principles recognise the importance of this relationship:

Working in partnership with the teacher
It is the teacher whose curriculum and lesson planning and day-to-day direction set the framework within which teaching/classroom assistants work. The teaching/classroom assistant works under the direction of the teacher, whether in the whole class or on their own with an individual or a small group of pupils. Teaching/classroom assistants, therefore, need to be fully briefed about the teacher's plans and intentions for teaching and learning and her/his contribution to these. Ideally, teaching/classroom assistants will be involved by teachers in their planning and preparation of the work.

(LGNTO 2001 p. 5)

Partnership

The way in which the TAs perform is dependent on the quality of the rela-tionship with the teacher. Good teachers are always aware of the learning needs of their class, and adapt their teaching programme to match those needs. These needs may reflect the ways in which the pupils learn, or it may be adjusting to physical, emotional, social, cultural or spiritual differences. In all the approaches to classroom organisation, teaching and learning the teacher needs to communicate as much as possible with the TA in order that they can share tasks and understand what each can contribute.

Case study evidence
In one school they enjoyed a joke together: one teacher laughingly said 'We row the whole time!' in front of her TA. She followed it up by 'We couldn't have a better working relationship than we have now'. Another teacher described how the TA knew where the boundaries were: 'She would never go off and do something new or different without [asking me]. It's all sort of within our routine, and she would always come and check things out or say [what she was doing]'. The way in which this depended on the goodwill of the TA was apparent, but it was also clear that the TAs did things in their own time because it was appreciated by the teachers. The teachers chose the children with whom the TAs worked, explained what they wanted and the format of the lesson.

The *Good Practice Guide* (DfEE 2000a) has a whole section on creating part-nerships with teachers on pages 24 to 27. It has a paragraph on each of the following:

1 Differentiating the roles of teacher and TA
2 Ensuring teacher participation in planning

3 Creating a climate that encourages high-quality TA input
4 Developing feedback mechanisms
5 Dealing with behaviour management issues under teacher guidance
6 Ensuring TAs are informed of the learning needs and any behaviour difficulties of children with SEN
7 Including TAs in IEP reviews
8 Inviting TAs to staff meetings
9 Including TAs in the staffroom
10 Including TAs in written communications
11 Recognising the legal responsibilities of TAs
12 Encouraging reviews of the classroom relationships

Items 8 to 11 have already been covered in dealing with whole school strategies for developing TAs, but items 1 to 7 and 12 will be included in the discussions to follow in this chapter.

Exploring the teacher – TA partnership

In order to address item 12, it is possible to use a joint questionnaire, get all the TAs and teachers to complete it separately, return the sheets to a third party – the senior manager, the head or an external facilitator – who sends the collated anonymised results to the group. If TAs work in close partnership with one teacher they can share their replies with each other and see where they were similar or different. The closer the partnership, the closer the similarity will be. Feedback of results otherwise can take place, with the collated results, at a staff meeting, opening up a general debate about how TAs work with teachers in the school. Clearly, the school staff have to be ready for such an exercise and want to look at their own practice and relationships – not always an easy situation to achieve. Ground rules of purpose, confidentiality and use of results have to be established before such an investigation. The whole of Balshaw's (1999) book *Help in the Classroom* is based on the assumption that once the climate for development is right, teachers and TAs together can investigate how to improve their joint practice through various exercises in collaboration.

Questions to ask both parties can be about:
The main aims of the school
Each other's roles – whether each knows what the other does both in their classroom and elsewhere in the school
What their partner's experience and qualifications are for doing what they do
What feelings they have about their respective roles

The partnership
>   What they think is happening
>   What they get out of it
>   What makes it work well and whether it could be improved and how

Any professional development and support given by the school
>   Changes they might like to make

What expectations should they have for the future?
>   What aspects of the TA's role they are most happy with
>   What aspects are they least happy with?

Other comments

Morgan *et al.* (1998) pointed out the advantages of teacher and TAs learning together, as strengthening the team. They recognised that both in the USA and the UK teachers have had little training in collaborating with other adults. They also found when carrying out their training sessions that the biggest issue was having time to collaborate. Moyles and Suschitzky (1997 p. 30) referred to this as 'the perennial problem', a feeling reiterated by most headteachers when interviewed. Farrell *et al.* (1999) talked of the teacher and TA sharing the preparation of job descriptions, of planning reflecting the needs of the TA, including entitlement to support for the learner and the flexible use of space. They recognised the TA can bring experience of other classrooms and teachers to the partnership, and suggest that wider understanding of the management of TAs can bring about 'more participation, independence in learning and higher standards' for TAs and pupils (Farrell *et al.* 1999 p. 55).

Lacey (2001) explored the whole issue of teacher–TA partnership in a book about many kinds of partnerships. She gave some useful audit suggestions if partners are trying to address particular issues such as finding time to talk together, an essential element of partnership. She concludes the relevant chapter:

> The partnership between teachers and assistants that are effective, have to struggle in the face of many adversities. When they work, the partners are supportive of each other and of children. They have sufficient time to plan and evaluate how best to work as well as efficient systems for communication . . . This partnership appears to be built on mutual respect and trust, support of each other and a shared understanding of how to meet pupils' learning needs. It is underpinned by clear lines of communication, commitment to provide planning time and the security of a permanent job supported by a career structure and relevant training Nothing less is sufficient.
>
> (Lacey 2001 p. 112)

Later in the book she gives a list of certain systems and strategies to promote partnership, based on work with many kinds of partners. It recognises that even where two people want to improve a relationship there are other constraints within any organisation. It needs to attend to:

- management systems
- management support
- flexible time management
- leadership
- communication
- common focus
- shared learning
- team building.

She also suggested that schools or other services need to look at three levels if they wish to sort out their priorities – strategic, operational and fieldwork levels.

Boundaries

One of the things that has to be established between each teacher and TA working with them is the boundaries of the professional relationship. Each teacher has their own way of working and will need time to explore what their expectations are with TAs, making explicit things that may otherwise be implicit. When things are not talked about, misunderstandings can arise or it takes much longer to establish how to work together.

Farrell *et al.* (1999 p. 3) found no problems over boundaries with teachers: 'there is a clearly understood distinction between the role of LSAs and teachers'. They also remarked on the lack of opportunities for class teachers to receive training for working with LSAs in any phases of education. Lacey (1999 p. 33) concluded that, when considering inclusion at classroom level, it was vital that there were 'clarity of roles and responsibilities' and 'collaboration between teachers and LSAs, including time to plan and work together'.

There are various ways to facilitate this. Teachers can be more involved in drawing up the TAs' job descriptions, enhancing the mutual understanding of roles. Another suggestion is to use a diagram such as Figure 7.1 and for the partners to work through it to establish mutual understanding of the components.

If a teacher is having a new TA, the following might be the questions in the TA's mind, and it is worth the TA spending time just clarifying the answers to them.

What do you particularly want me to do?
What do I do if a pupil in your room asks to go to the toilet?
Can I write in any pupil's books?

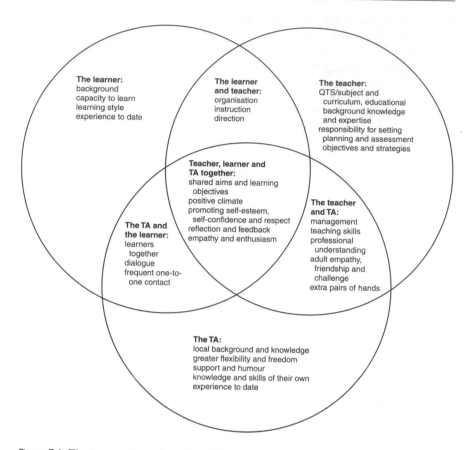

Figure 7.1 The interactions of teachers, TAs and learners in the classroom
Source: Watkinson 2002a p. 51

What contact with parents or carers do you expect of the TA?
Do you want me to attend consultation evenings?
Do I take part in SEN reviews?
Can I do anything at the request of a parent such as change a child's reading book or search for lost equipment?
Can I tidy the rooms? Your desks? The resources area?
Is there anything you do not want me to do?

(Watkinson 2002b p. 63)

Supporting teaching and learning

The school will have already decided what its approach is to teaching and learning and many schools have established policies for just this area; all teachers and TAs should have copies of this. It will address areas such as

- differentiation – mixed ability, setting and support for SEN
- pupil involvement in active learning strategies
- investigative/problem-solving approaches to be used
- written work – presentation and who marks what in what way
- oral work – appropriate questioning skills
- pupils' study skills.

TAs teach

When TAs are observed in action, it is clear that they also teach. This question has long been a contentious one. Teacher unions rightly need to protect the perceived roles of their members. The debate has again been in the public eye with the reducing workload ideas and the subsequent proposals for enabling this to happen.

Moyles and Suschitzky (1997 p. 52) recognised that 'CAs (classroom assistants) do have a role to play in helping children to learn – a role in teaching. What this has raised so clearly for the researchers, is a key question about what is "teaching"?' When they explored the views of teachers on the CAs, they found 'less perceived differences expressed within the responses of trained teachers and mainly untrained CAs (non STAs), than might have been anticipated' (p. 50). My case study teachers were clear: 'I'd like to see her as an authority role . . . as a teacher for that section'.

The problem seems to be the semantics of the words: teach, teaching and teacher. Parents teach their children; peer and sibling teaching is well known. By teachers, the government, the general public, and more particularly the media, seem to mean adults with QTS. TAs teach, but do not have all the attributes of a qualified teacher. As Ofsted said. 'Although no one should pretend that teaching assistants are teachers, when they are most successful they show many of the skills characteristic of good teachers' (Ofsted 2002a p. 18). The new proposals attempt to define what only a qualified teacher can do, but admit

> In practice, the difference between the contribution of a qualified teacher and a higher level teaching assistant, or a cover supervisor, will not be defined in terms of simple words but by the quality to what each member of staff can reasonably be expected to demonstrate. It is not reasonable to look to a teaching assistant to demonstrate the full subject expertise and professional judgement of the qualified teacher.
>
> (DfES, 2002a p.20)

They act under the direction of qualified teachers at all times, and these qualified teachers take responsibility for the learning of the pupils in the class. For this organisation and responsibility, teachers are well trained and paid on different scales.

Views of teaching

Defining teaching and learning is complex, and has been the focus of much research. Watkins and Mortimore (1999 p. 3) defined pedagogy as 'any conscious activity by one person designed to enhance learning in another'. Kyriacou (1986) offered three models or levels of teaching, the first of which he refers to as surface – maximising active learning time and quality of instruction. His second level covers the conceptual or psychological level, and the third or craft level relates to classroom skills. He has rating scales on preparedness, pace and flow, transitions (beginnings and ends of lessons) clarity, business-like manner, withitness and encouragingness. I have observed TAs who would score highly on all of these. Dunne and Wragg (1994) describe nine dimensions of teaching, levels through which teachers can progress. TAs can manage the first ones easily: ethos, direct instruction and management of materials; most of the second three: guided practices, structured conversation and monitoring; and often parts of the last ones: management of order, planning, preparation and written evaluation.

A definition of teaching used by inspectors is that found in the Ofsted *Handbook* (Ofsted 1999). While it is possible to suggest that managers use this framework on TAs, which has been used very occasionally in formal inspections on TAs, Ofsted are currently revising the framework. In using the framework definition as a checklist for TAs, I found good TAs could operate in all the suggested aspects except setting homework and managing support staff themselves (Watkinson 2002b).

> The headings cover:
> The impact on pupils' learning
>
>> outcomes
>> acquisition of knowledge, skills and understanding
>> development of attitudes – application, concentration, pace, interest
>> development as independent learners and thinkers
>
> Subject knowledge
> Methods used, technical competence and skills
> Management of time and resources
> Planning and assessment strategies
> Presentation, challenge and inspiration of learners.

Qualified teacher status

In the words of a postgraduate student teacher observed by Jim Rose (ex-HMI), 'There is so much more to teaching than teaching'. Looking at the old QTS standards published by the Teacher Training Agency (TTA 1998),

Planning and class management, from Section B and Section C, Monitoring assessment, recording, reporting and accountability could be seen as in the field of the qualified teacher. However, much of the 'teaching' of Section B can apply to TAs, for example:

- dealing with individuals or groups of pupils, with an understanding of responsibilities regarding those with SEN
- establishing a safe, purposeful learning environment including the use of resources
- setting higher expectations for all pupils both academically and in behaviour
- using skills such as monitoring, intervening, stimulating, communicating, fostering enthusiasm and motivation, structuring and presentation of material, instructing and demonstrating, listening and questioning
- matching approaches used to subject being taught
- developing pupils' skills and opportunities for consolidation and collaboration
- reflective practice.

The current standards for QTS (TTA 2002) came into effect in September 2002. Planning, target setting, monitoring and assessment still remain the clear prerogative of the qualified teacher but many aspects of the teaching and class management section could apply to TAs, often with little alteration. They refer to clarity of purpose, promoting active and independent learning, differentiating, taking account of linguistic and cultural backgrounds, managing space, organising time, high expectations of behaviour, use of ICT, recognising equality of opportunity and school policies, as well as seeking help from more experienced teachers.

The Values and Principles underpinning the NOS (LGNTO 2001) cover similar areas to the principles described for teachers:

- working in partnership with the teacher
- working within statutory and organisational frameworks
- supporting inclusion
- equality of opportunity
- anti-discrimination
- celebrating diversity
- promoting independence
- confidentiality
- continuing professional development.

There are common strands though all these definitions. The new proposals define specified teaching work as follows:

a. planning and preparing lessons and courses for pupils;
b. delivering lessons to pupils;
c. assessing the development, progress and attainment of pupils;
d. reporting on the development, progress and attainment of pupils; and
e. marking the work of pupils.

(DfES 2002a p. 20)

but admit that 'these statements do not convey the degree of challenge and complexity of different learning situations'. They also define twenty-five tasks that teachers should not routinely be expected to do (DfES 2002c p. 20).

Areas of practice in which TAs support teaching and learning

The following sections are organised to reflect both the attributes which can be observed in TAs and the elements of teaching as described in the various texts quoted above such as points 1 to 7 in the *Good Practice Guide*. They expand on the list used in Chapter 2 (see p. 20).

Planning and preparation

Case study evidence
In one school, the planning for the target groups supervised by the TAs during assembly was done by the TA on their own, as well as for other small activities such as snack time for the EY children. It was a TA who had come up with the first draft of a planning/recording sheet for the target group time. Coming up with ideas was seen as supporting the teachers in their work, as was the reporting back to them about the progress of children during a session.

It is important that teachers share their planning with TAs in someway. It is the in-depth knowledge of the pupils which enables the TA to carry out the teacher's curriculum objectives – the fine-tuning. So, the TAs must know the teacher's curriculum objectives for the lesson. Practice in transmitting this knowledge is variable, depending not only on the school systems but also on the individual ways of working of the teachers.

Case study evidence

Some schools shared planning time on a Thursday, one TA had a copy of the teacher's planning on a Monday morning, two worked on differentiation on a Monday afternoon. One TA said: 'We are getting to know about the planning. I don't have to hang about for 20 minutes of a half-hour session, waiting to find out what I've got to do while the teacher finishes talking'. In one school, the long-term and medium-term planning was available in a folder in the staffroom; not all the TAs saw planning, although all seemed to sit in on IEPs' formulation. In another the TAs' personal planning was done by some at home at the weekend, after the teachers had given them their plans on a Friday and for some, in the holidays with the teachers. One went to the planning on the teacher's desk. The TAs were able to contribute to them saying what in their opinion the child needed to work on next. One TA said she spoke with her teacher every night about the next day's work. Another said:

> [The teacher] hadn't done Fuzz Buzz before, she just lets me get on with that side of things while she does the rest of the class. That's what we do first thing on a Tuesday and then we all get together to do whatever work goes on from there and I just cover that group whatever. I do look at the planning on a Monday afternoon for the whole week for that class, specifically because I support Cathy, so I know roughly what's coming up – not always when, sometimes it's changed round, but we know roughly, and how she approaches things, so, what words and things like that.

One teacher commented: 'Because, I think, that as we've got [it] more together on what we're doing, they're getting more done. Because, there's no point you [the TA] coming in, and I'm going "they're writing a story, there you go". We actually need to spend more time together knowing what I actually do want from the children, so it's focused'. However, the same teacher also admitted:

> Because we plan on Thursday I won't really minutely sort out what I'm doing on each lesson until Sunday night exactly, I know the subject basis but exactly what I'm doing and where the children need to be – I won't know that until Sunday night, so when Dorothy comes in on a Monday all I can do is write it down and give it to

her, which is not the same as talking about it and going through it, is it?

Another teacher described how the pair usually communicated first thing in the morning after the TA had seen the planning previously, then doing her own planning, then doing a final check. The teacher admitted that if the TA was late it could throw her, but nevertheless the preparation and rapport enabled the TA to 'pick up instantly what was wanted – you see, she coped'.

Teachers can decide to have separate plans for the TA, copy their planning where the TA role is spelt out or some kind of system for the TAs to have oversight of the planning before the lesson. Some suggestions for formats are with those for feedback pages. While formats save time and are useful for everyday working, it is important that managers provide paid time for the TAs and teachers to plan together. This may be at an individual class level, or at a more collegiate level. It will depend on the nature of the planning, whether it is for short-term individual class strategies or introducing longer term, whole school or whole subject strategies. It is also important that managers enable the TA to have preparation time, both to prepare things for the teacher and to make their own preparations for what is expected of them. Too often both planning and preparation have been done in the past by TAs in their own time (Figure 7.2).

Performance

TAs will watch the various teachers with whom they work and see how they approach their teaching. Teaching is a performance, an act. One of the challenges since the early 1980s for some teachers, used to total autonomy in their classrooms, has been to be watched. Being in the presence of pupils did not faze them, but another adult watching meant that the act had a possible critical audience. Acting demands courage, forethought and practice, as does teaching. One of the problems TAs sometimes talk of is being labelled by the pupils as a non-teacher. Pupils pick up unspoken messages of 'presence' very easily. Words, gestures and stance when asking pupils to do something needs to assure them that adults mean what they say: TAs must be encouraged to show sufficient authority to operate effectively. Their speech needs to be clear, grammatically correct, and with a confident but not loud tone of voice. They may need to practise this. They may need to be trained in the use of gestures for the subtle behaviour management which can be achieved without a word such as signalling 'turn it down' maintaining eye contact. A TA sitting look-

Figure 7.2 TAs planning together

ing bored will signal to pupils that the lesson is boring – it may be, but the TA must act not bored.

Exposition

Most teachers and lecturers have tried practising at home before a new lesson, and TAs can be told of the benefit of such experiences. The development of 'critical friendships' between teachers and TAs where tips can be passed on frequently in an amicable way without waiting for an annual appraisal or a formal training session will pay dividends. The following checklist might be useful to give to TAs (Watkinson 2002a pp. 54–55).

Exposition

> Try to put your ideas in a logical sequence, and if possible note the key points.
> Try to have a beginning, middle and end, if it is prepared.
> Find the right words, speak clearly, watch the tone and inflections in your voice.
> Be sure of what you say or do – not too many 'ums' and 'ers'.
> Try to involve the pupils. Television presenters try to do this, even without a live audience. Just watch *Blue Peter* presenters – their eyes, their pace, their pauses. It all looks 'off the cuff', but is the result of practice.

Get the pupils' attention, maintain eye contact when you can. Use appropriate gestures.

Explain what you are going to do or cover, and what the pupils should get out of it – or learn.

Try to get their interest from the start. Find out what they already know in the area if you have time, as this provides the scaffolding for the learning you are trying to promote.

Where you can, link what you are saying to other lessons they have had in the same area, or what the teacher is particularly wanting to do. Even if you are working with pupils with SEN, try to make what you are doing relate to what the rest of the class are doing to allow them to keep up.

Emphasise the important bits. You may have to adapt as you go along, so be sensitive to the way in which pupils are reacting to you and what you are saying. This will help you decide the next step, or how large a jump you can make in assuming understanding.

Use examples or analogies, objects or pictures, maps, diagrams, sounds, anything to create curiosity, motivate or add interest. Have a 'here is one I made earlier' item ready if that is relevant.

Draw or put key words down as you go along. You may even get to use the blackboard, whiteboard or overhead projector. Make sure you have paper, pencils, pens or chalk if you need them. Do not get up to get things: this is an ideal opportunity for any pupils to lose interest and some to become disruptive.

Try to get feedback, and promote discussion, again if you have time. Did they understand what you were talking about? Dialogue keeps them both awake and participating. Respond to them.

Try to leave time to get one pupil to recall what you have been saying to another pupil. This helps them clarify their mind as well as give you an idea how well they have taken things in.

Summarise at the end.

(Watkinson 2002a pp. 54–55)

Questioning and challenging

One of the most important ways in which TAs can help children learn, achieve and think is to question for themselves. Questions encourage thought and ideas, and as pupils get older, enable them to ask questions themselves. Education is about imparting knowledge, for without it there is no context for understanding and any questioning is superficial; but without questioning, how can we be sure we understand, or make any progress.

Questions can be used purely to check knowledge and understanding, class teachers often use questions as a teaching strategy, asking for answers that one or two students may know, thus relieving the monotony of just their voice and increasing the participation of the group. They will ask questions of various levels of difficulty to encourage all the children to feel able to answer and thus participate. They can be closed, needing only 'yes' or 'no' answers, or open, sometimes called 'higher order' questions, where the answers can be varied. Open questions are not so often used in a large class situation because there just is no time for them – but a TA with a small group may have the time and opportunity to use them. The actual asking of the questions needs just the same kind of clarity, eye contact and structure as an exposition. Questioning needs practice, like the other skills.

Teachers could also ask a TA to collect the pupils' questions in written form, as they may show how far their thinking about a subject has progressed, or take note who answers the teacher's questions with a tick grid with names on one side and columns just to note who answers, or who never even tries.

This is an area in which TAs respond well to training. A video of a lesson like history can be used at a meeting to explore how the teacher filmed questions the class's ideas. This will raise the TAs' awareness of what types of questions could be asked in various contexts. If the TAs or teachers are willing to be videoed themselves, they can watch for their own verbal strategies used to promote the pupils thinking.

Intervention and non-intervention

TAs may need to be helped with this very important area, yet most seem to have an instinctive feel about allowing pupils to do what they can for themselves. TAs are not there to do the pupil's work for them, they may need to interpret, scribe, repeat instructions give an example, but the pupil must be clear as to the purpose of the TA's presence (Figures 7.3 and 7.4).

The class teacher may need to monitor this, particularly being vigilant over marking any written work from the pupils, asking whose work is it? Teacher observation of a TA as part of the supervision process or appraisal can show how the TA is working.

The way learning takes place, the need for active participation and independence on behalf of the learner, will soon be understood by the TA, who will welcome any discussion on such matters. Basic learning psychology should be part of any TA course and usually fascinates TAs. With such a current emphasis on factual information to be gained from direct class teaching or secondary sources, it would be easy for an adult recently returned to the school world to feel that telling is the only way of teaching. TAs are adept at making activities into games, finding ways of going over the same ground with a slow learner in a different way, of bringing out the less vocal participant in a group, particularly if they are encouraged to do so. Preparing materials for varying activities also takes time and resources, and this has to be set against other demands on the teacher's time. Courses and SENCO support can help those who have difficulties in this area, networking and meeting with other TAs can also help in providing a way of exchanging ideas.

Figure 7.3 Encouraging independent learning: standing back

Figure 7.4 Encouraging independent learning: intervention

TAs may need help in understanding that listening to pupils is a very valuable way to spend time: 80 per cent of time in school can be the teacher or TA giving out and only 20 per cent of the time the pupils actively participating. Again, one of the opportunities of having a TA in the room is to give the pupils the opportunity of a listening ear.

TAs at first may need to be encouraged to leave their 'charges' to get on on their own for some learning strategies, or some tasks. Once the pupils understand what they have to do, and have the tools to do it, they must be allowed to work as unaided as possible. This may mean the teacher ensuring that TAs are mobile, and can offer support to other pupils, or have other classroom tasks with which to busy themselves.

Case study evidence
This is an observation made in a Year 2 class, where the TA, Sheila, is working with Barbara, who has Down's syndrome. It is a literacy hour, with a supply teacher. No formal observation was done during the teacher input session at the beginning. The concentration and sensitivity of Sheila are impressive. She is sensitive to the needs of Barbara, able to act mild anger, to comfort or sit back as appropriate and in doing so enable her to complete a simple task. Sheila is firm, the boundaries of the situation are clear for both, she repeats phrases to ensure they go in such as 'birthday – b'. She challenges using 'quickly', 'no', 'you do know', 'come on   don't show off' along with 'I'm pleased', 'well done'. She bends to Barbara's level; hand and eye movements are particularly significant. She is not static, she supports other children when she can, and in doing so enables Barbara to have space and time to perform. She is sensitive to the fidgets, offers to change chairs at one point to get round them, but persists, not letting Barbara get away with not completing a task she feels the child is capable of.

Sheila's support of other children in the class ensures that Barbara is not totally dependent on her. Her body language during this support of other children is important, ensuring the children's attention, as is her concentration on the task. Her questioning is varied and skilful. She uses 'what' and 'why' questions.

The skill of the TA is to know when to intervene and when to stand back, and offering help appropriately when requested needs to be cultivated if it is not instinctive. This may mean looking at some of the classroom strategies for pupils' support as a whole. Primary teachers, working on their own, still find it quicker sometimes to give a child the correct spelling in a word book or to give the answer to a mathematical problem, rather than check a 'try'; they send the child to a possibly unsuccessful attempt to find the word in a dictionary or allow insufficient thinking time. Having a TA to oversee such strategies should help active and independent learning.

Working with individual pupils, groups or the whole class

Some of the work of TAs will necessarily be at an individual level, particularly where the physical needs of the pupils have to be addressed in order that the pupil can participate in class activities. These needs will be spelt out in statements or IEPs. This whole area of dealing with the individual needs of those with SEN is well supported by a wide literature and the role of the SENCO in the school. All pupils benefit at some time from the individual attention which a TA can give, but a teacher with a whole class to teach and monitor can rarely spare time for them. Teachers can give TAs time to explore ideas and listen to individual stories, to develop appropriate individual strategies for learning, catch the learning moments and boost self-esteem, provided it does not create a dependency culture. One way in which this can be prevented is for managers to ensure that two or more adults are linked to a child, working at different times. A TA can monitor the work of the class, if appropriately briefed and trained, while the teacher works with an individual. It should not be the case that the least qualified and trained member of staff works with the pupils with the most complex needs. IEPs can also include targets to include and integrate a pupil more with their peers.

Case study evidence
TAs recognise that, in helping the children, they help the teachers. 'Basically we are there to support the teacher to support him ... we come away and work on our own to give the teachers some space and to allow the other children not to be distracted'. 'It has a knock-on effect. If I can manage Francis, then the teacher can manage her class ... Being there for him and in turn being there for her and also for her children'.

Managers need to determine how much the TA should know about individual pupils. Weddell, a retired educational psychologist, reported that when he was an LSA

it can be quite difficult to get specific information about what the teacher finds a child can and cannot do – and under what conditions. It is usually more difficult to obtain information about what a child can do than about where the child is failing. There is a similar problem about discovering the particular situations in which a child performs better than in others, so as to get an idea about teaching approaches.

(Weddell 2001 p. 92)

Farrell and colleagues told of LSAs implementing programmes designed and monitored by the teachers. A variety of practice in withdrawal of children and appropriate contact with the pupils with SEN was seen while visiting seventeen schools and four LEA support services. Positive findings included the views of teachers and managers about their work, the understanding of parents and the pupils themselves, the 'active and pivotal role ... in supporting pupils' (Farrell *et al.* 1999 p. 3). Lacey looked at the role of LSAs in the inclusion of pupils with severe or multiple learning difficulties. She found that while LSAs may have been appointed to support individual children, 'they did not want to isolate him or her and felt they could work most effectively with a small group' (Lacey 1999 p. 19).

Learners need language and social interaction to aid them, another area in which the TA can support, but keeping the talk on the subject not about last night's soap on television, the forthcoming football match or my mum's latest boyfriend. Circle time, however, is not something to leave to an untrained TA. The TA can become a participant in the circle to help set an example and properly trained in how to manage such situations, enable more sensitive topics to be discussed as there will be a person present who can counsel any pupils disturbed by their own feelings. Some schools deliberately get TAs trained in counselling skills, in order that they can be of use in any emotionally charged situation. Any school ground rule of safety for active or practical group work must be discussed before any such activity. Monitoring group work for the teacher and reporting back can be a most useful added dimension to the lesson. Figure 7.5 shows a sheet designed by teachers in a secondary school to aid TAs in supporting pupils with specific learning difficulties (SpLD).

Occasionally, TAs are asked to take a whole class. This is an area likely to be covered in the developments following the new proposals. Keeping a large group on task takes a great deal of skill, and is a great responsibility. The position used to be that any adult can stand in front of a class in an emergency, provided they do not teach. My rule of thumb, as a manager, was to ensure that if any situation was planned, whereby the TA took a class so that the teacher could work with a specific group or an individual, that the teacher remained within call, and if possible in the same room as the TA – that is, the TA, and the class, was still obviously under the supervision of the qualified teacher. This sort of situation often happened with younger ones, when a TA may read a story or sing with a large group and the teacher does something special. Even student teachers had to have a qualified teacher present for lessons like PE.

Suggested General Strategies for Pupils on the SpLD Spectrum

• Provide multi sensory learning opportunities involving mind maps, diagrams, drawings, sound role play etc. Produce handouts or mind maps where possible. Emphasise visual and kinaesthetic learning modes.

• Avoid dictation and reduce copying from the whiteboard to a minimum.

• Regularly direct open ended and challenging questions to pupil in class.

• Provide repeated opportunity for recall during lesson.

• Check that he/she corrects mis-spelt words (spellcheck, ace dictionary).

• Promote *visual strategies* for learning spelling (see INSET sheets).

• Ask him/her to prepare visual key words for display above eye level in classroom.

• Identify a 'role' for pupil in group or pair work.

• Check that homework is correctly recorded in planner, or provide stick in note.

• Exploit opportunities for literacy and numeracy across the curriculum.

Figure 7.5 A suggestions sheet for a TA regarding special provision
Source: Stewards School, Harlow, Essex

The new proposals indicate that TAs could cover classes in the case of short-term absence of the teacher

> for example when teachers are ill or undertaking professional develop-
> ments or planning, preparation and assessment (PPA) activities. A mem-
> ber of support staff *with appropriate training and skills, who knows the*
> *pupils' needs and school procedures* [my italics], may be a more appropri-
> ate choice to undertake cover than another qualified teacher or a supply
> teacher.
>
> (DfES 2002a p. 21)

Practical work

TAs can work with a group, organise resources or equipment, use some explaining and tuition, question and observe what is going on. The pupils will be active, mobile and need to be as autonomous as possible. For these activities it is important that TAs are aware of all the health and safety procedures involved. For assisting in a subject like secondary science this may well mean that managers have to set up a training session for the TA or TAs involved, to ensure they understand the principles of risk assessment and the safe ways of

dealing with bunsen burners, chemicals, glass, microbes and radioactive sub-
stances, all used in school laboratories.

There may be some activities that the teacher needs to check the knowledge
and skills of the TA such as using measuring instruments correctly, understanding the level of accuracy that is required and the units to be used.
Sometimes, in science tasks, pupils believe they have to find the answer, when
actually the teacher's objective is to give them experience of certain equipment, or find a way to test, that can be repeated. In art, the emphasis by the
pupil again may be on the end product, and whether or not they can achieve
what is required, or something to satisfy themselves, when the teacher's
objective has been to explore a variety of media, to find their potential for
some other purpose entirely. It is essential that TAs know the purpose of the
task; they can then use appropriate questions to help the pupils think.

Resource management

TAs need paid time to do this, especially if they are to relieve the teacher of
some of the tasks that teachers should not routinely be expected to do. TAs
can make work cards and work sheets given a prototype, make and mend
equipment and books, or sort and organise classroom resources and equipment. Some equipment preparation and maintenance should be part of the
pupils' tasks, and the distinctions need to be clarified for the TA. Even small
children can and should clear up after themselves. TAs can help the pupils
help themselves, with sufficient time allowed in the lesson for such activities.
They can be encouraged to carry a few sharp pencils, a pencil sharpener and
spare pens. If they are to use audio-visual equipment or a new software
program on a computer, they need time to make sure it all works before the
lesson, where to go for technical help or spare bits. They may not have used
an overhead projector or whiteboards before, so the manager or the class
teacher should check.

Multitasking

Another observable trait of teachers and TAs is their ability to multitask.
This, along with the relative mobility of TAs, compared with the teachers,
means they can become a 'flexible friend' in the classroom, a 'gofer' in times
of emergency, anything an extra pair of hands can do.

Case study evidence
Four different activities are observed in the one classroom with the
same TA. She sits close to her identified children during a short class
phonic/word recognition session and then supervises the follow-up

work set for the little group. She keeps up their pace, questions, challenges and maintains the standards she knows are expected. When it is complete she uses a changeover time to assist a group in the maintenance of their cress seedlings. She asserts discipline with gesture, indicating displeasure. She then supervises a group in an activity called by the class 'speedy maths', giving encouragement with humour, and promoting self-esteem and confidence so that the children can read out answers when required. In her final session before play, she teaches a group of seven children some handwriting skills, while the rest of the class go to assembly. The teacher is present in the room for this, but doing recording and preparation. The TA's style and skill, particularly in differentiating questions appropriate to the different children, are impressive. This is so 'teacherlike' that an Ofsted-style observation was later attempted on the video made at the time. The TA showed very good knowledge of the subject matter, preparation and presentation skills, the children were attentive, on task, contributing and challenging each other.

Assessment activities

All the time teachers work with pupils they inwardly make small judgements. Those with QTS recognise this as informal formative assessment. TAs will also judge but at first without training to realise what they are seeing. As they increase in understanding of how learning takes place, of the needs of pupils and the content of the curriculum, they will be increasingly useful in helping teachers in making more formal formative assessments. The feedback from TAs can be as important as the in-class support they are providing to the pupils and teachers need to make arrangements to obtain this.

Case study evidence
The TA is doing an assessment for reading with her charge, Elaine. She is using a highlighter to mark the appropriate line in the Essex/ Birmingham levelled assessment lists as Elaine reads from her reading book. Other children follow Elaine through this process. The TA has been shown how to use the Essex/Birmingham assessment tool, enabling the teacher to leave this time-consuming task to her. Her questioning goes beyond the 'what' and 'who', to 'why'. She works under the teacher, as when the teacher stops the class – they all stop. Her gestures are well emphasised, eyebrows up and so on to clearly show interest. She runs her fingers under words to help the child see particular words.

Feedback can be much more informal than the planning process, just a note on the planning sheet and handed back to the teacher will help. Post-it Notes are invaluable and can be attached to pupils' work, the teacher's desk or planning sheets. Sometimes just a verbal comment at the end of a lesson before the TA and teacher separate, in the corridor on the way to the staff-room or even in the car park on the way home can help the teacher plan the next step for the pupils with whom the TA has been working. In one school, the TAs themselves devised a separate written feedback system that would have some consistency for the teachers. Another school had a diary system for noting improvement and problem recording. TAs also use teachers' assessment forms after training and guidance, which can be ticked when things were achieved (Figure 7.6).

In general

The TAs need to know what to do throughout the lesson, and throughout any informal times in other areas of the school as well. They will need specific training in the techniques and language used to support or control challenging pupils, and practice skills which support whatever the philosophy or policy is in the school If they are working with disturbed children or children who are on identified SEN stages for problems with behaviour, the SENCO and class teachers need to be involved to ensure a consistent approach.

Even in schools where all the systems, structures, strategies and philosophy are all in place, standards and expectations are high time does not stand still. People change and can develop; staff can be assisted in this process by managers. Chapter 8 looks at ways of developing the TAs once they are in place and working well. Generally, it is hard to hold them back: their enthusiasm for work is matched by their keenness to know more!

Week beginning

Child ⟶							
Learning Objective							

General comments

1. Easily achieved   2. Achieved only with support   3. Did not achieve

* see over for more detail

Figure 7.6 Examples of planning and feedback formats
Source: Maldon Primary School and Beehive Lane Community Primary School

Child   Week beginning

Learning Objective	Mon	Tues	Wed	Thurs	Fri

General comments

1. Easily achieved   2. Achieved only with support   3. Did not achieve

* see over for more detail

Child   Week beginning

Learning Objective	Delivery Method	Outcome

General comments

Beehive Lane Community Primary School
LSA Working Document

on the IEP for...Year.........................

LSA...

Targets

Time Span

Activities

Resources

Comments and Evaluation

Chapter 8

TAs' personal and professional development

> TAs are entitled to feel that they can develop in their jobs, and get better at what they are doing. Some TAs wish to reach the point where they can move on into teacher training, an ambition which the Government is taking steps to encourage. But the majority that do not have such ambitions still have developmental needs that the good employer will address. It is also clearly in the interests of the school if its TAs are able to increase their expertise and their job satisfaction.
>
> (DfEE 2000a p. 34)

This chapter explores ways in which managers can support their TAs by encouraging and providing opportunities for professional development. It gives strategies for in-house work as well as explaining some of the external courses available to TAs. Consideration is given to whole school INSET and the need to train teachers to make the best use of TAs.

Personal development

Developing all staff

If much of the effective role in teaching and learning for TAs is down to their personal characteristics, skills, knowledge and understanding, the ways in which they and the school develop these are clearly important. 'The professional development of **all** staff can add to school improvement, and that the support staff directly in contact with the pupils and students can have a direct role in enhancing achievement' (Watkinson 1999b p. 63).

Many schools have seen gaining the IiP award as a route to developing their whole staff. This move is encouraged by the DfES. Key Issue 3 (IiP 2000) talks of supporting individual development which encourages individual performance, advances understanding of what is expected, promotes commitment and motivation and promotes staff taking responsibility for their own learning. Key Issue 6 talks of promoting values for life and increasing understanding of personal, social, cultural, spiritual, moral and health issues. It is pointed out that development is about personal as well as professional development.

Developing TAs

The development of TAs, as with their work, appears to depend on their personality. TAs' enthusiasm develops as their confidence increases, which itself is a reflection of attention and value being placed on their role and them as people. While they are invisible, they tend just to get on with what they are asked to do, keeping their potential also hidden. Given encouragement, they blossom not only in having increased knowledge and understanding, but also in realising that here is something they can do, which is valued and in which they can achieve. TAs of this calibre have been described as 'feisty', and setting out on their exploration of issues can be too much of a challenge to less confident teachers or heads. For some insecure managers this potential for challenge may be a characteristic of which to be wary, but for most it is happily welcomed. Despite the workload of university level study, many TAs have undertaken HE courses with no previous experience of sustained study or many formal external examinations.

> It was clear from informal feedback that many students saw a growth in confidence in the classroom as a critical effect of the course. Part of this may have derived from greater knowledge and understanding; informally students also hinted that the course had enabled them to share a technical vocabulary and set of concepts with the teachers that made it easier for them to take part in educational discourse.
>
> (Swann and Loxley 1998 p. 147)

The lack of clear pathways and qualification frameworks have made career pathway decisions hard for TAs. Blenkin and Kelly found that nursery nurses were uninterested in career progression, they 'only appear to engage in further training if it is the requirement of the post' (Blenkin and Kelly 1997 p. 20). They also reported some indifference towards training because of a distrust of higher levels, what they called 'anti-intellectualism' (p. 24). Robins suggested nursery nurses may be 'so overworked that they find it difficult to, or too time consuming to manage anything else, such as "getting advice"' (Robins 1998 p. 46). Possibly the more closed society of EY institutions prevents any vision of possible changes, or reflects a group of people already at the 'top' of what was attainable. My experience of TAs has usually indicated a lively interest in continued professional development and career progression with the emphasis on being a good TA rather than aiming for QTS, but a concern over lack of pay recognition for further training.

Variation

The TAs are often modest about their capabilities, and see their own personal education as a handicap; they value paper qualifications about their job, but recognise achieving these have not advanced their career or increase their pay. Farrell *et al.* (1999) surveyed the training providers of courses and also found that TAs 'valued the opportunity to receive training, both accredited and non-accredited, particularly if it related to their daily work' (p. 3), but stated such training had no impact on salary or career progression, both of which concerned the TAs. They wanted to be 'better LSAs and to be valued for doing just that' (p. 64).

Survey evidence
The consideration of career progression leading inevitably to them becoming teachers, while needed for a few, was not the desire of most TAs. On-site training including induction was variable, although some good practice was observed. Keeping up-to-date or meeting other TAs were as important to TAs as having a qualification. Only 10 to 20 per cent may want to go on to become teachers, but all were willing to go on learning.

Diary evidence
Advisers and trainers like tutoring TAs, often commenting that they were much more responsive than teachers coming out of school, 'they listen, work with their schools, produce materials of high calibre off their own bat'. Course portfolios get illustrated liberally with photographs and, in one case I saw, even with small watercolour paintings. TAs will buy themselves computers to undertake study, stay up when the rest of the family has gone to bed to watch videos, and complete work under strained domestic situations. It is rare for them to give up and even rarer for them to fail. Once they have a flavour of personal success, they want more.

The attitude of TAs to paper qualifications may have been determined in the current climate which is driving parents and pupils to believe that paper qualifications are the marker of quality, and only 'qualified' teachers matter or it may be caused by a need to boost their own confidence. It remains to be seen whether any form of qualifications will be required for any level of the job in the future.

Case study evidence

Only one TA interviewed was adamant that courses were not for her, but she got great satisfaction from her job as it was, and felt she got all the updating she needed from the in-house training. Her personal enthusiasm and commitment to the teachers with whom she worked meant she was always alert to their needs and the needs of the children. In no way was she complacent or inflexible. However, she was working in a school where there was considerable attention paid to the needs of TAs, and provision of paid time for meetings and INSET. The teachers interviewed spoke of the TAs' lack of confidence, and how they grew by talking together, watching the lessons and working alongside the teachers, particularly where the TAs experienced the work of more than one teacher. The talking took place at 'playtime or whatever, briefly at lunchtime, showing her forms and things like that'. One said, 'If you'd asked me 12 months ago she would have said she couldn't do it. It's quite nice, in 12 months she has just forged ahead because of the support of the teachers, and she can do anything now and she's more than adequate to do it with any of the children'.

They often asked, 'What next, is teaching the only route?' One teacher voiced a concern over the way their role had changed, not recognising that changes in their own role were also taking place. She said, 'There is this need to stretch them, and then you get into how much more of the teacher's role can they take over?'

The NOS values and principles state:

Continuing Professional Development

Teaching/classroom assistants will take advantage of planned and incidental self-development opportunities in order to maintain and improve the contribution that they can make to raising pupil achievement. Asking for advice and support to help resolve problems should be seen as a form of strength and professionalism.

(LGNTO 2001, pp. 5–6)

It was suggested (DfEE 2000c) that TAs should have professional development similar to teachers, but while this resulted in performance related pay and its legal status for teachers, no requirement is made of schools to ensure it takes place for TAs. Schools who value all staff will find the time and resources to appraise and develop all their staff.

Recognising value

One indicator of whether TAs consider they are being valued, but which must not be abused, is that of volunteer time. All staff in a happy school feel able to give time through goodwill, it is one of the things that disappears when morale is low. TAs themselves tend to be very happy with their work, despite their low pay, as they enjoy working with pupils and the hours fit in with family commitments.

> *Diary evidence*
> Talking with TAs from one of our first primary schools to get the IiP award showed a clear way in which the school worked as a team. One described how on returning to school after completing a course, the head had presented her course certificate in assembly, when the children had received their certificates for various things. She had been clapped, and at playtime children had come up to her and asked her what she had had to do to get her certificate. This same head used to put smiley face stickers in children's books from time to time and had special adult versions for the portfolios that the TAs maintained for their courses.

These may seem childish ways to recognise value, but all the adults there appreciated it. Schools can make sure the TAs contribute to the annual report to parents or that their photographs and those of all support staff appear in the school photo gallery, or all participate in the staff photograph. Any kind of celebration needs to include everybody.

In-house provision for development

Informal training and development

Hodgson and Kambouri (1999) discuss some of the underlying principles for teaching adults, pointing out that there is no one best way, and that it may take time to find out how each learns best. They give six principles, emphasising facilitation rather than formal courses:

* participation in learning is voluntary;
* effective practice is characterized by a respect among participants for each other's self worth;
* facilitation is collaborative;
* action and reflection are placed at the heart of effective facilitation (action in the sense of exploring a whole new way of interpreting one's own work, personal relationships or political allegiances);
* facilitation aims to foster in adults a spirit of critical reflection;

- the aim of facilitation is the nurturing of self directed, empowered adults.

(Hodgson and Kambouri 1999 p. 185)

Case study evidence

Teachers interviewed did not realise how much they were teaching the TAs both by example and through the TAs watching them – ' I don't teach her – no time' yet they gave time to sharing ideas. The daily meeting of teachers with TAs in the staffroom, however fleeting, often unwittingly added to the knowledge and understanding of the TAs, as teachers tell the TAs how they wanted something done or why. One TA said, 'I've been doing it for a couple of years – Fuzz Buzz – I learnt from Yvonne really, Yvonne talked me through how to cope with that' [Yvonne is the visiting SEN support teacher]. 'Yvonne suggested that the group needed Fuzz Buzz'.

The teachers in the open plan school indicated that part of the ease with which TAs developed transferable skills was due to the geography of the school. There were no physical divisions to the classroom, although the classes usually functioned separately, especially following the increased whole class teaching recommended by the NLNS. The senior management balanced the skills and desires of the TAs themselves and saw spreading TAs across the classes as part of the TA development process.

The problems could come for TAs if the fleeting nature of such intercourse in some schools, particularly secondary schools, meant less effective support for learning and teaching, and increased the potential for TAs to receive varied guidance.

Meetings

Case study evidence

In both study schools, the incorporation of the TAs into the staffroom culture was an essential part of their understanding of how the school operated and gave them an insight into how they could contribute. When I first visited one of them, they felt regular meetings were not necessary. 'So long as we can ask for a meeting'. 'We don't like to bother anyone'. 'We don't want a meeting just to say we are OK'. Yet six months later they were saying how much they appreciated the meetings with the visiting support teacher. They would have liked more time with their class teacher, and more direction as to working with children during teacher input time. By the end of my time in the school, the TAs were having regular weekly meetings with their line managers or the SENCO as well as having occasional input from the support teacher. The other school had started Wednesday morning meetings after the introduction of the morning literacy hour and mathematics lessons but prior to that there had been SEN training for the TAs by the headteacher in her SENCO capacity for the target group initiative. The meetings had an element of training, but were also seen as opportunities for the TAs to help themselves and initiate their own development. The meeting time was also paid time for the TAs whereas any attendance at after school sessions was not.

The *Good Practice Guide* has paragraphs on holding meetings and sharing in its section called 'Creating partnership among teaching assistants' (DfEE 2000a pp. 31–33). It recognises that the informal opportunities may not be sufficient and that more formal arrangements usually need to be made particularly for sharing information about pupils, the school and support groups; planning, problem solving and staff development.

Some useful topics for meetings that have been used by managers have been:

- any area of interest or concern raised by the TAs themselves
- questioning – using video material of teachers in action
- supporting IEPs and implementing other strategies to support those pupils with SEN
- the value of play – using video material
- using the materials from the NLNS
- using a visiting teacher, educational psychologist, literacy or numeracy consultant, school adviser or therapist to explain parts of their work.

Diary evidence

One secondary school visited had a regular weekly meeting of all TAs, chaired by the SENCO. At each meeting a topic of interest or concern to the TAs was logged for future debate, individual concerns about pupils were discussed, particularly where pupils had returned from a lengthy period of absence or were new to the school, and curriculum faculty heads and other teachers attended by arrangement. These teachers would examine with the TAs how they wanted their subject supported, and the TAs would suggest strategies or request support for the particular pupils for whom they had concern in that subject. As it took place weekly, these were not prolonged sessions, merely occupying one period of the school timetable, all present were paid for their time. Sometimes an individual TA would disclose a particular skill or knowledge area which could be used to support a particular curriculum area – one was a music graduate, who offered to help a particular group of pupils in practical sessions, two came from the local Bangladeshi community and could support EAL.

School based INSET

It seems obvious that if TAs are supporting the curriculum, they should have some understanding and training in the area they are supporting, and what the demands on the teachers are. This did not really develop on a large scale until the government strategies came. The attendance of the TAs at the in-house training for the National Literacy Strategy (NLS) was seen as part of the training programme for the strategies, and was undertaken willingly by the TAs, despite, in some instances, lack of payment for the time of this participation. In the NNS, guidance was given in the training materials and the framework itself. Giving copies of the guidance to the additional adults was recommended, along with thorough briefing. Aplin's (1998) book was recommended for use when working in schools with assistants for mathematics. The statement 'Make sure that they know not only what the children are to do but what they are to learn', recognised that adults other than teachers could understand 'why' as well as 'what' they were doing (DfEE 1999a p. 24).

It is helpful to purchase copies of the frameworks for all your TAs and many of the additional booklets that appear from time to time such as vocabulary lists, but the joint training with the teachers in the individual school is the most effective, in terms of ensuring joint understanding of subject matter, consistency of approach, understanding objectives and planning, and in team building.

Other joint training areas

There are some other areas where it is essential that staff are trained together. One of these is the principles and practice of behaviour management. The DfEE/DfES Induction training included modules in this area (DfEE 2000f), but in some ways it was ahead of its time – the teachers in many schools had not had similar training.

Diary evidence

In one school I visited to have a meeting with the TAs and provide some isolated training, they shared a problem which is possibly not uncommon: 'How can we stop a child sliding down the banisters, when the deputy head does not stop them?' Following the session, I shared this concern with the head, and it turned out he was having a problem with that member of staff.

Another school I visited frequently, had not only sent all their staff together to cluster training days but also had the trainer as a regular visitor to the school. He showed by example how children can be treated positively yet firmly, as well as taking whole school INSET sessions. After several years all the staff had developed this way of talking to children with some remarkable results. The school was in a deprived area, where social skills were often lacking at home, and discipline lacking; 5 year olds could be found on the street alone at night. The head reckoned the attitudes were beginning to rub off on the parents as well. This school not only achieved high levels of behaviour but also ensured that the children did well academically; the children were keen learners.

It is vital that child protection training should take place for all staff. The school must have clear child protection policies which are agreed by the governors and known to the parents. There are two aspects to this: one how to deal with a child or pupil who reveals and the other that of protection of staff against false allegations. TAs are particularly likely to be the ones to whom pupils reveal along with other support staff such as MDAs, as they work so often with individuals or small groups. These are the staff with whom individual children can make close relationships, often talking about home or leisure situations. The TAs often help small or physically handicapped pupils change their clothes and may see body marks, or recognise emotional distress. All staff must know about not questioning such pupils but providing a listening ear. They need to know what is important and what not, which member of staff is the Named Officer to deal with incidents and the whereabouts of the LEA guidance. All staff need guidance on when touch or comfort is appropriate for younger or vulnerable pupils and how to help in intimate situations, such as changing wet or soiled clothing. Training in restraint is essential if it is to be used.

First aid training is another very useful whole staff training session. It does a lot for team work, developing a sense of humour and morale when the elegant female school secretary has to settle the male PE teacher in the recovery position, or the deputy head has to bandage the site manager.

Any school briefings given in the areas of equal opportunities, celebrating multiculturalism and or developing strategies to support pupils with EAL and their families, should also be for all staff, not just the teachers.

Some headteachers have suggested having an LEA adviser for TAs, and this post already exists in some LEAs. They also felt that TAs should be on the agenda of the regular visits from the general School Development Adviser. The existence of advisers is different in different LEAs, and their role even more so. It is worth asking what advice is available in your local area, although usually this will now come at a price.

Cascading

One of the problems in any school is the cascade model of in-service, where only limited numbers of staff go off site to 'receive the message' and then have to come back to inform or train other staff. A system is needed whereby all staff attending courses feed back in some way. The caretaker who receives guidance about the use of bleach, for instance, needs to inform all those who might feel the need to use it as a disinfectant. The TAs, particularly, need to feed back about the ways in which they are being trained, otherwise the teaching staff do not know of what their TA is capable. Where the TAs have been asked to take part of a staff meeting and tell the teachers what they were studying, their own confidence has been boosted as well as the information being exchanged.

The *Good Practice Guide* (DfEE 2000a) has useful audit sheets for managers concerning in-house provision for TAs. Indicator 5 (p. 48) can be used to find out whether TAs meet with other TAs for purposes of planning, problem solving and staff development and Indicator 6 (p. 49) as to whether TAs are supported in relation to their induction, mentoring and development needs.

Off-site training

The changes in role brought about by the NLS were followed up by specific training for the TAs involved. It was in 1999 that the ALS training for TAs and teachers together was introduced. This was funded, but there was some cynicism, as little rationale was spelt out in the materials (DfEE 1999b Module 1) other than the achievement of government targets for 2002. TAs were to become the recommended way of delivering catch-up work for children in Years 3 and 4, who seemed unlikely to attain level 4 when they reached Year 6, because they achieved only level 1 or only just attained level 2 in their Year 2 tests. The funding supported the development of specific tasks for these children, special materials for the TAs, and training for the TAs and a teacher from each school. The DfEE and DfES TA Induction training for the NLNS included whole days of off-site training for TAs, but unless the TAs knew how their own school was interpreting the information they were being given, it would not have been helpful. Teachers were not invited to attend these days as they were for other parts of the NLNS training and other induction modules.

Visiting other schools

Case study evidence

One TA observed had accompanied the SENCO to visit schools special-ising in dealing with autistic children and the subsequent discussions in the school had been very helpful for them in confirming the appropriateness of their practice. In the special school, the pupils had continual one-to-one support from an adult, and the pupils saw only similar autistic children. In the mainstream school, the autistic pupil was surrounded by children who could sit still and listen without adult support. Parents and staff agreed that despite the difficulties, the main-stream placement for Andrew was correct while he was young. He slowly became more part of his class, able to sit unaccompanied through a whole school assembly, and participate in class and group activities. The visit also gave the staff professional specialised contacts with whom to liaise over specific problems.

Local cluster groups have started up in some places, where the heads have supported meetings in their schools. The TAs visit each school in the cluster in turn, say once a term, talk to each other and about their schools, and may have visiting speakers. Some schools' cluster INSET days have special sessions for their TAs, as well as MDAs, caretakers and so on.

Short courses

Case study material

Andrew's TA spoke at length about the three-day conference she had been to which enabled her to set up the TEACCH programme for Andrew which I had seen in action. This conference or training session had had a major impact on the way in which she worked with the child, and with the encouragement of the teacher and the school she had been able to implement the strategies suggested. The school management of both study schools, and their TAs, recognised that external courses, and one or two Teachers' Centre (LEA) courses had provided training of greater depth than was possible from school staff.

Funding has been an issue for the TAs, being so poorly paid, and realising no amount of training or qualifications would change their rate of pay. Sometimes TAs will fund their own course, some are funded by the school professional development budget and others by the school from earmarked Standards funding. But, of course, funding for TAs does not stop at fees. TAs are often required to attend in their own time, not paid time. They may not have access to a car, or access to the family car means expenditure or inconvenience to other members of the family. Public transport is not an option in rural areas as it rarely provides the right direction at the right time. Some schools do recognise all the above and make efforts to provide additional support to enable the TAs to go to off-site training, knowing the school and pupils will benefit as well as the TA. A welcome gesture would be for the school to provide paper, files, set books or other materials suggested by the courses, none of which cost a great deal, but show an interest and support of the TAs' training.

Courses put on by local further education (FE) and HE colleges and universities will attract funding through the Learning and Skills Council, the body that replaced the Training and Enterprise Councils (TECs) and the FE and HE Funding Councils (FEFC and HEFC). Thus, the real cost of such courses as they appear in the handbooks is already subsidised. Some LEA courses will be free to participants, as they will be funded through Standards Grants, such as the DfEE/DfES Induction courses, other courses may have to run at cost and thus appear very expensive. Some LEAs may still retain central funding for training, particularly where they still operate their own TA teams. It is possibly worth considering local sources of funding: charities, industries or businesses who may see bursaries as a way of supporting local communities. Such activity can be time-consuming for managers, but can build up useful local contacts. TAs should be paid for their time if they would normally be working, and the school could consider helping with travelling expenses. Where schools are 'growing their own', governors are usually only too supportive of providing such finance.

A larger funding issue to consider is the release of teachers to accompany the TA on the course, mentor release time and paid time for the TA to complete tasks for the course. All the TA courses will demand some TA participation, observation and recording of school activities. They need access and time to do these.

Qualifications and experience

The proliferation of qualifications at each level has increased the confusion over training and fitness for purpose, as the levels of the awards, and the diversity of content and standards has left managers without any ability to recognise their acquisition in terms of fitting qualification to purpose or a pay structure. 'Qualifications for teaching assistants' is available to be down-loaded from the www.teachernet/teachingassistants website and lists many of the awards which have been used by TAs to date.

Whatever award or course the TAs undertake, managers should try to make contact with the college, provider or course tutor. All courses will have an element of school based work in them, carrying out activities or observations. Not all colleges are good at liaising with host schools and providing them with details, or appropriately backing up the student's work. If the manager and the TA are to make the most of any training, it should be a joint effort.

Induction level

The Green Paper initiatives (DfEE 1998a) for recruitment also included training. England-wide training for all new recruits in primary schools was proposed, produced and funded by the government and delivered by the LEAs. It included training to support literacy and numeracy, and also covered the generalist role of the TA as well as, possibly most innovatively, the behaviour management module. The emphasis was put in the course on ensuring that TAs were part of a whole school team and process, had job descriptions, and briefing on relevant school policies, particularly literacy, numeracy and behaviour management support (DfEE 2000a, 2000d, 2000h, 2000i). In 2001, the DfES addressed the induction needs of TAs in secondary schools (DfES 2001a, 2001c, 2001d, 2001e, 2001f). Part of these courses was the requirement to do some observational work back in schools, and the compilation of a personal professional portfolio. While these courses only attempt to provide the off-site input for a possible lengthy induction process undertaken by the school, its content has been matched already with the NOS. TAs successfully completing all the off-site days, and the tasks required of them back at school, would have covered many of the competencies, knowledge and understanding components of a level 2 TA. The matching tables are available on the LGNTO website www.lgnto.gov.uk as are the NOS themselves. The new proposals intend that this programme should be extended.

Levels 2 and 3

Not only has the variety of qualifications increased over recent years, but also the levels of availability of training specifically geared to TAs have expanded. In September 2002, the first courses matched by QCA against the new NOS had started, as well as the new NVQs. Existing awards will be allowed to continue until 2003, and many TAs applying for jobs in the next few years will already have qualifications achieved under the old free-for-all system. NVQs may prove a problem for schools. TAs do not have to attend a course, but have to compile a portfolio of evidence of competence, both practical and of their understanding and knowledge. In order that this can achieve an award, they have to register with an awarding centre, usually an FE or adult education college, or it can be an independent centre or run by the LEA. The centre has to appoint assessors to sign off the evidence as true. In order to do this they have to watch the TA at work and assure themselves of the underpinning knowledge either by verbal questioning or written or recorded material provided by the candidate. This can be a long, time-consuming and tedious process, depending on the kind of paperwork required by the centre and the awarding body accrediting the centre. In order that standards are compatible across the UK the centre also appoints internal verifiers, and is inspected by external verifiers from the awarding bodies. This all costs money and further time and paperwork. Ideally, the assessor should be a member of staff in the TA candidate's workplace. The assessor can then observe the TA at work, and get to know his or her real competence and knowledge base. However, it is difficult to see, particularly with the current worry about overload, how teachers or senior TAs will find the time to carry out the observations and questioning that has been required of educational NVQs in the past. Managers must consider carefully, when agreeing to a TA undertaking an NVQ, and understand what the implications are, not only for mentoring but also for assessing such awards. Awarding centres may provide peripatetic assessors who come in from time to time to perform this task, but this can incur an extra cost.

Other courses which should be considered is the attendance of relevant TAs on specialist SEN courses, undertaking counselling training, or specific curriculum courses such as ICT.

Table 8.1 shows the main new awards known to be available in August 2002.

The STA qualification still exists and seems outside the QCA remit for approval. STA training was recommended by the NNS, 'but we are convinced that the first priority for the strategy should be to train teachers' (DfEE 1998b, p. 64). There is some confusion as some STA courses are presented by some FE colleges as level 3 awards, and others are clearly undergraduate modules, thus requiring study at level 4. This discrepancy has caused some problems for TAs wishing to go on to further HE study. Each HE institution is able to set its own entry criteria for its courses, and some will accept the STA qualification as part of a first year study, and others will not.

Routes to teaching

With the increasing development this year of foundation degrees for TAs, based on two years' full-time or four years' part-time study, this anomaly will be part of the rationalisation of the qualifications scene. The new proposals (DfES 2002a) recognise that there is a wide range of qualifications

Table 8.1 Teaching assistant qualifications accredited to the national qualifications framework in August 2002

Level	Vocationally related qualifications	Occupational qualifications
2	CACHE level 2 certificate for teaching assistants NCFE level 2 certificate for teaching assistants Edexcel BTEC certificate for teaching assistants *ABC level 2 certificate for teaching assistants (under development)* *NOCN level 2 intermediate award for teaching assistants (under development)*	NVQ level 2 for teaching assistants (awards by CACHE, OCR, City and Guilds *Edexcel expected September 2002*)
3	CACHE level 3 certificate for teaching assistants *Edexcel BTEC level 3 certificate for teaching assistants (submitted)*	NVQ level 3 for teaching assistants (awarded by CACHE, OCR, City and Guilds *Edexcel expected September 2002*)

Source: Employers' Organisation 2002 p. 7
Notes: Items in Italics were qualifications submitted but which had not received accreditation when the document was published.
ABC: Awarding Body Consortium
BTEC: Business and Technology Education Council
CACHE: Council for Awards in Children's Care and Education
NCFE: Northern College of Further Education
NOCN: National Open College Network
OCR: Oxford and Cambridge and RSA Examinations
RSA: Royal Society of Arts

available, some accredited and some not. The development of new standards by the TTA suggested in the consultation, alongside the existing NOS should enable training providers to provide credits which will be recognised by HE institutions and even QTS credits if that is the chosen route of the TA. It is also envisaged that there will be funding for such a programme.

The TTA commissioned research into the pathways to teaching for TAs partly to look at career pathways for TAs who might wish to develop along that route several years ago, although it was also seen as an attempt to address the teacher shortage (Smith *et al.* 1999). The TTA (2000) published a first guide to what was available. Since then the numbers of TAs who can be accepted on Graduate and Registered Training Programmes have increased, although over the country as a whole this route still only accounts for few trainees a year. Most try to complete their degrees, and get onto a School Centred Initial Teacher Training Course in their area or a postgraduate certificate of education (PGCE) course at their local college.

Training the teachers

One of the areas that has been neglected in the past has been the training of teachers to use and manage other adults. I hope that there have been sufficient suggestions in this book for schools to use in this aspect. Managers must remember that teachers new to the school including newly qualified teachers and supply teachers will all need to know the school policies regarding the use of TAs, and should be introduced to the relevant TAs as people. Such teachers may need a short induction session to aid their understanding.

TAs cannot 'be skilled up away from the teachers' as one head requested, suggesting that teachers were already too busy and burdened to want to understand what the TAs were to learn. Keeping teachers aware of what training the TAs are undertaking is important, and where possible having joint attendance at external courses.

The future training of teachers will include an element of provision in this area as the new standards (TTA 2002) include 'understand[ing] the contribution that support staff and other professionals make to teaching and learning' (p. 6), planning 'with the help of support staff where appropriate' (p. 9) and 'manag[ing] the work of teaching assistants or other adults to enhance pupils' learning' (p. 12). Knowing the varied allocation of time to such preparation in Initial Teacher Training Courses, managers would be wise to check with future newly qualified teachers how knowledgeable they are about the use of TAs. The new proposals indicate the 'development of further in-service training materials' for teachers.

> It will be important for schools to help teachers make an up-front investment in these skills of management, communication and delegation, to ensure that support staff who complement them are well managed to raise standards and reduce teachers' own workloads over time.
>
> (DfES 2002 p. 41)

Headteachers and senior managers in the past have been very reluctant to include the management of support staff, and TAs in particular, in their own priorities for training. It rarely appeared as a subject at conferences, and attendance at such courses offered was often very low. Headteachers need to be involved in many of the issues described in this book for theirs is the final responsibility, delegated to them by governors for staffing distribution and delegation, communication systems creating an appropriate climate, understanding the roles and work of TAs, addressing problems of pupils with special needs or the stress and workload issues of staff. The new proposals indicate that they will 'work with the National College for School Leadership and other key stakeholders to ensure that training programmes and networks for school leaders support these needs' (DfES 2002a p. 9).

Change is continual and managing change is a prime consideration for all who work in schools as well as managers and the developing TAs. Some of the most exciting times in schools can be when managers think ahead, and initiate ideas and plans before they are imposed from outside. Chapter 9 looks at how schools might like to look ahead as well as to their status quo.

Looking ahead

Why bother? In this instance, we believe there are good reasons, both educational and financial, for bothering. We believe it is time to look again at the traditional patterns of staffing in schools. Over the years, teachers' roles have become unnecessarily rigid ... We think there is much scope yet to be explored and we are sure that there will be benefits not only to associate staff and their teacher colleagues able to focus more properly on pedagogy, but also to individual pupils and to the school as a whole. It is right they should be staffed by colleagues from a variety of backgrounds, bringing appropriate skills to the corporate life of the institution.

(Mortimore *et al.* 1994 p. 222)

Chapter 9 takes a broader look at the possible implications of developing the work of TAs within a school. The new initiative of the pathfinder schools, looking at the use of support staff, particularly in relation to ICT is explored. The need for creating a new profession of teaching assistance and of a pedagogy for TAs is considered in relation to the development of effective schools as learning organisations. The book ends by touching on the use of TAs in the development of a truly inclusive society.

TAs develop

This book has described the process by which adults who have outward-going, caring personalities and a commitment to education and who are prepared to develop and undergo training of a variety of kinds can provide responsive, sensitive and knowledgeable aides to the teaching and learning process. Figure 9.1 shows how training and personality can combine to produce a professional TA.

After auditing and training, TAs should be able to be placed well into the upper right-hand quartile of Figure 9.1.

The book has emphasised, however, that the provision of highly skilled, competent and professional TAs will not in itself provide the most effective support to the pupils, teachers and the school. TAs are only as effective as

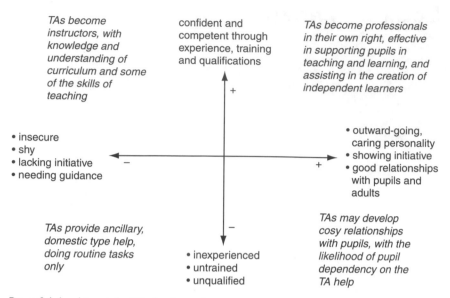

TAs become instructors, with knowledge and understanding of curriculum and some of the skills of teaching

confident and competent through experience, training and qualifications

TAs become professionals in their own right, effective in supporting pupils in teaching and learning, and assisting in the creation of independent learners

+

- insecure
- shy
- lacking initiative
- needing guidance

–

+

- outward-going, caring personality
- showing initiative
- good relationships with pupils and adults

TAs provide ancillary, domestic type help, doing routine tasks only

–

- inexperienced
- untrained
- unqualified

TAs may develop cosy relationships with pupils, with the likelihood of pupil dependency on the TA help

Figure 9.1 Looking at the TAs by themselves

their use, deployment and management, and much depends on the relationships developed with teachers and the ethos of the school. Where the school systems and structures support the formation of a whole school team, the consistency of practice, and contribution of the TAs to the teaching and learning of the school is enhanced. The training and qualifications provided by universities, local authorities and colleges and national initiatives are all helpful in facilitating professional development. They can provide a standard of professional practice and national consistency. It is the use to which the school management puts these initiatives, and the use they make of the skills, knowledge and understanding developed by TAs in training, that will create support for pupils, teachers and the school. Managers aim to place their own school in the upper right-hand quartile of Figure 9.2. But does it stop there?

The effective school

The moves towards self-evaluation, the school effectiveness research movement and recognising that change is a fact of life to be planned for, not coped with, have moved leadership thinking from managing an organisation to a more exciting, innovative plane. The sight of the headteacher, settled for life in a cosy school, a pillar of the local community revered by staff, parents and children has long gone. The challenges of leading school initiatives, taking hold of the potential in LEA and government driven initiatives are not for those seeking a quiet life, and some have opted for the early retirement route.

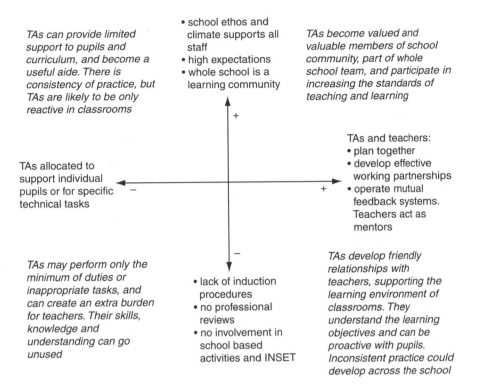

TAs can provide limited support to pupils and curriculum, and become a useful aide. There is consistency of practice, but TAs are likely to be only reactive in classrooms

- school ethos and climate supports all staff
- high expectations
- whole school is a learning community

TAs become valued and valuable members of school community, part of whole school team, and participate in increasing the standards of teaching and learning

TAs allocated to support individual pupils or for specific technical tasks

TAs and teachers:
- plan together
- develop effective working partnerships
- operate mutual feedback systems. Teachers act as mentors

TAs may perform only the minimum of duties or inappropriate tasks, and can create an extra burden for teachers. Their skills, knowledge and understanding can go unused

- lack of induction procedures
- no professional reviews
- no involvement in school based activities and INSET

TAs develop friendly relationships with teachers, supporting the learning environment of classrooms. They understand the learning objectives and can be proactive with pupils. Inconsistent practice could develop across the school

Figure 9.2 Looking at the whole school scene in relation to TAs

In a changing world, not only do schools have to plan for change, but part of their curriculum must be to help children and young people learn to live with and use change. Sammons talks of 'efficient organisation, fitness for purpose, flexibility of approach and intellectual challenge' when discussing the centrality of teaching and learning – a challenge in itself (Sammons 1999 p. 215)!

Thomas and colleagues describe an effective school as being 'recognised to be one where all members are included and have a stake, not simply one which achieves high scores on academic criteria . . . reducing inequality . . . is about providing the chance to share in the common wealth of the school and its culture' (Thomas *et al.* 1998 pp. 8–9). Creemers (1994) suggests multiple outcomes as criteria for effectiveness: basic skills and knowledge – the traditional ones; compensation – providing equity; social skill and attitudes – including towards learning itself; higher order skills – such as problem solving; metacognitive knowledge and skills – learners' control over the cognitive processes; and 'new' educational goals such as educational technology, creativity and moral behaviour.

The following principles could be seen as 'fundamental to the task of enhancing the quality of education':

- All children can learn, albeit in different ways at different rates
- Individual schools can make a substantial difference to the development, progress and achievement of all pupils
- Effective schools add value to pupils' lives
- Effective schools focus on a range of learning outcomes, including academic, practical, creative, personal and social
- Schools improve most by focussing on learning and teaching, while also addressing their culture and internal conditions
- Partnership is a fundamental element of successful school improvement
- Intervention work needs to be based on appropriate research findings.

(Sammons 1999 p. 340)

If teaching and learning are at the 'heart of school improvement ... real, lasting change can only come from what teachers and learning assistants do consistently in classrooms and other learning areas of the schools' (Brighouse and Woods 1999 p. 83). They go on to describe the development of a teaching and learning climate with 'staff taking individual and collective responsibility to improve on their previous best'. They describe ten factors which 'if adopted would help to improve all schools':

1 an agreed policy about the practice of teaching and learning
2 a teaching and learning staffroom
3 collaborative teaching planning and assessment
4 the effective use of resources
5 monitoring and evaluation/collective review
6 professional development
7 action research
8 community involvement in the learning school
9 curriculum enrichment and extension
10 the celebration of teaching and learning.

(Brighouse and Woods 1999 p. 85)

When these contributions are added to the research findings of Farrell *et al.* (1999) about TAs whose 'general findings ... suggest that effective practice'

- fosters the **participation** of pupils in the social and academic processes of the school;
- seeks to enable pupils to become more **independent learners**;
- helps to **raise standards** for all pupils

(Farrell *et al.* 1999 p. 4, their emphasis)

it can be seen that working to improve the work with TAs in the school can be a real move towards enhancing the education in a school.

Professionalisation of the role of the TA

Responsibility

The pronouncements (Morris 2001; PricewaterhouseCoopers 2001) which have led to the concentration of initiatives to relieve teacher workload, reinforced the need for appropriate TA training and qualifications: for their own professional status, self-esteem and self-confidence; to ensure recognition by the teaching profession; and to enable continued professional development. While they might have many of the characteristics of teachers, they need a career structure in their own right.

The TAs I interviewed, and some of the respondents of the survey, indicated that one of the reasons they are so keen and lively is that they are not overwhelmed by responsibilities, assessment implications and the requirements of the NC, the NLNS, a view reiterated in the press. Most do not want to be teachers. The balance between TAs' job description, status and recognition and appropriate systems of support and pay has to be carefully examined.

While QTS level is seen as the entry door into the teaching profession, the TA foundations remain underground, their grade rating as zero or minus if the scale of QTS is seen as level 1. The quandary is to find a way of increasing their visibility without upsetting some of the real support they give. They are currently like the roots of a tree, below ground, but a gardener knows that the roots upon which the life of a tree depends often extend beyond the canopy of the tree, and need appropriate nourishment.

Voice

TAs form part of the support staff structure of the school, the foundations on which the more senior staff members depend. The headteachers and teachers in the case studies often commented on the value of their TAs 'absolutely vital', 'terrific burden off my shoulders'. Edwards (1997) makes a case for the professionalisation of support staff, making them a team in their own right.

> The growth of the professionalisation of support staff in colleges has greatly increased the efficiency and effectiveness of operation and there is no doubt that the quality of provision for students has benefited in consequence.
>
> (Edwards 1997 p. 15)

TAs need a voice of their own, just as nurses, technicians and librarians do. While the teacher unions and Unison, the local government union, are voicing support for the TAs, none speak primarily for them, yet it is these organisations that are speaking for TAs in the DfES and with employers. The TAs themselves are not represented. There are various groups around the UK but they seem to meet informally, largely where senior managers or heads have encouraged them, offered to fund refreshments, circulate notices around the local communication systems and offered the school's hospitality. I hope that your school will also encourage such meetings and groups, and if possible also encourage them to take the next step, and form a properly constituted TA association.

TAs are perfectly capable of running such groups, and these could quickly grow, as with parents' and governors' groups to a representative national association – let us hope without some of the rancour and arguments that have dogged these other associations. The PreSchool Learning Alliance grew from a letter in the *Guardian* newspaper in 1961 from Brenda Crowe; perhaps the TA movement will soon grow its own association. The General Teaching Council has taken a long time coming; let us hope that the TA Council will not take so long. A TA Council could establish standards, operate a register, and provided professional advice as well as a voice in the public and political arena.

A profession?

Morris (2001 p. 19) talked of six characteristics being present in a modern profession. She then detailed how that can bolster the teaching profession. They could also be used to support the case for a profession in teaching assistance for the great majority of TAs (probably about 80 per cent) who are not aspiring to be teachers. I have taken each of her points and outlined how TAs could progress to also being a modern profession.

High standards at key levels of the profession, including entry and leadership, set nationally and regulated by a strong professional body

For TAs, the NOS are already in existence, nationally recognised qualifications including NVQs are on their way and should become well established during 2003 and the standards for higher level TAs become available during 2003. However, the entry requirements or basic qualifications for some levels such as GCSEs in English and mathematics for competent level, a level 3 for higher level, and a higher level of 'supervisor, manager, and/or instructor' needs attention. A letter from the DfES (Wright 2002) says it 'will be considering whether further, higher level qualifications may need to be developed' (p. 2). While there is no national council, association or regulatory body for TAs, LGNTO, QCA, TTA, the exam boards, Unison and teacher unions all recognise the existence of TAs and support their developments in varied ways.

A body of knowledge about what works best and why, with regular
training and development of opportunities so that members of the
profession are always up to date

There is a great need for the development of a pedagogy for TAs, to include
teaching and learning theory and practice, curriculum knowledge and understanding, child development, SEN etc. The body of literature and research is
growing. Along with a professional association, there could be a journal or
magazine, national and local conferences to aid dissemination. Can schools
through their interest in TAs provide pump priming, facilitation, starter support, some funding?

Efficient organisation and management of complementary staff to
support best professional practice

The *Good Practice Guide* (DfEE 2000a) and the associated research done by
Balshaw and Farrell (2002) has made a great start in supporting schools in
their management strategies. Books by Lorenz (1998), Balshaw (1999) and
Kerry (2001) all assist with various aspects, and I hope that this book adds
to their contributions. While the DfES understandably stays away from the
pay debate as it is so contentious and the domain of the employers, its lead
along with some more 'hands off' LEAs would really help in giving guidance
on codes of practice in such areas. Case studies and exemplar job descriptions
are helpful, but some distinct criteria would assist, especially if the additional
responsibilities of taking a class are added.

Effective use of leading edge technology to support best professional
practice

The Pathfinder project should sort out some of the concerns the schools have
regarding equipment and training to maintain this leading edge. Still, TAs
have to negotiate access to resources and technology to give learning
environment support, and this includes simpler things like photocopying or
laminating facilities for preparation of lesson resources, resource ideas, their
own professional development and training to support of ICT in pupils.
Rarely have TAs been included in any National Opportunities Fund training
given to teachers.

Incentives and rewards for excellence, including through pay
structures

While case studies of effective use of TAs are increasing, it is hard to get
concrete evidence of costs and meaningful performance related pay. Real
examples of creative budgeting would help. While the new money from the

three year spending review is welcome, the discrepancy between primary (£10,000 per school) and secondary (£50,000 per school) seems anomalous. Just handing out lump sums is no answer: schools need funding for target levels of staff numbers and their associated competence. LEA and school partnerships need to promote best practice in pay scales, but is this discussed at headteacher conferences or senior managers' gatherings? Governor training in best employment practices is also patchy; schools could ensure that their own governors are well informed as to the issues.

Relentless focus on what is in the best interests of those who use the service – in education, pupils and parents – backed by clear and effective arrangements for accountability and of measuring performance and outcomes

Inspection already looks at use and deployment of support staff; but do schools? Perhaps all those who read this book do. What is the TA accountability to governors and parents for higher level responsibilities in your school? The philosophy behind this book supports the need for school vision, stakeholder involvement, effective school self-review systems, ways of looking at the affective effectiveness of TAs – raising teacher morale, providing additional staff expertise, maintaining inclusive practices, promoting pupils' self-esteem and independence, allowing flexibility of teaching groups etc. as well as test outcomes. Above all, it encourages the celebration of good practice.

Pedagogy

If TAs are to become a profession, assisting and supporting learning and teaching, then there must develop a pedagogy for them. They must have a proper understanding of the learning processes in which they are involved, be learners themselves and be aware of the processes in which they will become engaged. Ireson *et al.* (1999) consider the tools which will be needed to enhance learning in the future, and identify some key ideas. These relate well to the things that anyone considering a pedagogy for TAs will need to think about.

1 A reappraisal of the very word pedagogy, which for TAs means a reappraisal of the words 'teach' and 'teaching', a strand developed in Chapter 7.
2 No universal panacea. TAs need to understand that different learners, at different ages and stages from different cultural backgrounds have differing learning needs, and different subjects have different teaching needs.
3 Teachers are important – those with QTS, TAs, parents and anyone interested enough to share their knowledge and skills with others.

Teachers – in their attempts to promote learning – have to provide information, challenge their learners to find information for themselves, asses understanding, measure skills and provide formative feedback. Most of all they have to inspire in their learners the desire to learn and reinforce their self-confidence. They will achieve this more readily if they have high self esteem themselves and are regarded as members of a respected profession rather than one that faces constant criticism.

(Ireson *et al.* 1999 p. 229)

4 Context matters: the learning environment is important.
5 Some general principles which can apply to TAs just as well as teachers with QTS: the general pedagogic principles outlined by Ireson *et al.* (1999) were drawn up after they undertook various literature searches. These could well be adapted to make a set of principles for TAs. It appears beneficial if teachers:

- are clear about their aims and share them with learners
- plan, organise and manage their teaching effectively
- try to formulate the highest expectations about the potential capabilities of learners within a general context of inclusivity
- provide learning tasks which will challenge and interest and which are aligned to appropriate assessment procedures
- seek to relate academic learning to other forms of learning and promote 'boundary crossing' skills
- make explicit the rules and at times, the hidden conventions of all learning institutions so that all learners become aware of ways in which they will be judged
- include an understanding of metacognition in their objectives so that all learners can benefit from this knowledge and – as they advance through their learning careers – take increasing responsibility for their own learning
- motivate and enthuse learners.

(Ireson *et al.* 1999 p. 230)

6 Teachers are learners, TAs too, and need to retain their capacity to change and improve.

The learning organisation

Watkins and Mortimore (1999) warn against considering schools as learning factories rather than learning organisations. While schools are not factories making a product, or a business setting out with the main aim of making a profit, there is much to learn from studying some of the management litera-ture, which has developed. Senge, an American management expert, has been a great influence to those managers interested in some of the less mechanistic ways of approaching organising a business or industry. His basic tenet is that successful organisations, whether factories or not, are learning organisations where all who work there need to participate in the way they operate. Indi-vidual people matter, but what all the people in the organisation can do together is greater than the sum of all the individuals. Senge describes five disciplines of organisations. He wrote: 'teams not individuals are the funda-mental learning unit of organisations' (Senge 1990 p. 10). While his is an industrial model, if you read each one of the details of his five disciplines which he says characterise a learning organisation, and put them against what goes on in your school you will how his ideas can apply to as school. This is summarised in Table 9.1.

What Senge's Five Disciplines can mean for an individual TA

Clearly, it is the responsibility of the head or senior management to enable the systems described in the table to work, but the TAs themselves have to play their part in the team. They must take responsibility for being part of the organisation.

First discipline – systems thinking

They need to be consulted, to respond honestly. They should have access to the SDP, especially where it relates to their work. They should receive copies of the annual report to parents, their work be recognised in it and may even contribute to it. They should attend the annual meeting as a member of staff. They should have access to governor minutes and not only know who the support staff governor is but also participate in any election process for that member. They should be encouraged to participate in suggesting changes in systems, particularly where it improves communication.

Second discipline – personal mastery

This is about ensuring that TAs take responsibility for their own learning and professional development, of finding out more about the job, their perform-ance and acting on suggestions. The school can ensure these things are written into the job description and enable the TAs to take personal responsibility for fulfilling the job description appropriately and punctually. But for managers it is also about keeping up to date with management strat-egies for TAs, and enabling teachers to understand how to make the best use of their TAs.

Table 9.1 What Senge's Five Disciplines might mean for a school

The disciplines of the learning organisation	What it can look like in a school
Systems thinking	
Contemplating the whole	The head and governors consultation processes
Interrelated actions	Timetables and curricula
Conceptual framework – seeing the patterns	The school development plan
Putting the snapshots together	The annual report to parents
Personal mastery	
Proficiency	Having a skilled and qualified staff, taking personal responsibility for developing one's own skills and understanding
Clarifying and deepening the personal vision	Having a motivated staff – taking personal responsibility for aspects of school work
Focusing energy	Not wasting time and energy on non-essentials
Connecting personal development to the organisational	Having annual appraisals which inform a staff development plan for all staff
Mental models	
Unearthing the existing mental models	Deciding what sort of school everybody thinks it is
Challenge and scrutiny	Revisiting every few years the principles and policies of the school
Balancing enquiry and advocacy	Asking questions and answering them about how the school works
Opening minds	Everybody being prepared to go on learning
Building shared vision	
Not the 'vision statement'	Knowing what your school stands for, not just quoting a motto
Unearthing pictures of the future	Knowing where the school wants to be in the future
Cannot be detached.	You are all part of the school and have responsibilities as well as rights
Team learning	
The whole is greater than the sum of the parts	Working together can increase children's achievement, and the school's standing, where individuals may only succeed with a few children or in a limited subject area
Dialogue means thinking together	You have to talk together to understand the problems and the directions. Talking together achieves a joint understanding of words used, which means you can work together and think together.
	Joint staff meetings, planning together, feeding back ideas
Recognise patterns that undermine learning	Think and talk about together what might be problems or could be improved.
Recognise patterns that can accelerate learning	Think and talk about together what is working well and can be built on

Source: Senge 1990 pp. 6–10

Senge himself says

> As individuals practice the discipline of personal mastery, several changes take place within them. Many of these are quite subtle and often go unnoticed. In addition to clarifying the 'structures' that characterise personal mastery as a discipline (such as creative tension, emotional tension and structural conflict) the systems perspective also illuminates subtler aspects of personal mastery – especially integrating reason and intuition; continually seeing more of our connectedness to the world; compassion; and commitment to the whole.
>
> (Senge 1990 p. 167)

Third discipline – mental models

In the past TAs were often the forgotten members of the school team, invisible, coming and going when others were occupied elsewhere. They can now be recognised as important partners in the learning and teaching process, induction procedures ensuring a much greater understanding of what the school is about and how it works. They will have sufficient confidence and enthusiasm to ask if they do not understand.

Fourth discipline – building the shared vision

This follows on from the first and third discipline. TAs need to know not just how the school operates but where it wants to go. Sharing the vision is one of the indicators of IiP.

Fifth discipline – team learning

Senge talks of having dialogue. It was difficult in the days when TAs were not part of the staffroom culture, came at the beginning of lessons and left at the end of lessons, unless they gave time from their goodwill. As more and more time is paid for TAs to participate in staff meetings, they become part of the whole team, not just their team. Good relationships with pupils and other staff alike not only make the whole place a better place to work but also make it possible to raise difficult, subtle and confidential issues essential to work.

Learning schools

The concept of a learning school is one put forward often and in various ways. Fullan (1991) talks of 'institutional development' and 'interactive professionalism' (p. 349) when discussing change in institutions. He also warns: 'There are no short cuts, and there is no substitute for directly engaging in improvement projects with others. Like most complex endeavours, in order to get better at change we have to practice it on purpose' (Fullan 1991 p. 350). Sammons *et al.* (1995) saw a learning organisation as one of the eleven key factors identified in effective schools. Sammons (1999 p. 195) lists them thus (the items in parentheses are selected from her list by me as being particularly pertinent to the employment of TAs):

1 Professional leadership (which includes a participative approach)
2 Shared vision and goals (which includes consistency, collegiality and collaboration)
3 A learning environment (which includes an orderly atmosphere and an attractive environment)
4 Concentration on teaching and learning (which includes maximising learning time)
5 Purposeful teaching (which includes efficiency and adaptive practice)
6 High expectations (which includes communication and challenge)
7 Positive reinforcement (which includes feedback)
8 Monitoring progress (which includes evaluation)
9 Pupils rights and responsibilities (which include raising self-esteem and control of work)
10 Home–school partnership
11 A learning organisation (school-based staff development).

Sammons (1999) give two particular features which appear to be recognisable in the climate of a learning organisation: an orderly atmosphere and an attractive working environment. She describes them as calm rather than chaotic, 'the most effective way of encouraging order and purpose amongst pupils is through reinforcement of good practice and learning behaviour' (p. 201). She also quotes Southworth (1994) as giving the features of a learning school which stress 'the need for learning at five interrelated levels – children, teacher, staff, organisational and leadership learning' (Sammons 1999 p. 213).

Change

All the above talk of effectiveness, using outside initiatives, of innovation, of improving all possible aspects indicates change – change in systems but also change in attitudes. Fullan talks of taking one innovation at a time as 'fire-fighting and faddism' (Fullan 1991 p. 349). He suggests the problem not as one of resistance but 'taking on too many changes indiscriminately'. He insists that institutional development means developing the people in them, institutional and individual development go together.

> The only solution is that the whole school – all individuals – must get into the change business; if individuals do not do this they will be left power-less. The current school organisation is an anachronism. It was designed

for an earlier period for conditions that no longer hold. It constrains the creation of a new profession of teaching that is so badly needed . . . The only way out of this dilemma is for individuals to take responsibility for empowering themselves and others through becoming experts in the change process . . . to create a new ethos of innovation . . . successful individuals will be highly involved with their environments, influencing and being influenced in this continuous exchange.

(Fullan 1991 pp. 352–354)

Hargreaves and Hopkins (1991) give some useful tips on strategies and tactics for managing development and change:

A *strategy* provides the framework for solving problems in development planning, and includes:

- a definition of the purpose or goal to be reached;
- an outline of the main pathways for reaching the goal, a planned time frame for reaching the goal;
- an estimate of the costs (time, money, personnel and other resources) needed to reach the goal.

Tactics are the detailed operational activities required to put the strategy into effect. A strategy can be implemented by a variety of tactics, the choice being constrained by the circumstances of the time and location. Tactics are sometimes changed in the light of experience or prevailing conditions and constraints.

Keeping in mind the distinction between strategy and tactics can help effective development planning in the following ways:

- Do not get distracted by, or bogged down in, tactical details until the strategy is clear – to do so makes decision making more difficult.
- Do not abandon a strategy just because a particular tactic will not work or fails – choose another tactic.
- Remember that tactical variation makes strategies more flexible and adaptable than they seem.
- Remember that tactics are opportunities for those involved to use their creativity and inventiveness whilst implementing the strategy.

(Hargreaves and Hopkins 1991 p. 128)

It is time to have a radical rethink on the way schools are run and staffed. Weddell (2001) comments:

The experience [of being an LSA] has brought home to me, even more, the superhuman intellectual demands made on individual teachers and LSAs faced with meeting the diversity of learning needs in class groups of children. It is really time we moved away from the rigidity which this organisation imposes on the education of our children. The contribution LSAs can make is slowly becoming recognised as part of the ways in which the nature and levels of learning needs can be served by the nature and levels of expertise that a range of professional approaches can offer in schools.

(Weddell 2001 p. 96)

Even with the development of ICT there will be the need for people, for personal interventions, guidance, help, encouragement and shared joy in success for all learners – pupils or adults. Noss and Pachler (1999) are convinced that teachers' professional judgement will still be needed in an ICT-rich learning environment: 'providing "scaffolding" . . . to maximise the effectiveness of the contribution of ICT to the learning process' (p. 206). Learning never stops. The school buildings and equipment can be used by retired people and those not physically at work as well as those who are legally bound to attend – but it takes people to organise it, run it and act as learning facilitators. The role of teachers is already becoming that of a learning consultant, with a team of teaching and learning assistants, all themselves part of the learning organisation. The necessity for all pupils from 5 to 16 attending the same establishment for a stipulated number of hours to participate in 'lessons' which take place in similar sized units needs examining. Some things can be taught most effectively in groups of hundreds, other things need individual attention: pupils have a variety of needs at different times of their lives, ICT can help, but the learning environment, the support of trained people working in a team adaptable to the needs of the curriculum, society and the learners can enhance the learning achievement of all.

A survey of teaching and teachers carried out by the Organisation for Economic Cooperation and Development (OECD 2001) posed the scenarios, presented in Table 9.2 for the future.

The 'status quo extrapolated'	The 'reschooling scenarios'	The 'deschooling scenarios'
Scenario 1: *Robust bureaucratic school systems*	Scenario 2: *Schools as core social centres*	Scenario 3: *Learner networks and the network society*
Scenario 4: *Extending the market model*	Scenario 1: *Schools as focused learning organisations*	Scenario 1: *Teacher exodus – the 'meltdown' scenario*

Table 9.2 The OECD vision of schools of the future
Source: OECD 2001

With TAs playing a professional role, the business and market models need not dominate. They can play their part in a scenario which could see the schools as a learning organisation, networking and enabling young people to take a full and satisfying place in society, as well as enabling the staff to live fulfilled adult lives.

Inclusion taken to the furthest degree is not about closing special schools and sending all pupils to mainstream establishments, but about including all staff in the team of the school, of having specialisms within the staff, and special units with specialist staff, resources and equipment working together and not in competition. It is not just rural communities in the north of Scotland that are isolated – villages in our shire counties and suburban communities are often in a similar state. By looking at the employment and deployment of TAs, we may be opening up a whole new vision of education in the twenty-first century. Why not?

Bibliography

Adamson, S. (1999) 'Review of published literature on teaching assistants', in unpublished Teaching Assistant Working Group papers, London: Department for Education and Employment.

Aplin, R. (1998) *Assisting Numeracy*, London: BEAM, National Numeracy Project and London Borough of Tower Hamlets.

Balshaw, M. H. (1991) *Help in the Classroom*, London: David Fulton.

Balshaw, M. (1999) *Help in the Classroom* (2nd edn), London: David Fulton.

Balshaw, M. and Farrell, P. (2002) *Teaching Assistants: Practical strategies for effective classroom support*, London: David Fulton.

Ben-Peretz, M., Schonmann, S. and Kupermitz, H. (1999) 'The teachers' lounge and its role in improving learning environments in schools', in H. J. Freiberg (ed.) *School Climate*, London and Philadelphia: Falmer Press.

Blatchford, P., Martin, C., Moriarty, V., Bassett, P. and Goldstein, H. (2002) 'Pupil adult ratio differences and educational progress over reception and key stage 1 (RR335)', London: Institute of Education, University of London for the DfES.

Blenkin, G. M. and Kelly, A. V. (eds) (1997) *Principles into Practice in Early Childhood Education*, London: Paul Chapman.

Booth, T., Ainscow, M., Black-Hawkins, K., Vaughan, M. and Shaw, L. (2000) *Index for Inclusion: Developing learning and participation in schools*, Bristol: Centre for Studies on Inclusive Education.

Brighouse, T. and Woods, D. (1999) *How to Improve your School*, London and New York: Routledge.

Burnham, M. (1988) 'The forgotten staff', *Special Children*, 22: 31.

Creemers, B. P. M. (1994) *The Effective Classroom*, London and New York: Cassell.

DES (1978) *The Warnock Report*, London: Department of Education and Science.

Dew-Hughes, D., Brayton, H. and Blandford, S. (1998) 'A survey of training and professional development for learning support assistants', *Support for Learning*, 13: 179–183.

DfEE (1997a) *Excellence in Schools* (White Paper), London: Department for Education and Employment and The Stationery Office.

DfEE (1997b) *Investors in People and School Self Improvement*, London: Department for Education and Employment.

DfEE (1998a) *Teachers Meeting the Challenge of Change* (Green Paper), London: Department for Education and Employment.

DfEE (1998b) *The Implementation of the National Numeracy Strategy* (final report of the Numeracy Task Force), London: Department for Education and Employment.

DfEE (1999a) *The National Numeracy Strategy* [Framework for teaching mathematics], London: Department for Education and Employment.

DfEE (1999b) *National Literacy Strategy – Additional Literacy Support (ALS)* [Teaching materials], London: Department for Education and Employment.

DfEE (2000a) *Working with Teaching Assistants – A Good Practice Guide*, London: Department for Education and Employment.

DfEE (2000b) *Teaching Assistant File – Induction training for teaching assistants*, London: Department for Education and Employment.

DfEE (2000c) *Performance Management – Guidance for Governors* (Guidance 0059/2000), London: Department for Education and Employment.

DfEE (2000d) *Professional Development* (Information 0008/2000), London: Department for Education and Employment.

DfEE (2000e) *Behaviour Management Module – Induction training for teaching assistants*, London: Department for Education and Employment.

DfEE (2000f) *Progress File – Supplement 3* (Information – curriculum and standards PFSUPP3), London: Department for Education and Employment.

DfEE (2000g) *Role and Context Module – Induction training for teaching assistants*, London: Department for Education and Employment.

DfEE (2000h) *Literacy Module – Induction training for teaching assistants*, London: Department for Education and Employment.

DfEE (2000i) *Mathematics Module – Induction training for teaching assistants*, London: Department for Education and Employment.

DfES (2001a) *Teaching Assistant File – Induction training for teaching assistants in secondary schools*, London: Department for Education and Skills.

DfES (2001b) *Special Educational Needs Code of Practice*, London: Department for Education and Skills.

DfES (2001c) *Behaviour Management Module – Induction training for teaching assistants in secondary schools*, London: Department for Education and Skills.

DfES (2001d) *Role and Context Module – Induction training for teaching assistants in secondary schools*, London: Department for Education and Skills.

DfES (2001e) *Literacy Module – Induction training for teaching assistants in secondary schools*, London: Department for Education and Skills.

DfES (2001f) *Numeracy Module – Induction training for teaching assistants in secondary schools*, London: Department for Education and Skills.

DfES (2001g) *Special Educational Needs Module – Induction training for teaching assistants in secondary schools*, London: Department for Education and Skills.

DfES (2002a) *Developing the Role of School Support Staff* (Consultation DfES/0751/2002), London: Department of Education and Skills.

DfES (2002b) *Time for Standards* (Proposals DfES/0751/2002), London: Department of Education and Skills.

DfES (2002c) *The Education (Teaching Work and Registration) (England) Regulations 2002* (Draft Circular and guidance), London: Department of Education and Skills.

Dunne, R. and Wragg, T. (1994) *Effective Teaching*, London and New York: Routledge.

Edwards, J. (1997) 'The professionalism of support staff', *Education Journal*, January: 15.

Employers' Organisation (EO) (2002) *Qualifications for Teaching Assistants* (Guidance Version 1), London: Employers' Organisation.

Farrell, P., Balshaw, M. and Polat, F. (1999) *The Management, Role and Training of Learning Support Assistants* (RR161), Manchester: University of Manchester and DfEE.

Freiberg, H. J. and Stein, T. A. (1999) 'Measuring, improving and sustaining healthy schools', in H. J. Freiberg (ed.) *School Climate*, London and Philadelphia: Falmer Press.

Fullan, M. G. (1991) *The New Meaning of Educational Change*, London: Cassell.

Funding Agency for Schools (FAS) (1999) *Making Changes: Effective use of support staff in schools*, York: FAS.

Galton, M. and Simon, B. (eds) (1980) *Progress and Performance in the Primary Classroom*, London: Routledge and Kegan Paul.

Gartner, A., Reissman, F. and Jackson, A. C. (1977) *Paraprofessionals Today*, Vol. 1: *Education*, New York: Human Sciences Press.

Gipps, C. and MacGilchrist, B. (1999) 'Primary school learners', in P. Mortimore (ed.) *Understanding Pedagogy and its Impact on Learning*, London: Paul Chapman.

Haigh, G. (1996) 'To boldly go beyond washing the paintpots', *Times Educational Supplement*, Primary Update 21, 9 February.

Hall, G. E. and George, A. A. (1999) 'The impact of principal change facilitator style on school and classroom culture', in H. J. Freiberg (ed.) *School Culture*, London and Philadelphia: Falmer Press.

Hargreaves, D. H. and Hopkins, D. (1991) *The Empowered School*, London: Cassell.

HMCI (1996) *The Annual Report of Her Majesty's Chief Inspector of Schools 1994/1995*, London: Ofsted.

HMCI (1998) *The Annual Report of Her Majesty's Chief Inspector of schools 1996/1997*, London: Ofsted.

HMI (1992) *Non-teaching Staff in Schools* (Education Observed Series), London: DES and HMSO.

Hodgson, A. and Kambouri, M. (1999) 'Adults as lifelong learners: the role of pedagogy in the new policy context', in P. Mortimore (ed.) *Understanding Pedagogy and its Impact on Learning*, London: Paul Chapman.

Investors in People (IiP) (2000) *Investors in People in Schools*, London: DfEE.

Ireson, J., Mortimore, P. and Hallam, S. (1999) 'The common strands of pedagogy and their implications', in P. Mortimore (ed.) *Understanding Pedagogy and its Impact on Learning*, London: Paul Chapman.

Kerry, T. (2001) *Working with Support Staff: Their roles and effective management in schools*, London: Pearson Education.

Kerry, T. and Mayes, A. S. (1995) *Issues in Mentoring*, London and New York: Routledge with the Open University.

Kyriacou, C. (1986) *Effective Teaching in Schools*, Cheltenham: Stanley Thornes.

Lacey, P. (1999) *On a Wing and a Prayer*, London: Mencap.

Lacey, P. (2001) *Support Partnerships*, London: David Fulton.

Lee, B. and Mawson, C. (1998) *Survey of Classroom Assistants*, Slough: National Foundation for Educational Research for Unison.

LGMB (1996) *Survey of Non-teaching Staff and Volunteers in Primary and Nursery*

Schools, London: Employment Surveys and Research Unit of the Local Government Management Board.

LGNTO (2001) *Teaching/Classroom Assistants National Occupational Standards*, London: Local Government National Training Organisation.

LGNTO, EYNTO and DfEE (2000) *Survey of Education Support Staff and Volunteers in Nursery and Primary Schools in England 1999*, London: Local Government National Training Organisation, Early Years National Training Organisation and Department for Education and Employment.

Lorenz, S. (1998) *Effective In-class Support*, London: David Fulton.

Loxley, A. and Swann, W. (1997) 'Beyond the paintpots', *Head Teachers' Review – NAHT*, spring: 19–21.

MacBeath, J. (1999) *Schools must Speak for Themselves: The case for school self-evaluation*, London and New York: Routledge.

MacBeath, J., Boyd, B., Rand, J. and Bell, S. (1996) *Schools Speak for Themselves: Towards a framework for self-evaluation*, Glasgow: National Union of Teachers for the University of Strathclyde.

MacGilchrist, B., Myers, K. and Reed, J. (1997) *The Intelligent School*, London: Paul Chapman.

Marr, A. (2000) 'A very visible means of support', *Times Educational Supplement*, 28 April: 22.

Morgan, J., Ashbaker, B. and Forbush, D. (1998) 'Strengthening the teaching team: teachers and paraprofessionals learning together', *Support for Learning*, 13: 115–117.

Morris, E. (2001) *Professionalism and Trust*, London: Department for Education and Skills.

Mortimore, P., Sammons, P., Stoll, L., Lewis, D. and Ecob, R. (1988) *School Matters*, Wells: Open Books.

Mortimore, P., Mortimore, J., Thomas, H., Cairns, R. and Taggart, B. (1992) *The Innovative Uses of Non-teaching Staff in Primary and Secondary Schools Project* (Final report), London: Institute of Education, University of London and DfE.

Mortimore, P., Mortimore, J. and Thomas, H. (1994) Managing Associate Staff: Innovation in primary and secondary schools, London: Paul Chapman.

Moyles, J. and Suschitzky, W. (1997) 'Jills of all trades?. . . .', Leicester: Association of Teachers and Lecturers with Leicester University.

Moyles, J. and Suschitzky, W. (1998) 'Roles and responsibilities of support staff in KS1 classrooms', *Early Years*, 18: 49–54.

NACCCE (2000) *All our Futures: Creativity, culture and education* (Report to Secretaries of State for Education and Employment and for Culture, Media and Sport), London: National Advisory Committee on Creative and Cultural Education.

Nicholas, C. (2001) 'Chris' story: looking inside my head', in T. O'Brien and P. Garner (eds) *Untold Stories: Learning support assistants and their work*, Stoke on Trent: Trentham Books.

Noss, R. and Pachler, N. (1999) 'The challenge of new teachnologies: doing old things in a new way, or doing new things?', in P. Mortimore (ed.), *Understanding Pedagogy and its Impact on Learning*, London: Paul Chapman.

NUT (1998) *Associate Staff: Support for Teachers*, London: National Union of Teachers and Pricewaterhouse Coopers.

O'Brien, T. and Garner, P. (eds) (2001) *Untold Stories: Learning support assistants and their work*, Stoke on Trent: Trentham Books.

OECD (2001) 'Challenges to the teaching profession', paper presented at The Management of Human Resource in Education conference, Barcelona, 25–27 October.

Ofsted (1997) *Training Specialist Teacher Assistants: A guide to good practice*, London: Ofsted.

Ofsted (1999) *Handbook for Inspecting Primary and Nursery Schools*, London: Ofsted.

Ofsted (2002a) *Teaching Assistants in Primary Schools: An evaluation of the quality and impact of their work* (HMI 434), London: Ofsted.

Ofsted (2002b) *The Curriculum in Successful Primary Schools* (HMI 553), London: Ofsted.

Parry, M. and Archer, H. (1974) *Pre-school Education*, School Council Publications, London: Macmillan.

Plowden, B. (1967) *Children and their Primary Schools*, Report of the Central Advisory Council for Education (England), London: HMSO.

PricewaterhouseCoopers (2001) *Teacher Workload Study* (Draft final report, 12 November 2001), London: PricewaterhouseCoopers.

QCA (1999) *Early Years Education, Child Care and Playwork* (A framework of nationally accredited qualifications), London: Qualifications and Curriculum Authority.

Robins, V. (1998) *The Invisible Professionals: Nursery nurses working in schools*, London: Professional Association of Teachers incorporating the Professional Association of Nursery Nurses.

Rose, C. (2001) 'Carole's story: looking back', in T. O' Brien and P. Garner (eds) *Untold Stories: Learning support assistants and their work*, Stoke on Trent: Trentham Books.

Sallis, J. (1999) 'One school team?', *ACE Bulletin*, 92: 10.

Sammons, P. (1999) *School Effectiveness: Coming of age in the twenty-first century*, Lisse, The Netherlands: Swets & Zeitlingeer.

Sammons, P., Hillman, J. and Mortimore, P. (1995) *Key Characteristics of Effective Schools*, London: Ofsted.

Senge, P. M. (1990) *The Fifth Discipline*, London: Century Business.

Smith, A. (1996) *Accelerated Learning in the Classroom*, Stafford: Network Educational Press.

Smith, K., Kenner, C. and Barton-Hide, D. (1999) *Career Ladder for Classroom Assistants*, Southampton: University of Southampton and Hampshire County Council.

Southworth, G. (1994) 'The Learning School', in P. Ribbens and E. Burridge (eds) *Improving Education: Promoting quality in schools*, London: Cassell.

Swann, W. and Loxley, A. (1997) 'The impact of school based training on classroom assistants in primary schools', paper presented at the Open University Specialist Teacher Assistant Certificate Conference, Milton Keynes, June.

Swann, W. and Loxley, A. (1998) 'The impact of school-based training on classroom assistants in primary schools', *Research Papers in Education*, 13: 141–160.

Tennant, G. (2001) 'The rhetoric and reality of learning support in the classroom: towards a synthesis', *British Journal of Learning Support*, 16(4): 184–188.

Thomas, G., Walker, D. and Webb, J. (1998) 'Using support in inclusive classrooms', in Thomas, Walker and Webb, *The Making of the Inclusive School*, London and New York: Routledge.

TTA (1998) *National Standards for Qualified Teacher Status*, London: Teacher Training Agency.

TTA (2000) *Progression to Initial Teacher Training for Teaching Assistants* (Information on training courses – survey), London: Teacher Training Agency.

TTA (2002) *Qualifying to Teach: Professional standards for Qualified Teacher Status and requirements for Initial Teacher Training*, London: Teacher Training Agency and Department for Education and Skills.

Watkins, C. and Mortimore, P. (1999) 'Pedagogy: what do we know?', in P. Mortimore (ed.), *Understanding Pedagogy and its Impact on Learning*, London: Paul Chapman.

Watkinson, A. (1998a) 'Supporting learning and assisting teaching: 1', *Topic*, Spring: 1–6.

Watkinson, A. (1998b) 'Supporting learning and assisting teaching: 2', *Topic*, Autumn: 1–5.

Watkinson, A. (1999a) *The Use and Deployment of Teaching Assistants in Essex Primary Schools in the Summer of 1998* (Education Research Digest 3/99), Chelmsford: Essex County Council.

Watkinson, A. (1999b) 'The professional development of teaching assistants', *Professional Development Today*, 2(3): 63–69.

Watkinson, A. (2002a) *Assisting Learning and Supporting Teaching*, London: David Fulton.

Watkinson, A. (2002b) 'When is a teacher not a teacher? When she is a teaching assistant', *Education 3–13*, 30: 58–65.

Watkinson, A. (2003) *The Essential Guide for Competent Teaching Assistants: Meeting the National Occupational Standards at level 2*, London: David Fulton.

Weddell, K. (2001) 'Klaus's story: the experience of a retired professor of special need education', in T. O'Brien and P. Garner (eds) *Untold Stories: Learning support assistants and their work*, Stoke on Trent: Trentham Books.

Wright, I. (2002) 'Developments for teaching assistants and other school support staff', Letter to Chief Education Officers, London: Department for Education and Skills.

Index